Bernard D. Katz

Understanding
Symbolic Logic

GERALD J. MASSEY

Professor of Philosophy
Michigan State University

Understanding
Symbolic Logic

Harper & Row, Publishers
New York, Evanston, and London

For Ann

CONTENTS

Preface, xv

PART ONE.   TRUTH-FUNCTIONAL LOGIC

  1 Preliminaries, 3
     1.0   Scope of Text, 3
     1.1   Symbolic Logic; the Logistic Method, 4
  2 Truth-Functional Sentence Connectives (I), 7
     2.0   Conjunction, 7
     2.1   Disjunction or Alternation, 9
     2.2   Negation, 10
  3 Exercises, 11
  4 Language Schema P, 12
     4.0   Vocabulary, 12
     4.1   Formation Rules, 12
     4.2   Use and Mention; Quotation Marks and Corners, 15
  5 Exercises, 17
  6 Semantics of Language Schema P, 18
     6.0   Semantics, 18
     6.1   Truth Tables, 19
     6.2   Interpreting Language Schema P, 25
  7 Exercises, 27
  8 Logical Truth and Analyticity, 29
     8.0   Logical Truth and Logical Falsehood, 29
     8.1   Analytic and Synthetic Sentences, 30
  9 Exercises, 33
 10 Abbreviation and Equivalence, 34
     10.0   Some Abbreviative Conventions, 34
     10.1   Equivalence, 36
     10.2   Tolerably Ambiguous Abbreviations, 38
 11 Exercises, 40
 12 Functional Completeness, 42

12.0 Mutual Entailment, Equivalence, and Expressive Power, 42
12.1 Functional Completeness of the Tilde, Wedge, and Dot, 43

13 Truth-Functional Sentence Connectives (II), 46
13.0 Truth-Functional Sentence Connectives; a Second Look, 46
13.1 Redundancy of the Tilde, Wedge, and Dot, 48
13.2 Sheffer's Stroke, 49

14 Implication and Equivalence, 52
14.0 The Conditional, 52
14.1 The Biconditional, 54
14.2 Implication; Consequence Relation, 56
14.3 Short-cut Test for Validity and Implication, 58
14.4 More Abbreviative Conventions, 60
14.5 Equivalence and Implication, 61

15 Exercises, 62

16 Normal Forms; Duality, 64
16.0 Normal Forms, 64
16.1 Reduction to Normal Form, 67
16.2 Simple Disjunctive Normal Form, 71
16.3 Duality, 72

17 Exercises, 74

18 Boolean Equations; Electrical Circuits, 76
18.0 Boolean Equations, 76
18.1 Design of Electrical Circuits, 81

19 Exercises, 86

20 Application of Formalized Languages to the Logical Analysis of Natural Languages, 89
20.0 Proving Correctness of Arguments, 89
20.1 Proving Incorrectness of Arguments, 93
20.2 Rendering Logical Structure Explicit, 94
20.3 Bringing Logical Form to the Surface, 101
20.4 The Semantics of Atomic Sentences, 104

21 Exercises, 107

22 Functional Incompleteness, 109
22.0 Mathematical Induction, 109
22.1 Strong Mathematical Induction, 112

22.2   Functional Incompleteness of the Dot and Wedge, 115

23   Exercises, 117

24   Alternative Notations, 118
    24.0   Trivial Alternatives, 118
    24.1   Nontrivial Alternative: Polish Notation, 119

25   Exercises, 122

**PART TWO.   AXIOMATIZATION OF TRUTH-
              FUNCTIONAL LOGIC**

26   Axiomatic System of Truth-Functional Logic, 125
    26.0   Primitive Basis of System P, 125
    26.1   Basic Concepts of Axiomatics, 127

27   Exercises, 130

28   Metatheory of System P (I), 132
    28.0   Consistency of System P, 132
    28.1   Independence of Axioms and Rules, 134
    28.2   Independence and Consistency, 140

29   Exercises, 141

30   Metatheory of System P (II), 144
    30.0   The Deduction Theorem, 144
    30.1   Some Key Theorem Schemata, 147
    30.2   Maximal Consistent Classes, 149
    30.3   Completeness Theorem, 151
    30.4   Compactness Theorem and Concluding Remarks, 154

31   Exercises, 157

PART THREE.   SENTENTIAL MODAL LOGIC

32   Truth Tables and Modal Logic, 163
    32.0   Motivation, 163
    32.1   Actual and Possible Truth-Value Outcomes, 163
    32.2   Language Schema M, 164
    32.3   Full and Partial Truth Tables, 165
    32.4   Fundamental Truth Tables Revisited, 169

33   Exercises, 173

34   Validity in LSM, 175

34.0   Value Assignments; Plenary Sets of Truth Tables, 175

34.1   Validity, 179

34.2   Relation of LSP to LSM, 179

34.3   Analytic Truth, Logical Truth, Entailment, Implication, and Equivalence, 180

35   Exercises, 181

36   Truth-Tabular Connectives, 183

36.0   Possibility, 183

36.1   The Singulary Truth-Tabular Connectives, 185

36.2 N-ary Truth-Tabular Connectives; Strict Implication, 188

36.3   Strict Equivalence; Compatibility; the Star, 191

37   Exercises, 195

38   Functional Completeness; Reduction of Modal Wffs, 197

38.0   Functional Completeness, 197

38.1   Reduction of Modal Wffs, 200

38.2   The Six Modalities, 201

39   Exercises, 204

40   Axiomatic Modal Logic, 205

40.0   Primitive Basis of the System S5, 205

40.1   Relationship to System P; Consistency of S5, 207

40.2   Deduction Theorem; Key Theorem Schemata, 208

40.3   Completeness Theorem for S5, 211

40.4   The System S5′ (Completeness), 216

40.5   The System S5′ (Consistency), 218

41   Exercises, 220

PART FOUR.   QUANTIFICATION THEORY

42   Atomic Analysis, 225

42.0   Molecular Analysis versus Atomic Analysis, 225

42.1   Singular Terms, 225

42.2   Predicates and Circled Numerals, 226

42.3   Transparent versus Opaque Predicates, 228

42.4   Individual Variables and Predicate Variables, 230

43   Exercises, 231

44   Semantics of Atomic Wffs, 232

44.0   Semantics of Individual Variables, 232
44.1   Semantics of Predicate Variables, 233
44.2   Semantics of Atomic Wffs, 234

45   Exercises, 236

46   Quantifiers, 237
46.0   Existential and Universal Quantifiers, 237
46.1   Grammar of LSQ, 238
46.2   Free and Bound Variables, 239
46.3   Interpretations; Minimal Interpretations, 240
46.4   Inductive Definition of the Value of a Wff Under a Minimal Interpretation, 242
46.5   Applying the Inductive Definition, 243

47   Exercises, 245

48   Model Theory, 248
48.0   Models: Satisfiability and Validity, 248
48.1   Inflation Theorem, 249
48.2   Löwenheim Theorem; Spectrum Problem, 251
48.3   Generalized Inflation Theorem; Löwenheim–Skolem Theorem, 252
48.4   Implication and Truth-Functional Implication; Equivalence, 254

49   Exercises, 255

50   Logical Analysis of English Discourse, 259
50.0   Logical Truth and the Empty Domain, 259
50.1   Universes of Discourse of English Statements, 261
50.2   Translating English into Q-Languages, 262

51   Exercises, 268

52   Quine's System of Natural Deduction (I), 273
52.0   Instances, 273
52.1   Natural Deduction Systems versus Logistic Systems, 274
52.2   Rule of Premiss, 275
52.3   Rule of Truth Functions, 276
52.4   Rule of Universal Instantiation, 277
52.5   Rule of Existential Generalization, 278
52.6   Rule of Conditionalization, 278
52.7   The Five Soundness-Preserving Rules, 280

53   Exercises, 281

54 Quine's System of Natural Deduction (II), 284
    54.0 Conservative Instances, 284
    54.1 Rule of Universal Generalization, 285
    54.2 Rule of Existential Instantiation, 287
    54.3 Rationale Behind Universal Generalization and Existential Instantiation, 288
    54.4 Finished Deductions; Proofs; Metatheorems, 289
    54.5 Proof of the Consistency Theorem, 293
55 Exercises, 296
56 Applying the Natural Deduction System, 300
    56.0 Deductive Strategies, 300
    56.1 Time-Savers, 303
    56.2 Identity, 304
    56.3 Postulate Systems; Calculus of Individuals, 307
    56.4 Completeness Theorem for System QI, 313
57 Exercises, 316
58 Proof of the Completeness Theorem for System Q, 320
    58.0 Corollaries of the Skolem–Gödel Theorem, 320
    58.1 Maximal, Consistent, ω-Complete Classes, 321
    58.2 Proof of the Lemma of Section 58.0, 323
59 Quantification with Function Variables, 325
    59.0 Function Variables; Terms, 325
    59.1 Natural Deduction Rules for System QIF, 327
    59.2 Peano Arithmetic, 328
60 Exercises, 333
61 Decision Problems and Incompleteness, 335
    61.0 Decidability; Church's Thesis, 335
    61.1 Church's Theorem, 338
    61.2 Gödel Incompleteness Theorem, 341
62 Special Cases of the Decision Problem, 343
    62.0 Special Cases, 343
    62.1 Syllogisms, 344
    62.2 Reduction of Decision Problems; Prenex Normal Forms, 348
63 Exercises, 350

APPENDIXES

Appendix A.   Set Theory, 355
  Introduction to Set Theory, 355

Exercises, 357

Appendix B.   Semantic Tableaux, 358
Semantic Tableaux for Truth-Functional Logic, 358
Exercises, 364
Semantic Tableaux for Quantificational Logic, 365
Exercises, 369

Appendix C.   Alternative Proof of the Completeness of System P, 372
Exercises, 374

Appendix D.   Alternative Proof of the Compactness Theorem for System P, 376
Exercises, 378

Appendix E.   Alternative Proof of the Completeness of System Q, 379
Exercises, 383

Appendix F.   Alternative Approaches to the Semantics of Quantifiers, 384
Exercises, 386

Appendix G.   Quantification Theory with Modality, 389
Kripke's 1959 Semantics; LSQ-M, 389
System Q-M; Natural Deduction System of Quantification Theory with Modality, 392
Alternative Semantics for Quantification Theory with Modality (KA), 397
Alternative Semantics for Quantification Theory with Modality (KB), 398
Exercises, 401

Appendix H.   Tense Logic, 404
Exercises, 411

Appendix I.   Logistic System of Quantification Theory, 414
Exercises, 415

Index, 417

PREFACE

The author has tried to write a textbook suited to the needs and preferences of the largest possible number of those who teach symbolic logic. The book presupposes no special preparation in logic or mathematics. It treats a large variety of topics and allows the instructor considerable latitude in the selection of topics to cover, and in the order in which to cover them. Consequently, the book lends itself to adoption in courses whose lengths vary from one quarter to a full academic year. (See Table of Suggested Courses.) The author has endeavored to achieve clarity of exposition, hoping the book will also be useful to those engaged in an independent study of symbolic logic.

There are many good symbolic logic textbooks available. Of these each will be found superior in one or several respects to the others. The author felt it to be his primary pedagogical obligation to imitate, so far as he was able, the various excellences of these books. Thus what novelty the present book possesses springs from necessity, not design.

The author confesses to a rather loose and cavalier treatment of meaning. The book exploits a sharp analytic-synthetic distinction and presents synonymy as an intuitively clear relation. The author is aware of the difficulties surrounding the aforementioned distinction and relation, but he is unaware of less problematic surrogates that have comparable pedagogical and expository value.

Finally, the author acknowledges with gratitude his personal indebtedness to many colleagues, students, and associates who in myriad ways contributed to whatever merits this book has. To name them all would be impossible, but special mention must be given to Herbert E. Hendry and James E. Roper.

GERALD J. MASSEY

Pittsburgh, Pennsylvania
October, 1969

TABLE OF SUGGESTED COURSES

Course length	Topics (in order)	Chapters and appendixes to be covered (Braces indicate desirable supplementary material)
One quarter	Truth functions, quantification	§1–15, 20–25, 42–47, 48–49 (rapidly), {F}, 50–56.1
One quarter	Truth functions, axiomatics	§1–15, {B(1st half)}, 20–30.1, {30.2–31}
One quarter	Truth functions, sentential modal logic	§1–15, {B(1st half)}, 20–25, 32–39
One semester	Truth functions, quantification	§1–15, B(1st half), 20–25, 42–49, F, 50–56.1, {B(2nd half)}, 56.2–56.3, 59–60
One semester	Truth functions, axiomatics, quantification	§1–15, {B(1st half)}, 20–30.1, 42–47, 48–49 (rapidly), {F}, 50–56.1, {B(2nd half)}, 56.2–56.3
One semester	Truth functions, quantification, axiomatics	§1–15, {B(1st half)}, 20–25, 42–47, 48–49 (rapidly), {F}, 50–56.1, {B(2nd half)}, 26–30.1, 56.2–56.3
One semester	Truth functions, sentential modal logic, quantification	§1–15, {B(1st half)}, 20–25, 32–39, 42–47, 48–49 (rapidly), {F}, 50–56.1, {B(2nd half)}, 56.2–56.3
One semester	Truth functions, quantification, sentential modal logic	§1–15, {B(1st half)}, 20–25, 42–47, 48–49 (rapidly), {F}, 50–56.1, {B(2nd half)}, 56.2–56.3
One semester	Truth functions, quantification, sentential and quantified modal logic	§1–15, 20–25, 42–47, 48–49 (rapidly), F, 50–56.1, 32–39, G, {H}
Two quarters	Truth functions, quantification	§1–15, B(1st half), 16–25, 42–49, F, 50–56.1, B(2nd half), 56.2–63, {D, E, I}

Course length	Topics (in order)	Chapters and appendixes to be covered (Braces indicate desirable supplementary material)
Two quarters	Truth functions, axiomatics, quantification	§1–15, B(1st half), 16–31, {C, D}, 42–49, {F}, 50–56.1, B(2nd half), 56.2–57, 59–60
Two quarters	Truth functions, quantification, axiomatics	§1–15, B(1st half), 16–25, 42–49, F, 50–56.1, B(2nd half), 56.2–57, 26–31, C, I
Two quarters	Truth functions, sentential modal logic, quantification, quantified modal logic	§1–15, B(1st half), 20–25, 32–39, 42–49, F, 50–56.1, B(2nd half), 56.2–57, G, {H}
Two quarters	Truth functions, quantification, sentential and quantified modal logic	§1–15, B(1st half), 20–25, 42–49, F, 50–56.1, B(2nd half), 56.2–57, 32–39, G, {H}
Two quarters	Truth functions, axiomatics, sentential modal logic, quantification	§1–15, B(1st half), 20–31, {C, D}, 32–49, {F}, 50–56.1, B(2nd half), 56.2–57, {E, I}
Academic year	Truth functions, axiomatics, quantification	§1–15, B(1st half), 16–31, C, D, 42–49, {F}, 50–63, I, {E}
Academic year	Truth functions, quantification, axiomatics	§1–15, B(1st half), 16–25, 42–49, {F}, 50–56.1, B(2nd half), 26–31, C, D, 56.2–63, I, {E}
Academic year	Truth functions, axiomatics, sentential modal logic, quantification, quantified modal logic	§1–15, {B(1st half)}, 16–31, {C, D}, 32–49, F, 50–56.1, {B(2nd half)}, 56.2–57, {58–60}, G, {H}
Academic year	Truth functions, quantification, axiomatics, sentential and quantified modal logic	§1–15, {B(1st half)}, 20–25, 42–49, F, 50–56.1, {B(2nd half)}, 26–31, {C, D}, 56.2–56.3, 59–60, 32–41, G, H, {E, 61–63}

EXPLANATION OF GRADING
OF EXERCISES

All the exercises in this book are graded according to difficulty and character. The symbols flanking the numeral that denotes the number of an exercise indicate the grade of the exercise in the following way. Ordinary parentheses indicate a straightforward exercise which the average student should be able to work without much trouble. Brackets designate a straightforward exercise of moderate difficulty. The student who finds himself unable to do some of the bracketed exercises should not despair, for he is not expected to be able to solve them all. Angle brackets designate straightforward exercises of considerable difficulty or complexity; superior students may take legitimate pride in solving them. Finally, braces indicate exercises which, in part or whole, are philosophical in character. These exercises are not straightforward in the sense of being well-defined questions admitting of answers which are objectively right or wrong. Rather, they raise philosophical issues on which the student is encouraged to reflect. Success with these exercises consists mainly in getting more and more clear about the issues involved.

The table below summarizes the foregoing explanation.

Exercise symbol	Example	Character of Exercise
Parentheses	(k)	Straightforward, within anyone's competence
Brackets	$[k]$	Straightforward, but moderately difficult
Angle brackets	$\langle k \rangle$	Straightforward, but quite difficult
Braces	$\{k\}$	Philosophical, no "right answer"

PART ONE
Truth-Functional Logic

1. PRELIMINARIES

1.0. Scope of Text

Whether or not one statement entails another statement is one of the principal concerns of logic. At the outset we can characterize entailment somewhat vaguely thus: A statement S_1 is said to *entail* a statement S_2 if, in virtue solely of their meanings, the statement S_2 would be true if the statement S_1 should be true.[1] This explanation of entailment is too vague to be of much use. Dissipating *some* of that vagueness is one of the most important tasks of logic. We said *dissipating some* rather than *all* the vagueness, because not every entailment is a matter of logic. Logic is concerned with entailment only insofar as it turns on the meaning of very special topic-neutral words, the so-called *logical words*, such as 'not', 'and', 'or', 'every', 'is the same as', 'possibly', and the like. Although 'John is a bachelor' entails 'John is unmarried', that entailment is not a matter of logic since it depends crucially on the meaning of non-logical words such as 'bachelor' and 'unmarried'. By restricting itself to entailments turning only on logical words, logic may give the impression of being irrelevant to headier disciplines such as sociology, physics, and mathematics. But quite the opposite is true. Precisely because the expressions it studies are topic neutral, the findings of logic are relevant to every subject matter. And because those expressions are extremely basic, the relevance to any given subject matter is so far reaching as to be truly profound.

Elementary logic treats of entailment insofar as it turns on nothing more than the meaning of such words as 'not', 'and', 'or', and 'every'. For example, it is by virtue of the meaning of 'and' that statement (1) entails statement (2):

(1) The Royal Society was chartered in 1662 and Louis XIV established the French Academy in 1666.

(2) The Royal Society was chartered in 1662.

Hence, that (1) entails (2) is a matter of elementary logic. *Elementary logic with identity* treats of entailment insofar as it depends

[1] In the context of definition, the word 'if' has the force of 'if and only if'.

3

also on the meaning of such expressions as 'is the same as' or 'is identical with'. For example, the assessment that 'The morning star is the same as Venus' entails 'Venus is the same as the morning star' comes within the province of elementary logic with identity. Parts One, Two, and Four of this book deal with elementary logic and elementary logic with identity. Part Three is devoted to *modal logic*, which studies entailment insofar as it turns also on the meaning of such expressions as 'necessarily' and 'possibly'.

1.1. Symbolic Logic; the Logistic Method

In former times one spoke of *logic;* nowadays one speaks of *symbolic logic* or, as it is sometimes called, *mathematical logic*. The adjective 'symbolic' is somewhat misleading since, as far as the use or study of symbols goes, symbolic logic does not differ significantly from the older logics. From the beginning (Aristotle, fourth century B.C.) logicians have been concerned with symbols, a concern that is part of their more general concern with language itself. It is, rather, the kinds of languages that are studied which distinguish symbolic logicians from their venerable ancestors. Formerly logicians studied *natural languages* (such as Greek, Russian, and English). More precisely, they investigated a number of stereotyped expressions of natural languages. But toward the latter part of the nineteenth century, a revolutionary change occurred. Logicians began to eschew natural languages, however stereotyped and supplemented with special symbols, in favor of so-called *formalized languages* (*artificial languages, symbolic languages*). Because formalized languages afford all the advantages of stereotyping without the pitfalls and complexities of natural languages, their study opened a new epoch in the history of logic.

The aforesaid way of doing logic—through detailed study of formalized languages—is known as the *logistic method*. A simple illustration may help to explain the method. It should be clear from the meaning of the conjunctive word 'and' that the order of conjuncts is immaterial to the truth value of a conjunction. (The truth value of a sentence consists simply in its being true or in its being false. A true sentence is said to have the *truth-value truth,* and a false sentence is said to have the *truth-value falsehood.*) For example, the conjunctions (1) and (3)

(3)   Louis XIV established the French Academy in 1666, and the Royal Society was chartered in 1662.

must have the same truth value, since they differ only by the order of their conjuncts. This feature of conjunction—that the order of the conjuncts is immaterial to the truth value of a conjunction—is called the *commutativity of conjunction*. Notice that the properties of conjunction are apparently mirrored or paralleled by the behavior of the word 'and'. This observation suggests a promising strategy for studying conjunction. Rather than speak of the properties of conjunction, why not instead speak of the behavior of the word 'and'? For example, instead of saying that conjunction is commutative, say rather that any compound sentence[2] of the form $\ulcorner A$ and $B \urcorner$ must have the same truth value as the compound $\ulcorner B$ and $A \urcorner$. The main drawback to this reformulation is that it is false. Consider, for example, these two conjunctions:

(4) Elizabeth got married and became pregnant.
(5) Elizabeth became pregnant and got married.

Now, depending on the sort of girl Elizabeth is, (5) may well be false even though (4) is true. So the behavior of 'and' fails to mirror or parallel the properties of conjunction well enough to turn talk about the latter into talk about the former.

It is not hard to see why the parallelism breaks down. As used in (4) and (5), the word 'and' does more than express conjunction; it also introduces a temporal element, signifying that the event described by the first conjunct antedates the event described by the second. In (1) and (3), on the other hand, the word 'and' expresses only conjunction. Words that have several different uses or meanings are said to be *ambiguous*. It is clearly the ambiguity of 'and' which upsets the desired parallelism. So, if talk about conjunction is going to be reduced to talk about 'and', that little word must be divested of all its other uses and meanings. One could do this by introducing distinct words for distinct uses of 'and'. For example, one might let 'and_1' express pure conjunction, 'and_2' correspond to the use to which 'and' is put in (4), and so on.

But the program to reduce talk about conjunction to talk about 'and' runs up against an obstacle even more serious than ambiguity: the communication-oriented character of English syntax. Unluckily for the logician, English grammar evolved so as to facilitate communication, not so as to mirror logical structure (at least not mainly so). If there were a strict parallelism between the properties

[2] Throughout this book we use the word 'sentence' to mean 'declarative sentence', and we treat 'sentence' and 'statement' as synonyms.

of conjunction and the behavior of 'and', sentence (6) would be synonymous with sentence (7) by virtue of the commutativity of conjunction:

(6)   Torricelli and Pascal experimented with the mercury barometer.

(7)   Pascal experimented with the mercury barometer and Torricelli.

But, privy to the meaning of (6), we know that 'Torricelli' is not one of its conjuncts. Rather, the conjuncts of (6) are the sentences (8) and (9):

(8)   Torricelli experimented with the mercury barometer.

(9)   Pascal experimented with the mercury barometer.

To make the conjunctive structure of (6) explicit, we could paraphrase it thus:

(10)   Torricelli experimented with the mercury barometer and Pascal experimented with the mercury barometer.

Albeit longwinded, (10) is better suited to our program (parallelism) than is the more idiomatic (6). Judicious paraphrase can thus bring out logical structure but usually at the sacrifice of brevity and ease of communication. Normally, therefore, a person will resort to paraphrase to the degree his concern is logical. At one extreme is the common man who employs it only to settle misunderstandings. At the other extreme is the symbolic logician who employs it as a matter of policy. *Qua* logician, he is willing to sacrifice economy of expression to render logical structure explicit. Paraphrase, however, is not systematic enough for him; it depends too much on insight into intended meaning. So the symbolic logician extends or perfects the device of paraphrasing in the following way. He designs languages in which syntactical structure is made to mirror logical structure, languages in which, for example, the properties of conjunction are faithfully reflected in the legislated behavior of the symbol for conjunction, be that symbol the word 'and' or some arbitrarily chosen design such as '∧' or '&' or '·'. These languages are the formalized languages alluded to above.

2. TRUTH-FUNCTIONAL SENTENCE CONNECTIVES (I)

2.0. Conjunction

The English conjunctive word 'and' is a binary sentence connective that has several uses or meanings only one of which we single out for study. As the label suggests, a *sentence connective* is an expression that joins or compounds sentences so as to produce another sentence. A *binary* sentence connective joins two sentences to produce a third. For example, we can join (8) to (9) by means of the binary connective 'and' to get the compound sentence (10). And (10) could be joined to (11)

(11)   The Royal Society was chartered in 1662.

to produce sentence (12), and so on:

(12)   (Torricelli experimented with the mercury barometer and Pascal experimented with the mercury barometer), and the Royal Society was chartered in 1662.

[Notice that parentheses were inserted in (12) to indicate the intended *groupings*, that is, to show which sentences were joined by which occurrence of the connective 'and'. Without parentheses or a similar device, there would be no way of knowing.]

A noteworthy feature of the use to which 'and' has been put in the foregoing examples is this: The truth values of the compound sentences (conjunctions) depend entirely on the truth values of the joined components (conjuncts). The compound is true if both components are true; otherwise, the compound is false. For example, (12) is true if and only if both (10) and (11) are true. By an *n-ary* sentence connective is meant a sentence connective that joins together n sentences to produce a compound sentence. An *n*-ary sentence connective is said to be *truth functional* if, whenever it joins n sentences to form a compound, the truth value of the compound depends on nothing more than the truth values of the joined components. Thus, as we have used it above, 'and' is a binary truth-functional sentence connective whose meaning is encapsuled in the simple chart below. This chart will be known as the *fundamental truth table for conjunction:*

A	B	A and B
t	t	t
t	f	f
f	t	f
f	f	f

In the above table the capital letters '*A*' and '*B*' stand for or represent any (declarative) sentences whatsoever. The rows of the table indicate the truth value of the compound when the components have the indicated truth values. For example, the second row informs us that when *A* is true and *B* false, the conjunction ⌜*A* and *B*⌝ is false.

The English conjunctive word 'and' has other uses which are not truth functional. For example, we remarked in Section 1.1 that the truth value of the compound sentence (5) depends on more than the truth values of its components (13) and (14):

(13)   Elizabeth became pregnant.
(14)   Elizabeth got married.

Even if (13) and (14) are both true, (5) may be either true or false according as pregnancy antedated ceremony or not. Were this use of 'and' truth functional, the truth value of (5) would be fixed or determined by the truth values of (13) and (14), which is clearly not the case. In the formalized languages of this book the raised dot '·' will be used as a binary sentence connective answering to the truth-functional use of 'and'. But unlike 'and', the (raised) dot will be put to no other uses. Thus the fundamental truth table given below for the dot looks exactly like the one given above for 'and', and we shall read expressions of the form ⌜*A* · *B*⌝ quite naturally as ⌜*A* and *B*⌝.

A	B	A · B
t	t	t
t	f	f
f	t	f
f	f	f

2.1. Disjunction or Alternation

Like 'and', the English disjunctive word 'or' is often used truth functionally. But unlike 'and', the connective 'or' has two truth-functional uses. Compound sentences formed by combining sentences by means of 'or' are called *disjunctions* or *alternations*. Depending on which truth-functional use is intended, the disjunction of (8) and (9), namely (15),

>   (15)   Torricelli experimented with the mercury barometer or Pascal experimented with the mercury barometer.

can mean either (16) or (17).

>   (16)   Torricelli experimented with the mercury barometer or Pascal experimented with the mercury barometer, or both.
>   (17)   Torricelli experimented with the mercury barometer or Pascal experimented with the mercury barometer, but not both.

If (15) is meant as (16), the disjunction is said to be *weak* or *inclusive*. An inclusive disjunction is true if at least one of its two components is true; otherwise, it is false. Both components of (15) are true, so (15) will itself be true if the disjunction is meant to be inclusive. In our formalized languages the binary connective 'v' will answer to the inclusive or weak use of 'or', and we will read $\ulcorner A \vee B \urcorner$ as $\ulcorner A$ or $B \urcorner$. The connective 'v' is called the *wedge* and derives from the Latin word 'vel', which means 'or' in the weak or inclusive sense. Below is the fundamental truth table for the wedge:

A	B	$A \vee B$
t	t	t
t	f	t
f	t	t
f	f	f

But if (15) is meant rather as (17), the disjunction or alternation is said to be *strong* or *exclusive*. An exclusive disjunction is true if exactly one of its two components is true; otherwise, it is false. For example, (15) is false if the disjunction is meant to be exclusive.

Exclusive disjunction will not be as basic to our formalized languages as inclusive disjunction. We will not even officially introduce a symbol answering to strong disjunction (unofficially, one will be introduced in an exercise). This omission does not mean that one who speaks our formalized languages will be at a loss for words to assert the exclusive disjunction of two sentences, but it does mean that he will have to make do with surrogates. Hereafter, when we speak without qualification of disjunction, inclusive disjunction will be meant.

2.2. Negation

The expression 'it is not the case that' can be applied to a sentence to form another sentence which negates or contradicts the first. For example, sentence (18)

(18)   It is not the case that Elizabeth got married.

contradicts (14). There is no harm but rather a great deal of advantage in looking upon (18) as a "compound" sentence which is produced by "joining" (14) to nothing by means of the singulary sentence connective 'it is not the case that'. Such a "compound sentence" will be called the *negation of* its single component sentence. The connective 'it is not the case that' is clearly truth functional; a negation is true or false according as its component is false or true. In our formalized languages, the symbol '∼', called the *tilde*, corresponds to the singulary connective 'it is not the case that'. We will read ⌜∼A⌝ as ⌜it is not the case that A⌝ or, for short, just ⌜not A⌝. The fundamental truth table for the tilde is shown below:

A	$\sim A$
t	f
f	t

The tilde, wedge, and dot are the only sentence connectives of the formalized languages about to be introduced. Whether this paucity of connectives means that speakers of these languages are truth-functionally inarticulate is a problem that will be discussed presently.

3. EXERCISES

(1) Let '≢' be introduced as a symbol for exclusive disjunction. Construct the fundamental truth table for this binary truth-functional connective.

(2) Is the binary connective 'because' truth functional in any of its uses? Defend your answer. Mention three or four English sentence connectives that are not truth functional.

(3) How many binary truth-functional connectives are there altogether? (*Hint:* How many different fundamental truth tables can be constructed for an arbitrary binary connective?)

(4) How many singulary truth-functional connectives are there altogether?

(5) Explain in detail why parentheses are needed to indicate the intended groupings within sentence (12).

(6) When A is true, B true, and C false, what is the truth value of each of the following:

$\sim A$	$A \vee [B \cdot C]$	$C \vee [A \cdot B]$	$\sim[A \cdot B]$
$\sim C$	$A \cdot [B \vee C]$	$C \cdot [A \vee B]$	$\sim[A \vee B]$
$\sim\sim A$	$A \vee [B \vee C]$	$C \vee [A \cdot C]$	$\sim\sim[A \vee [B \cdot C]]$
$\sim\sim C$	$A \cdot [B \cdot C]$	$C \vee [C \vee C]$	

(7) Use judicious paraphrase to bring out the two possible meanings of the ambiguous sentence 'Every number is greater than some number'.

(8) Suppose we were to introduce a binary truth-functional connective '&', called the *ampersand*, such that a compound ⌜A & B⌝ is true if and only if both A and B are true. In what sense would the ampersand and the dot be the same connective? In what sense would they be different? Go back to Exercises (3) and (4), remove the ambiguity, and answer the resulting unambiguous exercises.

4. LANGUAGE SCHEMA P

4.0. Vocabulary

It took you many years to learn tolerably well the syntax or grammar of your native English, but only a few minutes are needed to master the syntax or grammar of the formalized languages to be presented in this book. We will understand the *grammar* of a language to consist of two parts, its *vocabulary* and its *grammatical rules*. When dealing with formalized languages, we will often refer to grammatical rules as *formation rules*.

The first group of formalized languages that we will study have a common grammar; that is, they share the same vocabulary and have the same formation rules. We call this common grammatical frame *language schema P*, or, for short, "LSP." The vocabulary of LSP consists of infinitely many symbols. Specifically it consists of:

(i)   An infinite supply of *sentential variables:* 'p', 'q', 'r', 's', 'p_1', 'q_1', 'r_1', 's_1', 'p_2' , ...

(ii) One singulary sentence connective: '$\sim$'.

(iii) Two binary sentence connectives: 'v' and '$\cdot$'.

(iv) Two grouping indicators: '[' and ']'.

Notice that the vocabulary of a formalized language consists only of a set of signs or symbols, called the *primitive symbols* of the language system. This contrasts markedly with the vocabulary entries one finds, for example, in an ordinary dictionary, which introduces not only a sign or word but also its meaning. Logicians, however, keep the syntax or grammar of a language quite separate from its semantics or theory of meaning. As part of its syntax, the vocabulary of a formalized language is nothing but a list of signs or symbols. When these signs or symbols are (eventually) invested with meaning, one has passed beyond syntax into the realm of semantics.

4.1. Formation Rules

We easily recognize the expression 'Nice guys finish last' to be grammatical, although we might frown on the use of the slang word 'guys'. With equal ease we reject as ungrammatical the expression 'Nice finish guys last'. Intuitively, we deem grammatical those English expressions which "make sense", that is, those expressions which are put together in a way that respects the categories of the words that comprise the expressions. If, for example, an expression has a verb where a noun is called for, we regard it as ungrammatical. That by and large we can easily recognize the grammaticalness of English expressions seems an extraordinary accomplishment when we reflect on the complexity of English grammar. So complex is it that no one has yet produced a completely adequate set of grammatical rules for English, though there are linguists hard at work trying to produce one. Like grammatical English expressions, the grammatical expressions of LSP are those of its expressions that are put together with respect for the categories of the symbols that make them up. But unlike the grammatical rules of English, those of LSP are extremely simple. In fact, just four rules suffice to define grammaticalness in LSP, but their convenient formulation requires the prior introduction of several technical terms.

By a *formula* is meant any finite linear string of symbols of the vocabulary. For example, '$[p \vee q]$', '$\sim\sim\sim[p \cdot \sim q]$', and '$\sim]\sim[\sim$' are all formulas of LSP. Those formulas which are grammatical are called *well-formed formulas*, or *wffs*. (The singular is '*wff*'.) Here, then, are the formation rules, that is, the grammatical rules, of LSP:

(i)   Any sentential variable is a wff.
(ii) If B is a wff, then $\ulcorner \sim B \urcorner$ is a wff.
(iii) If B and C are wffs, then so are $\ulcorner [B \vee C] \urcorner$ and $\ulcorner [B \cdot C] \urcorner$.
(iv) A formula is a wff if and only if it can be constructed by a finite number of applications of the preceding rules.

The following are a few examples of wffs of LSP:

$$\sim p \qquad\qquad \sim\sim q_5 \qquad\qquad\qquad \sim\sim\sim\sim\sim q$$
$$[p \vee \sim q] \qquad \sim\sim[\sim p \vee \sim\sim p] \qquad [[[p \vee q] \vee q] \vee q]$$
$$[p \cdot [q \vee r]] \qquad [[p \cdot q] \vee [q \cdot p]] \qquad r_8$$

Wffs that consist of a sentential variable standing alone are called *atomic wffs* because no proper subformula of such a wff is a wff. Thus 'p' and 'r_8' are atomic wffs, whereas '$\sim p$' and '$[p \vee q]$' are not.[1] Wffs of LSP which are not atomic are said to be *molecular*.

---

[1] The expression 'r_8' is a single symbol; it is not a complex of symbols made up of the signs 'r' and '8'.

Molecular wffs contain proper parts which are themselves wffs.

When a language is used to discuss or talk about a language, the former is called the *metalanguage* and the latter is called the *object language*. For example, we are using English to discuss the grammar of LSP, so English is the metalanguage and LSP is the object language of our discussion. Notice that the capital letters '*B*' and '*C*', which figure prominently in the statement of the grammatical rules of LSP, do not belong to the vocabulary of LSP and, therefore, do not occur in either its formulas or wffs. These capital letters function as metalinguistic devices for mentioning or referring to arbitrary formulas of LSP. For example, whatever formula '*B*' may be used to refer to, the expression '$\sim B$' refers to the formula that results when a tilde is placed immediately to the left of the formula to which '*B*' refers. We shall let the capital letters '*A*', '*B*', '*C*', and '*D*', with or without subscripts, play this metalinguistic role throughout. And, for greater clarity, we shall use from time to time lowercase letters '*a*', '*b*', '*c*', '*d*', with or without subscripts, as metalinguistic devices for referring to sentential variables. Thus a sentential variable can be referred to either by capitals or by lowercase letters. Other formulas can be referred to only by capital letters.[2]

Formation rules are commonly said to *characterize inductively* or to provide an *inductive definition* of the concept *wff*. The characterization or definition is *inductive* in the sense that the rules indicate that a formula is well formed if smaller parts of it are well formed, and that these smaller formulas are well formed if smaller parts of them are well formed, and so on until the smallest possible formulas are reached—single symbols. No matter how many symbols a formula may contain, it can be analyzed as made up of sub-formulas (smaller formulas) in only finitely many ways. Accordingly, application of the formation rules to determine well-formedness always terminates; that is, the one applying the rules will know after a finite lapse of time whether or not a given formula is well formed. The formation rules thus give rise to an infallible mechanical procedure for recognizing well-formedness, that is, a method that is guaranteed to supply in every case the correct answer in a finite amount of time without demanding any ingenuity

---

[2] On certain rare occasions, Greek letters will also be used as metalinguistic variables.

on the part of the one applying it. Such methods or procedures are said to be *effective*. Effective procedures are also called *algorithms*. The formation rules of LSP, therefore, yield an effective method or algorithm for recognizing well-formedness. An effective method or algorithm for recognizing the presence of a property is called a *decision procedure for* that property. Thus the formation rules of LSP yield a decision procedure for well-formedness.

4.2. Use and Mention; Quotation Marks and Corners

To *mention* (speak about, refer to) an object we *use* (employ) a name or description of it. For example, to mention (speak about) the second planet from the sun, we can use a name or description of it, such as 'Venus' or 'the morning star' or 'the evening star'.[3] Although no one would confuse a name or description of a planet with the planet itself, it is not uncommon for people to confuse a name or description of an abstract entity (such as the number ten) with the entity itself. For example, many people fail to realize that in the decimal system the expression '10' is not the number ten but only a name of it. Consequently, they are quite puzzled by a simple *linguistic shift* to a different numeral system, such as the binary system, in which the expression '10' names not the number ten but the number two. (In the binary system, the number ten is named by the expression '1010', and the expression '1010 > 10' means 'The number ten is greater than the number two'; in the decimal system the latter expression means 'The number one thousand ten is greater than the number ten'.)

It is perhaps even more common for people to confuse linguistic entities (linguistic expressions) with certain of their names or descriptions. For example, students of logic and mathematics would hardly confuse the left bracket with its name 'the left bracket', but they might easily confuse the left bracket with its name ' '[' '. For example, the expression 'Clearly, [is a symbol of LSP' is nonsense if taken literally. The author of such an expression undoubtedly intended to mention (say something about) the left bracket but failed to use a name or description of it to do so, vainly trying to make the bracket itself do the job that its names do.

[3] It is a fact of astronomy that Venus, which happens to be the second planet from the sun, is the morning star, and that the morning star is also the evening star.

What he obviously meant was 'Clearly, '[' is a symbol of LSP'. The names of expressions that are apt to be confused with the expressions themselves are those names of expressions which are formed by flanking the expressions with single quotation marks. For example, the expression

'['

is not the left bracket but rather a name of the left bracket, whereas the expression

' '[' '

is not a name of the left bracket but a name of a name of the left bracket.

It is of paramount importance in logic to distinguish clearly use and mention, especially when linguistic expressions are the topic of discussion. Accordingly, we shall observe the use-mention distinction rather scrupulously, violating it only when we think such action will contribute significantly to clarity without being unduly misleading. But to observe faithfully the use-mention distinction with respect to using and mentioning linguistic expressions, we need a quasi-quotation device (which we have already used several times) to do easily an important job done only very awkwardly using single quotation marks. To illustrate what this job is, suppose we were to rewrite formation rule (ii) using single quotation marks:

(ii)'   If B is a wff, then '$\sim B$' is a wff.

Taken literally, rule (ii)' says that the two-symbols-long expression consisting of the tilde followed by the letter 'B' is a wff of LSP. That, of course, is sheer nonsense, because 'B' isn't even a primitive symbol of LSP. But rule (ii) was written with so-called *corners* ('$\ulcorner$' and '$\urcorner$'), not with single quotation marks. Corners function, so to speak, as *selective* quotation marks, applying to certain expressions that appear between them, not applying to others. Specifically, *corners apply to (quote) object-language symbols but do not apply to (quote) metalinguistic symbols*. Thus rule (ii) asserts that, if B is a wff of LSP, then the formula which consists of '$\sim$' followed by the wff B is a wff of LSP. And rule (iii) asserts in part that if B and C are wffs of LSP, the formula consisting of '[' followed by B followed by 'v' followed by C followed by ']' is a wff of LSP. As a last example, if A, B, and C are wffs of LSP, then $\ulcorner \sim [A \text{ v } [\sim B \cdot C]] \urcorner$ is the wff consisting of '$\sim$' followed by '[' followed by A followed by 'v' followed by '[' followed by '∼' followed by B followed by '·' followed by C followed by ']' followed by ']'. Corners are the invention of the distinguished logician and philosopher W. V. O. Quine. Without corners or some other device or convention for selective quotation, it would be very awkward to write an intelligible book on logic.

5. EXERCISES

(1) Can a language be used to discuss itself, that is, can the same language be both object language and metalanguage? If so, give examples; if not, explain why not.

(2) To show that the wff '$\sim[p \lor \sim q]$' is constructed from its atomic components in accordance with the formation rules, we proceed as follows. Rule (i) certifies both 'p' and 'q' as well formed. By rule (ii) we have that '$\sim q$' is well formed because 'q' is well formed. By rule (iii), we have that '$[p \lor \sim q]$' is a wff because both 'p' and '$\sim q$' are wffs. And finally, by rule (ii) again, we have that '$\sim[p \lor \sim q]$' is well formed because '$[p \lor \sim q]$' is a wff. For each formula presented as an example of a wff in Section 4.1, follow the above procedure to show that the formula is constructed from its atomic components in accordance with the formation rules.

(3) Prove that none of the following formulas are well formed: '$[p]$', 'pq', '$[\lor]$', '$[p \cdot [q \lor r]$', '$[\sim[p \lor q]]$', '$\sim[q]$'. To prove that a formula B is not well formed, one may show that there is no way to construct, in accordance with the formation rules, the formula B out of whatever atomic wffs it may contain.

(4) Why might one expect the grammatical rules of a formalized language to be simpler than those of a natural language?

(5) Indicate which of the following are true:

(a) Venus is Venus.

(b) Venus is named by 'Venus'.

(c) Venus is 'Venus'.

(d) 'Venus' is 'Venus'.

(e) Venus is named by Venus.

(f) 'Venus' is ⌜Venus⌝.

(g) ⌜Venus⌝ is ⌜Venus⌝.

(h) '$[p \lor q]$' is ⌜$[p \lor q]$⌝.

(i) Venus is named by ⌜Venus⌝.

(j) '⌜p⌝' is a name of ⌜p⌝.

(6)   Formulate in detail a decision procedure (algorithm) for well-formedness on the basis of the formation rules of LSP.

(7)   Which of the sentences that appear in Exercise (5) mention the second planet from the sun? Which mention the first sentential variable of LSP? Which mention a name of Venus?

(8)   The vocabulary of LSP contains infinitely many primitive symbols. Nonetheless, we could have got along just as well with only a finite number of primitive symbols if we had treated variables such as 'r_8' as complex symbols. For example, we might have let '$\sim$', 'v', '·', '[', ']', 'p', 'q', 'r', 's', '0', '1', '2', . . ., '9' be a complete list of the primitive symbols. Then we might have advanced an inductive definition of the numerals '1', '2', . . ., '9', '10', ... Then we could have defined a variable of LSP to be any of the letters 'p', 'q', 'r', 's', or any of those letters followed by a numeral. Reformulate the grammar of LSP on the basis of a finite vocabulary.

6. SEMANTICS OF LANGUAGE SCHEMA P

6.0. Semantics

The *semantics* of a language is the theory of the meaning of its grammatical expressions. As one might surmise from the simplicity of its grammar, the semantics of LSP is also extremely simple. Practically the entire semantics was presented in Chapter 2 and is summarized by the fundamental truth tables for negation, conjunction, and disjunction. There remains only one minor point that calls for explanation. The semantics of LSP stipulates that '[p v q]' has the value truth if either 'p' or 'q' has the value truth, and falsehood if both 'p' and 'q' have the value falsehood. But how do sentential variables, which are not bonafide sentences at all, have truth values? The answer is simple: They don't until we deliberately give them truth values. We speak of such action as *assigning truth values to* the sentential variables. For example, we might give to 'p' the truth-value truth and to 'q' the truth-value falsehood.

It then follows from the fundamental truth table for disjunction that the alternation '$[p \lor q]$' is true under that assignment of truth values to its sentential variables. How such truth-value assignments are made is the subject of Section 6.2.

6.1. Truth Tables

When all the sentential variables of a wff of LSP are assigned truth values, the semantical rules of LSP, which are summarized by the fundamental truth tables for the tilde, dot, and wedge, determine a unique truth value for the given wff. The truth value so determined is said to be the *value of* the given wff *for* or *under* the given value assignment to its variables.[1] Since the wffs of LSP are built up from sentential variables stepwise through negation, conjunction, and disjunction, repeated application of the three fundamental truth tables will disclose the value of a wff under any given value assignment to its variables. To illustrate this repetitive or inductive procedure, we will determine the value of the wff '$\sim[\sim p \lor [q \cdot p]]$' for a certain value assignment to its variables: truth assigned to 'p' and falsehood to 'q'. We do this by employing a *three-step evaluational procedure*.

Step One. Indicate beneath every occurrence of a variable the truth value assigned to that variable by the given value assignment. Where 't' and 'f' abbreviate 'truth' and 'falsehood', respectively, step one yields the following configuration:

$$\sim[\sim p \lor [q \cdot p]]$$
$$tft$$

Step Two. Appealing to the fundamental truth tables for the connectives, determine the values of the next smallest wffs, scratching out as you go those occurrences of 't' or 'f' which were relevant to this determination. (The motive for scratching out is simply to avoid mistakes that might arise from having too many 't's and 'f's close together.) Applied to the example, step two yields this configuration:

$$\sim[\sim p \lor [q \cdot p]]$$
$$f\ \cancel{t}f\ f\ \cancel{t}$$

Step Three. Reapply step two until it can no longer be applied; there will remain a single 't' or 'f' which indicates the value of the

---

[1] An assignment of truth values to the sentential variables of a wff, that is, a value assignment, is also called an *interpretation* of the wff.

wff under the given value assignment to its sentential variables. (The connective directly above this remaining occurrence of 't' or 'f' is said to be the *main connective of* the given wff.) Application of step three to the example yields first the interim configuration:

$\sim[\sim p \vee [q \cdot p]]$
  f f f f f f

and then the terminal configuration:

$\sim[\sim p \vee [q \cdot p]]$
 t f f f f f f

The terminal configuration shows that the wff '$\sim[\sim p \vee [q \cdot p]]$' comes out true for the values truth of 'p' and falsehood of 'q'. (It also shows that the first occurrence of the tilde is the main connective of the given wff.)

As a second illustration, application of the three-step evaluational procedure to determine the value of

$[[r \vee [\sim q \cdot \sim p]] \cdot \sim \sim p]$

for the value assignment of truth to 'p' and falsehood to both 'q' and 'r' terminates in the configuration

$[[r \vee [\sim q \cdot \sim p]] \cdot \sim \sim p]$
 f f f f f f f f f f f

which shows that the value of the wff is falsehood for the given system of values of its sentential variables. (The second occurrence of the dot is the main connective of this wff.) But, for the values truth of 'p' and 'r' and falsehood of 'q', we get the configuration

$[[r \vee [\sim q \cdot \sim p]] \cdot \sim \sim p]$
 f f f f f f f t f f f

which shows that the wff comes out true under this value assignment to its variables. A wff that, like the one just examined, comes out true under some value assignments to its variables and comes out false under other value assignments to its variables is called a *contingent* wff. Wffs that come out true under all possible value assignments to their variables are said to be *valid*. And wffs that come out false under all possible value assignments to their variables are called *invalid* wffs. By a *nonvalid* wff is meant a wff that comes out false under at least one value assignment to its variables. The concepts of *invalid wff* and *nonvalid wff* must be kept distinct; both contingent and invalid wffs are nonvalid, but contingent wffs are not invalid. The accompanying chart may help the reader get command of this terminology:

Nonvalid wffs

Valid wffs	Contingent wffs	Invalid wffs

The tripartite classification of the wffs of LSP into valid, contingent, and invalid wffs is mutually exclusive and jointly exhaustive of these wffs. The classification is *mutually exclusive* in the sense that no wff belongs to more than one of the three classes. It is *jointly exhaustive* in the sense that every wff belongs to at least one of them. Our three-step evaluational procedure furnishes us with an effective method or algorithm for determining to which class—the valid wffs, the contingent wffs, or the invalid wffs—a given wff of LSP belongs. The essence of the method lies in the construction of a chart known as a *truth table*, which shows the value of a given wff under each possible value assignment to its sentential variables.

For a wff such as '$\sim[p \vee \sim p]$', which contains occurrences of only one sentential variable, there are only two possible value assignments to its variables, that is, only two assignments of truth values to its variables. Namely, one can assign truth to the variable, or one can assign falsehood to it. These two possible value assignments are represented by the rows of the following table:

p	$\sim[p \vee \sim p]$
t	
f	

But there are four possible value assignments for a wff that contains occurrences of exactly two distinct sentential variables: One can assign truth to both variables, or truth to the first and falsehood to the second, or falsehood to the first and truth to the second, or falsehood to both. The rows of the following table represent the

four possible value assignments to the two variables of the wff
'[∼p ∨ [p · q]]':

p	q	[∼p ∨ [p · q]]
t	t	
t	f	
f	t	
f	f	

In general, it is easy to prove that there are exactly 2^k possible
value assignments to the variables of a wff that contains occurrences of exactly k distinct sentential variables. For example,
$2^3 = 8$, so there are eight possible value assignments to the variables of the wff '∼[[p ∨ q] · [q ∨ r]]', those represented by the rows
of the following table:

p	q	r	∼[[p ∨ q] · [q ∨ r]]
t	t	t	
t	t	f	
t	f	t	
t	f	f	
f	t	t	
f	t	f	
f	f	t	
f	f	f	

Suppose we wish to discover whether a given wff, say
'[∼p ∨ [p · q]]', is valid, contingent, or invalid. The three-step
evaluational procedure enables us to determine the value of the
wff for any given value assignment to its variables, so we merely
apply this procedure to each possible value assignment to the
variables of the given wff. For convenience, we first construct a
table like those above, the rows of which represent all the possible
value assignments to the variables. Then, moving from row to row,
we apply the three-step evaluational procedure to the value assignment represented by each row of the table to determine the value

of the given wff under each value assignment. The end result is a truth table. Applying the procedure just described to the wff '[$\sim p$ v [$p \cdot q$]]', we obtain the following truth table:

p	q	[$\sim p$ v [$p \cdot q$]]
t	t	f f t f f f
t	f	f f f f f f
f	t	f f t f f f
f	f	f f t f f f

The above truth table shows that '[$\sim p$ v [$p \cdot q$]]' is a contingent wff, because it comes out false under the value assignment represented by the second row (namely truth to 'p' and falsehood to 'q') and true under the three other value assignments. The truth table below shows that the wff '$\sim$[p v $\sim p$]' is invalid.

p	$\sim$[p v $\sim p$]
t	f f f f f
f	f f f f f

The truth table below shows that the rather complex wff for which it is constructed is valid.

p	q	r	[$\sim$[[$\sim p$ v q] $\cdot$ [$\sim q$ v r]] v [r v $\sim p$]]
t	t	t	f f f f f f f f f f t f f f f
t	t	f	f f f f f f f f f f t f f f f
t	f	t	f f f f f f f f f f t f f f f
t	f	f	f f f f f f f f f f t f f f f
f	t	t	f f f f f f f f f f t f f f f
f	t	f	f f f f f f f f f f t f f f f
f	f	t	f f f f f f f f f f t f f f f
f	f	f	f f f f f f f f f f t f f f f

Notice that the order of the rows of a truth table is quite irrelevant to the purpose for which a truth table is constructed, namely to show what values a wff takes on under the various possible value assignments to its variables. Thus the truth table below codifies the same information as the first truth table exhibited in this section.

p	q	$[\sim p \vee [p \cdot q]]$
t	f	f f f f f f
t	t	f f t f f f
f	f	f f t f f f
f	t	f f t f f f

Equally immaterial is the order of the columns headed by the various variables of the wff, because the order in which values are assigned to the variables of a wff in no way affects the value which the wff takes on under that value assignment. Thus the truth table below codifies the same information as does the one immediately above.

q	p	$[\sim p \vee [p \cdot q]]$
f	t	f f f f f f
t	t	f f t f f f
f	f	f f t f f f
t	f	f f t f f f

In short, as far as the construction of a truth table for a wff goes, it makes no difference in what sequence one enters the variables as column headings or in what order one indicates the various possible value assignments to those variables.

In the construction of truth tables we possess a simple and effective method or algorithm for deciding whether a given wff is valid, contingent, or invalid. Simplicity and effectiveness, however, often walk hand in hand with labor and tedium. To convince himself that the method can become tedious, the reader is invited to construct a truth table for a wff with occurrences of eight distinct variables. Such a table will contain 2^8, or 256, rows. The construction of such a table will not test in any way the intelligence or ingenuity of the reader, but it will tax his industry and patience. Fortunately for the dispositions of all concerned, the wffs of practical interest for logic rarely exhibit occurrences of more than four variables. (Our logical theory must apply, of course, to all wffs, however many variables they contain.)

6.2.   Interpreting Language Schema P

There are two quite different ways to assign truth values to sentential variables. The first and obvious way is merely to stipulate that certain sentential variables have certain truth values. For example, one might stipulate that 'p' has the value truth and that 'q' has the value falsehood. A wff all the variables of which have been assigned truth values is said to be *interpreted*, and the value assignment to its variables is called an *interpretation*. (Similarly, a class Γ of wffs is said to be *interpreted* if a truth value is assigned to every variable that occurs in any member of the class Γ. The above-mentioned value assignment to 'p' and 'q', for example, provides an interpretation of the set of all the wffs of LSP which contain no variables other than 'p' and 'q'.) Our three-step evaluational procedure enables us to determine the truth value of an interpreted wff, provided only that we know what truth values are assigned to its variables by the interpretation (value assignment).

The second way of assigning truth values to sentential variables is particularly important for the application of LSP to the logical analysis of English discourse. Rather than a mere stipulation that certain variables have certain truth values, this second way consists in stipulating that certain sentential variables are synonymous with, that is, mean the same as, certain English sentences. For example, one might stipulate that 'p' means the same as (is synonymous with) sentence (8) and that 'q' means the same as sentence (9). As a by-product of making a sentential variable synonymous with an English (declarative) sentence, the variable takes on a truth value, namely the truth value of the English sentence with which it is declared synonymous. For example, if 'p' is declared synonymous with (8), 'p' takes on or acquires the value truth, because (8) is true.

We will speak of the truth value of a sentence as *the referent of* the sentence. Thus truth is the referent of (8) and falsehood is the referent of (19).

(19)   Torricelli did not experiment with the mercury barometer.

Synonymous sentences will be said *to have the same sense*. For example, (6) and (10) have the same sense, whereas (6) and (8) do not. We *endow* a sentential variable *with reference*, that is, give it a referent, when we assign it a truth value. We *endow* it *with sense* when we declare it synonymous with some English sentence. The first of the two ways of interpreting or assigning truth values to sentential variables, therefore, amounts simply to endowing them with reference; the second consists in endowing them with sense, which, of course, brings reference along in its wake.

We have already seen that a value assignment to the variables of a wff confers a truth value on the wff itself. For example, the value assignment of truth to 'p' and falsehood to 'q' confers the value truth on '$\sim[p \cdot q]$'. In other words, a wff is endowed with reference once its variables are endowed with reference. Similarly, a wff is endowed with sense once its variables are endowed with sense. For example, when 'p' and 'q' are declared synonymous with (8) and (9), respectively, the wff '$[p \cdot q]$' becomes synonymous with both (6) and (10), as our grasp of the meaning of these sentences attests.

But synonymy is a slippery relation and it is fortunate that most direct applications of symbolic logic do not depend on the ability to recognize it. Many direct applications do depend, however, on the ability to discern *mutual entailment*, which is a much weaker relation than synonymy. (Two sentences are said to be *mutually entailing* if each entails the other.) Even our rather vague understanding of entailment is sufficient for us to see that sentences which are mutually entailing have the same truth value. For example, (6) and (10) have the same truth value; even though we might not know which truth value they have, we do know that they have the same truth value because they are mutually entailing. In general, synonymous sentences are mutually entailing, but the converse is not always true. Sentences (20) and (21), for example, are obviously not synonymous,

(20)   All bachelors are unmarried.
(21)   Whoever has a sister has a female sibling.

yet they are mutually entailing.[2] When '*p*' and '*q*' are declared synonymous with (8) and (9), respectively, even someone who hesitates to say that '[*p* · *q*]' becomes synonymous with (6) might concede that '[*p* · *q*]' and (6) become mutually entailing, and that is all that is needed for many of the applications of our logical theory to the logical analysis of English discourse.

By now it should be apparent that LSP is not itself a language but is rather the common structure or skeleton of the infinite array of languages that result when variables of LSP are endowed with sense. Each way of endowing them with sense gives rise to a different language. By a P-*language* we understand any of the languages that result when variables of LSP are endowed with sense. By studying the common structure of P-languages, LSP, we effect a notable economy in that our findings apply equally and impartially to each of the infinitely many P-languages.

It should also be clear now why the symbols '*p*', '*q*', '*r*', and so on, are called sentential variables. They are called *variables* because they take on whatever truth value we choose to give them. The adjective 'sentential' reminds us that these variables are to be given the sort of meaning which sentences have, that is, that once endowed with sense they become bonafide sentences of a genuine language.[3]

7. EXERCISES

(1) Mention several mutually exclusive and jointly exhaustive classifications of human beings.

(2) For each of the following wffs, construct a truth table to determine whether it is valid, contingent, or invalid.

---

[2] A statement such as (20) or (21), that is true in virtue of its meaning alone, is entailed by any statement.

[3] Sentential variables are called *propositional variables* by some authors, *truth-value variables* by others, and *sentence letters* by still others.

$\sim[p \lor p]$ $[\sim p \lor [p \lor q]]$ $[\sim p \lor [[p \cdot q] \lor [\sim p \cdot r]]]$
$[\sim p \lor p]$ $[[p \cdot \sim q] \lor [\sim \sim p \cdot q]]$
$\sim[[[\sim p \lor q] \lor [\sim q \lor p]] \lor r]$ $[p \cdot \sim p]$
$\sim[[p \lor [\sim p \cdot q]] \lor [\sim p \cdot \sim q]]$ $[\sim p \lor [[p \lor q] \cdot [p \lor r]]]$

Find the main connective of each of these wffs.

(3)   Which of the wffs exhibited in Exercise (2) are invalid? Which are nonvalid? Is every invalid wff also nonvalid? Is every nonvalid wff also invalid?

(4)   It is customary to call valid sentential wffs *tautologies*. That is, the tautologies of LSP are the same as the valid wffs of LSP. Similarly, it is customary to refer to invalid wffs as *contradictory*. Keeping this terminology in mind, determine which of the following classifications are mutually exclusive and jointly exhaustive of the wffs of LSP:

(a)   Classification into tautologies and nonvalid wffs.

(b)   Classification into contingent, contradictory, and valid wffs.

(c)   Classification into tautologies, contingent wffs, and nonvalid wffs.

(d)   Classification into tautologies, invalid, and contingent wffs.

(5)   Prove that there are exactly 2^k possible assignments of truth values to the variables of a wff of LSP which contains occurrences of exactly k distinct sentential variables.

(6)   Develop an effective procedure or algorithm for enumerating all the possible value assignments to the variables of an arbitrary wff of LSP.

[7]   As the construction of a truth table can be a tedious task, try to invent short-cut procedures for determining whether a wff is valid, contingent, or contradictory.

(8)   Where 'p' is synonymous with 'Washington was the first president of the United States' and 'q' is synonymous with 'Six is a prime number', determine the reference of (that is, find the truth value of) each of the following wffs:

$\sim[\sim p \lor q]$ $[[p \cdot q] \lor q]$ $[\sim p \lor \sim q]$

For each of the above wffs (sentences of the indicated P-language), write an English sentence that entails it and is entailed by it.

(9)   In what sense is mutual entailment a weaker relation than synonymy?

{10} If the wffs of practical interest in sentential logic rarely contain more than four distinct variables, why should the logician bother to develop a general theory that applies to wffs with an arbitrary number of sentential variables?

8. LOGICAL TRUTH AND ANALYTICITY

8.0.   Logical Truth and Logical Falsehood

We observed in Section 6.2 that a P-language is a genuine language; it boasts wffs (grammatical expressions) that are bonafide sentences exhibiting both sense and reference. A true sentence of a given language is said to be a *logical truth* of the language if the sentence's being true follows solely from the meaning of the logical words it contains. Sentence (22), for example, is a logical truth of English:

(22)   Either Torricelli experimented with the mercury barometer or he did not.

We will now show that the logical truths of a P-language are precisely the valid wffs which have been endowed with sense. Let A be a valid wff of some P-language L which has been endowed with sense. A is a bonafide sentence of L, so A has reference in L. What, if anything, may we conclude about the truth value or reference of A in L? Being valid, A comes out true under any value assignment to its variables. So, whatever the truth values that the variables of A take on in L as a result of the way they happen to be endowed with sense in L, the value of A will be truth in L. Notice that this demonstration that A is true in L made no appeal to the particular truth values that the variables of A happen to have in L. Nor did it appeal to the particular senses with which those variables happen to be endowed in L. The demonstration turned only on the validity of A, which depends solely on the meaning of the connectives (all of them logical words) of L as given by their fundamental truth tables. In short, the truth of A follows from the meaning of the logical words it contains, namely the tilde, wedge, and dot. Every interpreted valid wff, then, is a logical truth of a given P-language.[1] Moreover, a P-language will contain no other logical truths, because every other true wff of the P-language will be a nonvalid wff. And the fact that a nonvalid wff is true in a P-language does not follow from the meaning of its logical words alone, for the truth of a nonvalid wff depends crucially on just what truth values are assigned to its variables. In a P-language, therefore, validity is a necessary and sufficient condition of logical truth of interpreted wffs.

Besides logical truths, a P-language also contains *logical falsehoods*, that is, sentences the falsity of which follows just from the meaning of the logical words they contain. And, just as validity is both sufficient and necessary for logical truth in a P-language, so too all and only invalid interpreted wffs are logical falsehoods of a P-language. In other words, invalidity is both a sufficient and a necessary condition of logical falsehood of sentences (interpreted wffs) of P-languages.

A sentence that is neither logically true nor logically false is said to be *logically indeterminate*. From the definitions of logical truth and logical falsehood, it is evident that the truth value of a logically indeterminate sentence depends on more than the meaning of the logical words it contains. In a P-language, therefore, all and only contingent interpreted wffs are logically indeterminate.

8.1. Analytic and Synthetic Sentences

We consider now a much vaguer concept than logical determinateness (that is, being logically true or logically false), which, after all, involves only the meaning of a few select and very simple topic-neutral words, the so-called logical words. This vaguer concept, analyticity, involves the meaning of all words. A sentence is said to be *analytic* (*analytically true* or *analytically false* according as it is true or false) if its truth value depends only on the meaning of the words it contains (and not, therefore, on how the world hap-

[1] The context should make it obvious that we are here referring to interpreted wffs that have been endowed with sense and not merely with reference.

pens to be). A sentence that is not analytic is said to be *synthetic* (*synthetically true*, if true; *synthetically false*, if false). Clearly every logical truth is analytically true, and every logical falsehood is analytically false. But the converses do not always hold. Some analytic truths such as (20) are not logical truths, and there are analytic falsehoods such as (23) which are not logically false.

(23)   Some bachelors are married.

The foregoing facts have important consequences for the theory of P-languages. One consequence is that validity is a sufficient condition of analytic truth of interpreted wffs (in P-languages) but not a necessary condition. For example, in the P-language L let '*p*' and '*q*' be synonymous, respectively, with (20) and (23). Then both '*p*' and '$\sim q$' are analytic truths of L, though neither is logically true in L. Another consequence is that invalidity is a sufficient but not a necessary condition of analytic falsity of interpreted wffs. For example, both '$\sim p$' and '*q*' are analytically false in L but neither is logically false in L. The last consequence we wish to mention is that contingency is a necessary, although not a sufficient, condition of syntheticity of interpreted wffs. To see that it is a necessary condition, suppose that a sentence (interpreted wff) *A* of some P-language is synthetic but not contingent. Since it is not contingent, *A* is either valid or invalid, and therefore either logically true or logically false. But if *A* is logically true or logically false, then *A* is analytic, not synthetic. We may conclude, therefore, that if a wff of a P-language is a synthetic sentence, then it is a contingent wff. But obviously not every interpreted contingent wff of a P-language is synthetic. For example, '$[p \vee q]$' is a contingent wff of L that happens to be analytically true.

We have already suggested that analytic truth is a much vaguer and more questionable concept than logical truth. To appreciate this fact, one need only ask himself which of the following are analytically true:

Whatever is red is colored.
Gold is a dense metal that conducts electricity.
$F = ma$.

Fortunately our interest in analytic truth seldom goes further than those analytic truths which are also logical truths. To say that logical truth is clearer than analytic truth is not, of course, to say that logical truth is itself perfectly clear. The concept is no clearer than the notion of a logical word and the meanings of logical words. We have roughly described logical words as simple topic-neutral words such as 'not', 'and', 'or', 'every', and 'possibly', but we have offered no exact explanation or definition of a logical word. Our failure to offer one is simply due to the fact that we lack one. The best we can do is to offer crude characterizations (such as 'simple, topic-neutral words') supplemented by lists of examples and hope that the reader is thereby enlightened somewhat. With respect to P-languages, the situation is bright. There is no real doubt about which are the logical words, and their meanings are precisely stated. The situation is about the same for Q-languages (see Part Four) and perhaps only slightly worse for M-languages (see Part Three).

Although most philosophers believe that many sentences are synthetic, the philosopher Leibniz held the opposite view. Leibniz believed that, if one grasped perfectly the meaning of any sentence, he would see what its truth value is without need of recourse to empirical inquiry. Regarding those sentences commonly thought to be synthetic, Leibniz maintained that only the Divine Mind could penetrate their meanings deeply enough to determine their truth values by meaning analysis alone. The more orthodox philosophical opinion, which accords better with common sense than Leibniz's view does, acknowledges the existence of a multitude of synthetic sentences. Sentence (9) is a good example of one. Most philosophers would insist that no analysis of the meaning of (9) could ever by itself reveal whether or not Pascal experimented with the mercury barometer, that is, reveal whether or not (9) is true. If challenged to defend his belief that sentence (9) is synthetic, a philosopher might reply that he can conceive of Pascal's having experimented with the mercury barometer as well as conceive of Pascal's not having done so. That is, to justify his claim that a certain sentence is synthetic, the philosopher may appeal to his ability to conceive of it alternately as true and as false. In supplying examples of synthetic sentences, we will employ this criterion of syntheticity; *conceivability alternately as true and as false*. When convinced that we can alternately conceive a sentence as true and as false, we will not hesitate to offer it as an example of a synthetic sentence. Such a policy, be it noted, is purely pedagogical and in no way affects (or infects) the theoretical development of logic presented in this book.

9. EXERCISES

(1) Prove that a sentence (wff endowed with sense) of a P-language is logically false if and only if it is invalid.

(2) Prove that a sentence of a P-language is logically indeterminate if and only if it is a contingent wff.

(3) Establish that each of the following is true:

(a) Logical determinateness is a sufficient condition of analyticity (that is, every logically determinate sentence is analytic).

(b) Logical indeterminateness is a necessary condition of syntheticity (that is, every synthetic sentence is logically indeterminate).

(c) In a P-language, a sentence is logically true if and only if it is valid.

(d) If one member of a pair of mutually entailing sentences is analytically true (false), then so is the other.

(e) If one member of a pair of mutually entailing sentences is synthetically true (false), then so is the other.

(4) Indicate the status of each of the following wffs in the P-language L sketched in Section 8.1; that is, indicate whether each wff is logically true, logically indeterminate, logically false, analytically true, analytically false, synthetically true, or synthetically false:

(a) $[p \vee q]$ (e) $[p \vee \sim[p \vee q]]$

(b) $[p \vee \sim q]$ (f) $[p \vee \sim[p \cdot p]]$

(c) $[p \cdot q]$ (g) $[[p \cdot q] \vee \sim[p \cdot q]]$

(d) $[p \cdot \sim q]$ (h) $\sim\sim q$

{5} Try to formulate a better criterion of syntheticity than conceivability alternately as true and as false.

10. ABBREVIATION
AND EQUIVALENCE

10.0. Some Abbreviative Conventions

The brackets of LSP serve to indicate the intended groupings within wffs. For example, the second and third occurrences of brackets in '[[p ∨ q] · r]' show that the occurrences of 'p' and 'q' are connected by the wedge. The brackets in that same wff show that the dot connects the occurrence of 'r' to the occurrence of '[p ∨ q]' rather than to the occurrence of 'q'. Suppressing the inner pair of brackets we get the ill-formed formula '[p ∨ q · r]', whose intended groupings are ambiguous. Either the grouping '[[p ∨ q] · r]' or '[p ∨ [q · r]]' could be meant. Which is intended does matter, because the value assignment of truth to 'p' and 'q' and falsehood to 'r' would make the formula false if the first grouping were intended but true if the second were meant. That is why the ambiguity of '[p ∨ q · r]' is intolerable.

Unlike inner pairs of brackets, an *outside pair* (the first and last symbols of a wff) can be suppressed without rendering intended groupings ambiguous. Dropping the outside brackets of the above example, we obtain '[p ∨ q] · r', which, although ill formed, is unambiguous as to grouping. Dropping outside brackets will be our first step in a program for simplifying wffs, for making them easier to read and work with. An abundance of brackets tends to conceal the intended groupings within a wff; one must painstakingly match up brackets with their mates before he can grasp what groupings are intended. The crux of our program to make groupings more perspicuous will lie in the elimination of unnecessary brackets.

We initiate this perspicuity program by adopting the following abbreviative convention:

> Convention 1. If a wff is standing alone, that is, if it is not part of a larger wff, then we let the formula that results on deleting the outside pair of brackets (if any) of that wff abbreviate that wff.

For example, convention 1 stipulates that '$[p \lor q] \cdot r$' abbreviates the wff '$[[p \lor q] \cdot r]$' and that '$\sim p \lor q$' abbreviates '$[\sim p \lor q]$'. Notice that convention 1 does not authorize any brackets to be dropped from '$\sim[p \lor q]$' because that wff contains no *outside* pair of brackets; that is, it does not begin *and* end with brackets.

A system of abbreviative conventions will be said to be *formally acceptable* if it satisfies these two conditions: First, any abbreviation which they authorize must abbreviate exactly one wff; second, there must be an effective procedure or algorithm which can be applied to an abbreviation to recover the wff which it abbreviates. Taken by itself, convention 1, which permits us to omit outside brackets, is clearly formally acceptable.

Consider again the ill-formed formula '$[p \lor q \cdot r]$'. One way to render its intended groupings unambiguous without restoring brackets is to *rank order* the sentence connectives and let rank determine how brackets should be restored. An otherwise ambiguous formula will be understood to have the grouping whereby higher ranked connectives join or connect larger possible components. For example, if the wedge outranked the dot, then '$[p \lor q \cdot r]$' would be understood to abbreviate '$[p \lor [q \cdot r]]$'. Similarly, '$[p \cdot q \lor q \cdot r]$' would be taken to abbreviate '$[[p \cdot q] \lor [q \cdot r]]$'. As rank ordering renders grouping more perspicuous by eliminating messy interior brackets, we adopt the following convention, which subordinates the dot to the wedge and the tilde to both.

> Convention 2. We let the wedge outrank the dot, and we let both outrank the tilde.

In virtue of conventions 1 and 2, each formula in the left column below abbreviates the wff opposite it in the right column:

$p \cdot q \lor r$	$[[p \cdot q] \lor r]$
$p \cdot q \lor p \cdot r$	$[[p \cdot q] \lor [p \cdot r]]$
$\sim[p \cdot [q \lor r] \lor q]$	$\sim[[p \cdot [q \lor r]] \lor q]$
$\sim p \cdot [q \cdot r] \lor q$	$[[\sim p \cdot [q \cdot r]] \lor q]$

It can be shown that conventions 1 and 2 together constitute a formally acceptable system of abbreviations; the task is left to the reader as an exercise.

Henceforth we shall employ our abbreviative conventions freely. We will often write abbreviations but talk as if we had exhibited the unabbreviated wffs themselves. For example, we might say that '$p \vee q \cdot r$' is a wff with nine symbol occurrences. We would mean, of course, that the wff abbreviated by '$p \vee q \cdot r$' contains nine symbol occurrences, which is true.

To render groupings still more perspicuous, we shall employ an informal device which we will not bother to dignify as an abbreviative convention. Namely, we shall freely use parentheses and braces in place of brackets. The parentheses and braces are not to be regarded as new symbols but rather as poorly printed brackets. For example, instead of writing

$$\sim\sim q \cdot [[[p \cdot q] \cdot [q \vee \sim r]] \cdot \sim p]$$

we might write

$$\sim\sim q \cdot \{[(p \cdot q) \cdot (q \vee \sim r)] \cdot \sim p\}$$

in which the intended groupings stand out more boldly.

10.1. Equivalence

The truth tables below show that, for the same value assignments to their variables, the wffs '$p \cdot q$' and '$\sim[\sim p \vee \sim q]$' come out with the same truth values.

p	q	$p \cdot q$		p	q	$\sim[\sim p \vee \sim q]$
t	t	t		t	t	t
t	f	f		t	f	f
f	t	f		f	t	f
f	f	f		f	f	f

(Notice about these tables that the scratch work generated by the three-step evaluational procedure of Section 6.1 has all been erased. Hereafter most truth tables will be presented without the scratch work, which the reader can restore if he wishes.) Wffs so related are said to be *equivalent*. The precise definition follows. Let A and B be any wffs of LSP. If under every interpretation of the set $\{A,B\}$ of wffs the value of A is the same as the value of B, then A is said to be *equivalent to B*. The table below, which is formed by putting two truth tables together, shows that '$p \vee q$' is equivalent to '$\sim[\sim p \cdot \sim q]$'.

p	q	$p \vee q$	$\sim[\sim p \cdot \sim q]$
t	t	t	t
t	f	t	t
f	t	t	t
f	f	f	f

On the other hand, '$p \cdot p$' is not equivalent to '$p \vee q$', as the next table shows.

p	q	$p \cdot p$	$p \vee q$
t	t	t	t
t	f	t	t
f	t	f	t
f	f	f	f

It is obvious from the definition of equivalence that if A is equivalent to B, B must also be equivalent to A. A two-place relation on a set Δ of objects which relates an arbitrary member x of Δ to an arbitrary member y of Δ whenever it relates y to x is called a *symmetrical relation on* Δ or *among* the members of Δ. Marriage, for example, is a symmetrical relation among people, since a person x is married to a person y whenever y is married to x. And among wffs of LSP equivalence is clearly a symmetrical relation, for a wff B is equivalent to a wff A if A is equivalent to B.

It should also be evident that if A is equivalent to B, and B is equivalent to C, then A is also equivalent to C. This feature of equivalence makes it a *transitive relation* among the wffs of LSP. In general, a two-place relation R is said to be *transitive on* a set Δ or *among* the members of Δ if, for arbitrary members x, y, and z of Δ, R relates x to z whenever R relates x to y and y to z. For example, being larger than is a transitive relation on the set of numbers, and so is equality. The relation being older than is transitive among people, but the relation of marriage is not.

Some relations manifest the peculiar but noteworthy property of relating each object in a set to itself. Equality, for example, relates every number to itself; that is, every number is equal to itself. Such peculiar relations are said to be *reflexive on* such sets or *among* the members of the sets. Clearly, equivalence is a reflexive relation among the wffs of LSP, for every wff is, trivially, equivalent to itself.

To summarize, we have noted that equivalence possesses three noteworthy relational properties: reflexivity (or reflexiveness), symmetry, and transitivity among the wffs of LSP. Relations that possess these three properties with respect to a set Δ have come to be called *equivalence relations on* Δ or *among* the members of Δ. Equality, for example, is an equivalence relation among numbers, and congruence is an equivalence relation on the set of geometric figures. And, as we have just seen, equivalence is an equivalence relation among the wffs of LSP.

10.2.   Tolerably Ambiguous Abbreviations

We have already seen that (apart from convention 2) the formula '$p \vee q \cdot r$' is ambiguous with respect to intended grouping. It could be meant either as '$p \vee [q \cdot r]$' or as '$[p \vee q] \cdot r$'. The formula '$p \cdot q \cdot r$' is similarly ambiguous; it could be meant as '$p \cdot [q \cdot r]$' or as '$[p \cdot q] \cdot r$'. But there is an important difference between these two otherwise similar cases. The two wffs ambiguously abbreviated by '$p \cdot q \cdot r$' are equivalent, whereas the two abbreviated by '$p \vee q \cdot r$' are not. A convention that authorized '$p \cdot q \cdot r$' as an abbreviation of both '$p \cdot [q \cdot r]$' and '$[p \cdot q] \cdot r$' would, of course, be formally unacceptable, because it would violate the uniqueness condition imposed on formally acceptable systems of abbreviative conventions. Though formally unacceptable, such a convention could be tolerated if it were used only in those situations in which any member of a class of equivalent wffs would do as well as any other. To illustrate such a situation, suppose we wished to exhibit a contradictory wff. We could safely write '$p \cdot q \cdot \sim q$' because, whichever way the reader understood the intended grouping, the wff he would "recover" by restoring brackets would be a contradiction. As such situations arise frequently, we will now adopt, *for restricted use,* two additional conventions which are tolerably ambiguous in the sense just explained. The restriction on these conventions is that they be used only in situations in which any of a set of equivalent wffs would do.

Convention 3. If a conjunction is itself a component of a conjunction, one may drop the outermost brackets of the component or interior conjunction.

In virtue of convention 3, the formula '$p \cdot q \cdot r$' abbreviates (ambiguously) both '$p \cdot [q \cdot r]$' and '$[p \cdot q] \cdot r$'. As a second illustration, the formula '$p \cdot q \cdot r \cdot p$' abbreviates five equivalent wffs: '$[p \cdot q] \cdot [r \cdot p]$', '$p \cdot [q \cdot (r \cdot p)]$', '$p \cdot [(q \cdot r) \cdot p]$', '$[(p \cdot q) \cdot r] \cdot p$', and '$[p \cdot (q \cdot r)] \cdot p$'. An ambiguous abbreviation of the form $\ulcorner A_1 \cdot A_2 \cdot \ldots \cdot A_n \urcorner$ is called a *continued conjunction*. Convention 3 authorizes the restricted use of continued conjunctions as (ambiguous) abbreviations. What renders this controlled ambiguity innocuous is that all the wffs abbreviated by a continued conjunction are equivalent to one another.

All that was said above about conjunction applies equally to disjunction. Though ambiguous, the formula '$p \vee q \vee r$' abbreviates only wffs that are equivalent to one another: '$p \vee [q \vee r]$' and '$[p \vee q] \vee r$'. Ambiguous abbreviations of the form

$$\ulcorner A_1 \vee A_2 \vee \ldots \vee A_n \urcorner$$

are called *continued disjunctions*. Like continued conjunctions, continued disjunctions can be of limited but significant value as (ambiguous) abbreviations. Accordingly, we hereby adopt the following convention regarding continued disjunctions:

Convention 4. If a disjunction is itself a component of a disjunction, one may drop the outermost brackets of the component or interior disjunction.

In virtue of this convention, the formula '$p \vee q \vee r \cdot p \vee q$' abbreviates, for example, these five equivalent wffs: '$[p \vee q] \vee [r \cdot p \vee q]$', '$p \vee [q \vee (r \cdot p \vee q)]$', '$p \vee [(q \vee r \cdot p) \vee q]$', '$[p \vee (q \vee r \cdot p)] \vee q$', and '$[(p \vee q) \vee r \cdot p] \vee q$'.

The adoption of conventions 3 and 4 renders our total system of abbreviative conventions formally unacceptable but tolerably ambiguous. In contexts that demand an unambiguous abbreviation, conventions 3 and 4 must be eschewed. Suppose, for example, that one wished to exhibit a wff whose fourth symbol was a left bracket. It would be improper to write '$p \lor q \lor r$' in accordance with convention 4, because only one of the two wffs that '$p \lor q \lor r$' abbreviates has the desired characteristic. The byword for the use of these tolerably ambiguous conventions is caution!

11.   EXERCISES

(1)   Indicate which of the following are true and which false of the wffs of LSP:

Tautologies are equivalent to all tautologies.
Valid wffs are equivalent to only valid wffs.
Contradictions are equivalent to all contradictions.
Invalid wffs are equivalent to only invalid wffs.
Contingent wffs are equivalent to all contingent wffs.
Contingent wffs are equivalent to only nonvalid wffs.

(2)   Determine about each wff in the left column whether it is equivalent to the wff opposite it in the right column:

$p \lor q \cdot r$	$[p \lor q] \cdot [p \lor r]$
$p \lor q \cdot r$	$p \cdot q \lor p \cdot r$
$p \cdot [q \lor r]$	$p \cdot q \lor p \cdot r$
$p \cdot [q \lor r]$	$[p \lor q] \cdot [p \lor r]$
$\sim p \cdot \sim q$	$\sim [p \lor q]$
$\sim p \lor \sim q$	$\sim [p \cdot q]$
$\sim p \cdot \sim q$	$\sim p \lor \sim q$
p	$p \lor q \cdot \sim q$
p	$p \cdot [q \lor \sim q]$

(3)   Mention some relations among people which are
   (a)   reflexive, symmetrical, but not transitive;
   (b)   reflexive but neither symmetrical nor transitive;
   (c)   neither reflexive nor symmetrical nor transitive;
   (d)   reflexive and transitive, but not symmetrical;
   (e)   transitive but neither reflexive nor symmetrical;
   (f)   symmetrical but neither reflexive nor transitive;
   (g)   symmetrical and transitive but not reflexive.

(4) Exhibit all the wffs abbreviated by the following expression and show that they are equivalent to one another:

$$p \cdot q \cdot r \lor p \cdot q \cdot \sim r \lor p \cdot \sim q \cdot r$$

(5) Grouping conventions analogous to conventions 1 and 2 are used in elementary algebra to make the structure of formulas more perspicuous. In addition to dropping outside brackets, the algebraist stipulates that the equality sign outranks the plus sign of addition, which in turn outranks the dot of multiplication. For each of the following expressions, write out in full the algebraic formula it abbreviates.

$$a \cdot b + a \cdot c \qquad a \cdot (b + c) = a \cdot b + a \cdot c$$
$$a + b \cdot c \qquad a + b \cdot c = b \cdot c + a$$
$$a \cdot b + c \qquad (a + b) \cdot (c + d)$$
$$= ((a \cdot c + a \cdot d) + b \cdot c) + b \cdot d$$

(6) Besides formally acceptable abbreviative conventions, the algebraist also makes limited use of tolerably ambiguous ones. For example, he will at times use the continued sum '$a + b + c$' to abbreviate (ambiguously) both '$a + (b + c)$' and '$(a + b) + c$'. Similarly, he will occasionally use the continued product '$a \cdot b \cdot c$' to abbreviate ambiguously both '$a \cdot (b \cdot c)$' and '$(a \cdot b) \cdot c$'. In what contexts would the use of continued sums (continued products) as abbreviations be tolerable? Notice how much more perspicuous ambiguous abbreviation renders the last formula of Exercise (5), which becomes '$(a + b) \cdot (c + d) = a \cdot c + a \cdot d + b \cdot c + b \cdot d$'.

[7] Let the vocabulary of elementary algebra consist of the following:
   (a) An infinite list of numerical variables: 'a', 'b', 'c', 'a_1', 'b_1', 'c_1', 'a_2', ...
   (b) Two binary operation symbols: '$+$' and '$\cdot$'.
   (c) The equality sign '$=$'.
   (d) The grouping indicators '(' and ')'.
   Formulate formation rules for elementary algebra. [*Hint:* First give formation rules for well-formed terms, that is, the sort of terms which may flank the equality sign in an equation. Then add this rule: If A and B are well-formed terms, then $\ulcorner A = B \urcorner$ is a wff.]

[8] Prove that the system of conventions consisting of just conventions 1 and 2 is formally acceptable.

12. FUNCTIONAL COMPLETENESS

12.0. Mutual Entailment, Equivalence, and Expressive Power

Just as validity is a sufficient condition of analytic truth of sentences of P-languages, so equivalence is a sufficient condition of mutual entailment; that is, equivalent interpreted wffs of a P-language entail one another. To see that this latter claim is true, suppose that A and B are equivalent wffs that have been endowed with sense in a P-language L. Being equivalent, A and B will have the same truth value in L regardless of how they are endowed with sense in L. That A and B are equivalent can, of course, be determined by a simple truth-tabular test which is based entirely on the meanings given to the tilde, wedge, and dot by their fundamental truth tables. Thus it follows from the meaning of the logical words in A and B that A would be true if B should be, and vice versa. Hence, by the definition of entailment, A and B are mutually entailing. In P-languages, therefore, equivalence is a sufficient condition of mutual entailment among sentences. It is not, however, a necessary condition, as the reader can show by simple counterexamples.

In many important respects mutually entailing sentences are interchangeable. For example, a premiss or conclusion of an argument can be replaced by any sentence that both entails it and is entailed by it without affecting either the correctness or the soundness of the argument. (An argument is said to be *correct* if the conclusion follows from the premisses.[1] An argument is said to be *sound* if it is correct and, in addition, all its premisses are true.) Furthermore, there is an obvious sense in which mutually entailing

---

[1] What we have called a *correct argument* is called a *valid argument* by many authors. We prefer to reserve the term 'valid' for wffs that come out true under all interpretations. A sentence S is said to *follow from* a set Δ of sentences if, in virtue solely of their meanings, S would be true if every member of Δ should be true.

sentences convey the same information, that is, have the same content. In view of the foregoing remarks, let us say that a language L₁ is *as expressively powerful as* a language L₂ if, for every sentence S of L₂, there is some sentence S' of L₁ such that S and S' are mutually entailing. We have already called attention to the paucity of connectives in P-languages. Out of infinitely many truth-functional sentence connectives, P-languages contain only three. Might not the expressive power of a P-language be enhanced, therefore, by adding to it other truth-functional connectives? Surprisingly, the answer to this question is *no*! We will prove that a P-language is as expressively powerful as any language that would result by merely adding new truth-functional connectives to it. Notice that to prove this result we need only show that, for every wff of the supplemented P-language, there is a wff of the unsupplemented P-language that is equivalent to it. This last will be a corollary of the functional completeness of the tilde, wedge, and dot, which is proved in Section 12.1.

12.1. Functional Completeness of the Tilde, Wedge, and Dot

The "truth table" below determines or defines a certain truth function of the variables 'p', 'q', and 'r' in the sense of limiting or specifying the class of wffs of LSP that satisfy it:

p	q	r	
t	t	t	f
t	t	f	t
t	f	t	f
t	f	f	f
f	t	t	f
f	t	f	t
f	f	t	f
f	f	f	f

The above table, which we shall call "Table 1" or simply "T1," is *satisfied* by any wff that comes out true under the following two value assignments and falsehood under all others: the assignment of truth to 'p' and 'q' and falsehood to 'r', and the assignment of falsehood to 'p' and 'r' and truth to 'q'. For example, the wff '$p \cdot q \cdot \sim r \lor \sim p \cdot q \cdot \sim r$' satisfies T1, as the reader should verify. In general a table is said to be *satisfied by* a wff A if, were A to be put in the space appropriate to a wff (upper right-hand corner), there would result a correctly filled out truth table. Now is it purely fortuitous that there is a wff of LSP which satisfies T1? Or, to put the question differently, might we not have displayed a table which, unlike T1, happens not to be satisfied by any wffs of LSP? We shall prove that the answer to these questions is *no;* that is, we shall prove that the tilde, wedge, and dot form a functionally complete set of sentence connectives.

A set Γ of sentence connectives will be said to be *functionally complete* if, given any truth table whatsoever, there is a grammatical formula A which satisfies it and which contains no symbols except grouping indicators, variables of the given table, and connectives of Γ. To see that the set consisting of the tilde, wedge, and dot is functionally complete, consider an arbitrary truth table T:

a_1	a_2	$\ldots$	a_n	
α_1^1	α_2^1	$\ldots$	α_n^1	β_1
α_1^2	α_2^2	$\ldots$	α_n^2	β_2
.				.
.				.
.				.
α_1^k	α_2^k	$\ldots$	α_n^k	β_k

In the above table $a_1, a_2, \ldots, a_n$ are distinct sentential variables; α_1^1, $\alpha_2^1, \ldots, \alpha_n^k, \beta_1, \beta_2, \ldots, \beta_k$ are truth values; and $k = 2^n$. The rows of truth values under $a_1, a_2, \ldots, a_n$ represent all possible value assignments to $a_1, a_2, \ldots, a_n$. With each row $\alpha_1^i, \alpha_2^i, \ldots, \alpha_n^i$ of T we associate a certain continued conjunction which we call the *associated conjunction of* the given row of the table. The associated conjunction of $\alpha_1^i, \alpha_2^i, \ldots, \alpha_n^i$ is defined as the formula $\ulcorner B_1 \cdot B_2 \cdot \ldots \cdot B_n \urcorner$, where each B_j is either a_j or $\ulcorner {\sim} a_j \urcorner$ according as α_j^i is 't' or 'f'. For example, the associated conjunction of the second row of T1 is '$p \cdot q \cdot {\sim}r$', and the associated conjunction of the fifth row of the same table is '${\sim}p \cdot q \cdot r$'.

Notice that the associated conjunction of a row enjoys a privileged relationship to the value assignment represented by that row; that is, it comes out true under that one value assignment to its variables and false under every other value assignment to its variables. For example, '$\sim p \cdot q \cdot r$', which is the associated conjunction of the fifth row of T1, comes out true when falsehood is assigned to 'p' and truth to 'q' and 'r', and it comes out false under all other value assignments to 'p', 'q', and 'r'. We will exploit this privileged relationship to construct a wff, called the *characteristic wff of* the table, which satisfies the arbitrarily given table. Suppose T has some 't's in its last column; that is, suppose at least one of the β_i is truth. Let $C_1, C_2, \ldots, C_r$ be the associated conjunctions of those rows of T which end in 't' (there will be at least one such row). Then we let the continued disjunction $\ulcorner C_1 \vee C_2 \vee \ldots \vee C_r \urcorner$ be the characteristic wff of T. (In the event that $C_r = C_1$, that is, in the event that only one of the β_i is truth, $\ulcorner C_1 \vee C_2 \vee \ldots \vee C_r \urcorner$ will be just C_1 by itself.) That $\ulcorner C_1 \vee C_2 \vee \ldots \vee C_r \urcorner$ satisfies T is evident from the following considerations. Any value assignment represented by any of the rows associated with $C_1, C_2, \ldots, C_r$ clearly makes their continued disjunction true, since it makes one of them true. Any other value assignment clearly makes the continued disjunction of $C_1, C_2, \ldots, C_r$ false, because it makes every one of them false. For example, the characteristic wff of T1 is

$p \cdot q \cdot \sim r \vee \sim p \cdot q \cdot \sim r,$

a wff which obviously satisfies T1.

Suppose, on the other hand, that there are only 'f's in the last column of T; that is, suppose that none of the β_i is truth. Obviously what T requires as a characteristic wff is a contradiction. Accordingly, we let the contradictory wff $\ulcorner a_1 \cdot \sim a_1 \urcorner$, a wff which clearly satisfies T, be the characteristic wff of T. For example, '$p \cdot \sim p$' is the characteristic wff of the table below:

p	q	
t	t	f
t	f	f
f	t	f
f	f	f

Notice that the wff designated as the characteristic wff of T contains no symbols except variables of T, grouping indicators, and the tilde, wedge, and dot. The preceding sentence holds true whether there are any 't's in the last column of T or not. In summary, we have in this section shown how, given any truth table whatsoever, to write a wff that satisfies it; furthermore, the wff so written contains no symbols beyond grouping indicators, variables of the given table, and the tilde, wedge, and dot. Referring to the definition of functional completeness, therefore, we see that the set of connectives consisting of the tilde, wedge, and dot is functionally complete. It was not by chance, then, that there exist wffs of LSP that satisfy T1. Whatever table had been exhibited, there would have been wffs of LSP that satisfy it.

13.   TRUTH-FUNCTIONAL SENTENCE CONNECTIVES (II)

13.0.   Truth-Functional Sentence Connectives; a Second Look

Before considering what happens when new truth-functional connectives are added to a P-language, let us examine the nature of such connectives more closely. According to the definition given in Section 2.0, an n-ary sentence connective is said to be truth functional if and only if the truth value of any compound sentence formed by joining together n component sentences by means of the connective depends only on the truth values of the joined components. Accordingly, the semantics of a truth-functional connective can always be given by a fundamental truth table analogous to the fundamental truth tables for the tilde, wedge, and dot. For example, if '$\odot$' is a ternary connective[1] such that a compound

---

[1] If $\otimes$ is a singulary sentence connective, we write grammatically correct compounds as $\ulcorner \otimes A \urcorner$. And if $\otimes$ is a binary connective, we write grammatically correct compounds as $\ulcorner [A \otimes B] \urcorner$. For all other n-ary connectives, that is, when $n > 2$, we write grammatically correct compounds as $\ulcorner \otimes (A_1, A_2, \ldots, A_n) \urcorner$. (Remember that we are regarding parentheses as poorly printed brackets. Hence $\ulcorner \otimes (A_1, A_2, \ldots, A_n) \urcorner$ is no different from $\ulcorner \otimes [A_1, A_2, \ldots, A_n] \urcorner$.) The foregoing grammatical decisions are motivated by custom rather than uniformity, which would dictate that, if $\otimes$ is a singulary connective, a gram-

⌜⊙(A,B,C)⌝ is true if and only if exactly two of the components A, B, and C are true, its semantics could be given by the following fundamental truth table:

A	B	C	⊙(A,B,C)
t	t	t	f
t	t	f	t
t	f	t	t
t	f	f	f
f	t	t	t
f	t	f	f
f	f	t	f
f	f	f	f

As a second example, we give the fundamental truth table for the binary truth-functional connective '⊃', known as the *horseshoe:*

A	B	[A ⊃ B]
t	t	t
t	f	f
f	t	t
f	f	t

Let A be any grammatical formula that contains only sentential variables, grouping indicators, and truth-functional sentence connectives. Using the fundamental truth tables for the connectives in A, one can easily construct a truth table for A. For example, were A the formula '⊙(∼p, q, [p ⊃ q])', one would get the following table:

p	q	⊙(∼p, q, [p ⊃ q])
t	t	t
t	f	f
f	t	f
f	f	t

matically correct compound be written ⌜⊗(A)⌝, and that, if ⊗ is binary, a grammatically correct compound be written ⌜⊗(A,B)⌝. Notice too, that, were we to supplement LSP with ternary (or larger degree) connectives, we would also have to add the comma to the vocabulary as another grouping indicator.

The tilde, wedge, and dot are functionally complete, so we know that there are wffs of LSP that satisfy the above table, for example '$p \cdot q$ v $\sim p \cdot \sim q$'. Referring to the definition of equivalence, we see that any wff that satisfies the above table is equivalent to the formula '$\odot(\sim p, q, [p \supset q])$'. The same holds for any grammatical formula A which contains only sentential variables, grouping indicators, and truth-functional connectives; that is, there is at least one wff B of LSP equivalent to A. For, whatever the truth table of A turns out to be, there is at least one wff of LSP—the characteristic wff of the table—which satisfies the table and is thus equivalent to A.

Suppose, then, that L⁺ is any language that results on supplementing a P-language L with truth-functional connectives. Let A be any grammatical formula of L⁺. Then, as we saw in the preceding paragraph, there is at least one wff B of L that is equivalent to A. Hence, no matter how the variables of L⁺ are endowed with sense, B and A will be mutually entailing (provided only that the variables of L are endowed with sense in the same way). Thus L is as expressively powerful as L⁺; the supplementation of L with additional truth-functional connectives cannot increase its expressive power in the least.

13.1. Redundancy of the Tilde, Wedge, and Dot

Surprisingly, our choice of connectives for LSP was somewhat lavish. Without sacrificing expressive power, we could have omitted from the vocabulary either the dot or the wedge, but not both. For example, we could have eliminated the wedge in favor of the tilde and dot by espousing a convention to the effect that $\ulcorner A$ v $B \urcorner$ abbreviates the equivalent wff $\ulcorner \sim[\sim A \cdot \sim B] \urcorner$. In virtue of this convention, a wff of LSP containing occurrences of the wedge would abbreviate an equivalent wff devoid of wedges. For example, 'p v $[q$ v $r]$' would abbreviate '$\sim[\sim p \cdot \sim\sim[\sim q \cdot \sim r]]$', to which it is equivalent. That the tilde and dot are therefore functionally complete may be seen as follows. Let T be an arbitrary truth table. The connectives of LSP are functionally complete, so there is some wff A of LSP which satisfies T. The wff A, then, contains occurrences of no connectives other than the tilde, dot, and wedge. Applying the aforementioned convention to A to eliminate all occurrences of the wedge, we obtain an equivalent wff B with no connectives other than the tilde and dot. The wff B is equivalent to A, so it satisfies the arbitrary table T. By the definition of functional completeness, therefore, the tilde and dot form a functionally complete set of sentence connectives. And because those two connectives are already functionally complete, supplementing the tilde and dot by the wedge contributes nothing to the expressive power of a P-language.

Similarly, we could have eliminated the dot in favor of the tilde and wedge without impairing the expressive power of P-languages. For example, we might have adopted the convention that $\ulcorner A \cdot B \urcorner$ abbreviates the equivalent wff $\ulcorner \sim[\sim A \vee \sim B] \urcorner$. This convention would permit us to eliminate all occurrences of the dot in a given wff of LSP so as to obtain an equivalent wff devoid of dots. An argument exactly like the one of the preceding paragraph would then establish that the tilde and wedge are functionally complete.

13.2. Sheffer's Stroke

A fact as surprising as it is noteworthy is the existence of truth-functional connectives that are functionally complete by themselves. One of these, a binary connective called the *nonconjunction sign* or *Sheffer's stroke* or simply the *stroke*, is symbolized by a vertical stroke '$|$' and has the following fundamental truth table:

A	B	$A\,|\,B$
t	t	f
t	f	t
f	t	t
f	f	t

Because it answers to the fragmented English connective $\ulcorner$it is not the case both that ... and that ___$\urcorner$, we can read $\ulcorner A\,|\,B \urcorner$ as $\ulcorner$not both A and $B \urcorner$.

To prove that Sheffer's stroke is functionally complete by itself, it suffices to show how to eliminate the tilde and dot in favor of the stroke, because the tilde and dot together have already been shown to be functionally complete. Suppose for the moment, then, that C is a wff with no connectives besides the tilde and dot. Our problem is to convert C into an equivalent wff with no connectives other than the stroke. To this end we could adopt two abbreviative conventions, one to the effect that $\ulcorner {\sim}A \urcorner$ abbreviates the equivalent wff $\ulcorner A \mid A \urcorner$, the other to the effect that $\ulcorner A \cdot B \urcorner$ abbreviates the equivalent wff $\ulcorner [A \mid B] \mid [A \mid B] \urcorner$. In virtue of these conventions, for example, '${\sim}[p \cdot q]$' abbreviates the equivalent wff

$$[(p \mid q) \mid (p \mid q)] \mid [(p \mid q) \mid (p \mid q)].$$

These two conventions can be used to convert a wff written in the tilde and dot into an equivalent wff written in the stroke. Consequently, given any truth table whatsoever, there is a wff containing no connectives except the stroke which satisfies it. Sheffer's stroke, therefore, is functionally complete by itself; that is, its unit set is functionally complete.

Without sacrificing expressive power, we could have attained maximum economy by dropping the tilde, wedge, and dot from LSP in favor of a single binary connective, Sheffer's stroke. But the economy would have been achieved at the expense of clarity and perspicuity. Even very simple wffs such as '${\sim}[p \cdot {\sim}p]$' would give way to rather ponderous ones such as

$$[[p \mid [p \mid p]] \mid [p \mid [p \mid p]]] \mid [[p \mid [p \mid p]] \mid [p \mid [p \mid p]]].$$

Because of the pedagogical objectives of this book, considerations of clarity and perspicuity overruled those of economy in the choice of connectives for LSP.

There is just one other binary connective that is functionally complete by itself, the *nondisjunction sign*, which is commonly symbolized by '$\downarrow$'. Answering to the fragmented English connective $\ulcorner$ neither ... nor ___ $\urcorner$, the nondisjunction sign possesses the following fundamental truth table:

A	B	$A \downarrow B$
t	t	f
t	f	f
f	t	f
f	f	t

To eliminate the tilde and dot in favor of the nondisjunction sign, one could lay down the conventions that $\ulcorner {\sim}A \urcorner$ abbreviates the equivalent wff $\ulcorner A \downarrow A \urcorner$, and that $\ulcorner A \cdot B \urcorner$ abbreviates the equivalent wff $\ulcorner [A \downarrow A] \downarrow [B \downarrow B] \urcorner$. It follows that '$\downarrow$' is functionally complete by itself.

Conventions such as the one that $\ulcorner \sim A \urcorner$ abbreviates the *equivalent* wff $\ulcorner A \,|\, A \urcorner$ are often called *definitions*. In the given example, the tilde would be said *to be defined in terms of* the stroke, and the convention would be written

$$\sim A =_{\text{Df}} A \,|\, A$$

As another illustration, the convention that $\ulcorner A \cdot B \urcorner$ abbreviates the equivalent wff $\ulcorner \sim[\sim A \lor \sim B] \urcorner$ would be deemed a definition of the dot in terms of the tilde and wedge and would itself be written

$$A \cdot B =_{\text{Df}} \sim[\sim A \lor \sim B]$$

From time to time we will ourselves employ such terminology and write abbreviative conventions (definitions) in the manner just indicated.

Notice that a set Γ of truth-functional connectives is functionally complete if and only if every truth-functional connective is definable in terms of the members of Γ. The reason is obvious. Let '$\otimes$' be any n-ary truth-functional sentence connective. Construct a "truth table" for '$\otimes(A_1, \ldots, A_n)$', that is, a table in which the metalinguistic variables 'A_1', 'A_2', and so on, appear. Since Γ is functionally complete, there is a grammatical expression D, the connectives of which all belong to Γ, which "satisfies" T. This expression D may be used as the definition of '$\otimes$' in terms of the members of Γ thus:

$$\otimes(A_1, \ldots, A_n) =_{\text{Df}} D$$

because D is equivalent to $\ulcorner \otimes(A_1, \ldots, A_n) \urcorner$. This proves that every truth-functional connective is definable in terms of a functionally complete set Γ of truth-functional sentence connectives. The other half of the biconditional, that Γ is functionally complete if every truth-functional connective is definable in terms of members of Γ, is left to the reader as an exercise.

14. IMPLICATION
AND EQUIVALENCE

14.0. The Conditional

There is a truth-functional use of the fragmented English connective ⌜if ... then ___⌝ wherein the connective ⌜if ... then ___⌝ means the same as the complex connective ⌜either it is not the case that ..., or else ___⌝. For example, 'If my memory is correct, then I owe you a dollar' means 'Either it is false that my memory is correct, or else I owe you a dollar'. More generally, when the connective is used thus truth functionally, ⌜if A, then B⌝ means the same as ⌜either it is not the case that A, or B⌝ or simply ⌜not A, or B⌝. We already have fundamental truth tables for the truth-functional 'not' and (inclusive) 'or', so it is a simple task to construct the following fundamental truth table for ⌜not ..., or ___⌝.

A	B	not A, or B
t	t	t
t	f	f
f	t	t
f	f	t

And because ⌜not A, or B⌝ means ⌜if A, then B⌝, the above table is also the fundamental truth table for ⌜if ..., then ___⌝; that is, we have

A	B	if A, then B
t	t	t
t	f	f
f	t	t
f	f	t

A sentence of the form ⌜if A, then B⌝ is called a *conditional sentence* or simply a *conditional; A* is said to be the *antecedent of* the conditional, and *B* is said to be the *consequent of* the conditional.

The vocabulary of some of the formalized languages yet to be presented will contain the binary truth-functional connective '⊃', known as the *horseshoe* (briefly mentioned in Section 13.0), which answers to the truth-functional use of ⌜if ..., then ___⌝ just discussed. Accordingly, we will call wffs of the form ⌜$A ⊃ B$⌝ *conditionals*, and we will read ⌜$A ⊃ B$⌝ as ⌜if A, then B⌝. The fundamental truth table for the horseshoe is given below.

A	B	$A ⊃ B$
t	t	t
t	f	f
f	t	**t**
f	f	t

The connectives of LSP are functionally complete, so the addition of the horseshoe (or any other truth-functional connective) to its vocabulary would not in any way augment its expressive power. Any statement that could be made with the horseshoe can also be made without it. That is the principal reason we did not include the horseshoe in the vocabulary of LSP. Still, our decision to omit the horseshoe eventuates in some awkwardness. Conditionals bear an intimate and important relation to implication, as we will see in Section 14.2. This relation is of such a nature that someone who wished to investigate implication relations among the wffs of a language would find it very convenient to have the horseshoe belong to its vocabulary. Fortunately, abbreviative conventions (definitions) afford the same convenience without requiring the addition of the connective to the vocabulary. For the sake of future convenience, then, we adopt the following convention:

Convention 5.   We let ⌜$[A ⊃ B]$⌝ abbreviate ⌜$[{\sim}A ∨ B]$⌝. Or, more simply, $A ⊃ B =_{\mathrm{Df}} {\sim}A ∨ B$.

By virtue of conventions 1–5, each formula in the left column below abbreviates the wff opposite it in the right column:

$p ⊃ q$	${\sim}p ∨ q$
$[p ⊃ q] ⊃ q$	${\sim}[{\sim}p ∨ q] ∨ q$
$[{\sim}p ⊃ p] ⊃ p$	${\sim}[{\sim}{\sim}p ∨ p] ∨ p$
$[p · q] ⊃ [p ∨ q]$	${\sim}[p · q] ∨ [p ∨ q]$

The system of abbreviative conventions 1–5 is formally unacceptable because of the tolerable ambiguities that issue from 3 and 4. The subsystem formed by 1, 2, and 5, however, can be shown to be formally acceptable.

There was very little arbitrariness in our decision to let ⌜$A \supset B$⌝ abbreviate ⌜$\sim A \lor B$⌝, because the two are equivalent, as the construction of a truth table will show. Thanks to convention 5, a formula with horseshoes abbreviates an equivalent wff without horseshoes. For example, '$[p \supset q] \supset q$' abbreviates the equivalent wff '$\sim[\sim p \lor q] \lor q$'. Convention 5, then, eliminates the horseshoe in favor of the tilde and wedge. As we shall see, it permits us to act for many purposes as if the horseshoe belonged to the vocabulary of LSP.

14.1. The Biconditional

There is a truth-functional use of the binary English connective 'if and only if' in which a compound ⌜A if and only if B⌝ is true if the components A and B have the same truth value, and is false otherwise. For example, the compound sentence 'The butler is guilty if and only if the wife was faithful to her husband' is true if the two sentences that flank the connective either are both true or else are both false; if one of them is true and the other false, then the compound is false. Many formalized languages incorporate a binary truth-functional connective, symbolized by the triple bar '$\equiv$', which answers to the truth-functional use of 'if and only if'. A wff of the form ⌜$A \equiv B$⌝ is called a *biconditional* and will be read ⌜A if and only if B⌝. The components A and B are, respectively, called the *left* and *right sides of* the biconditional ⌜$A \equiv B$⌝. The fundamental truth table for the triple bar is given below.

A	B	$A \equiv B$
t	t	t
t	f	f
f	t	f
f	f	t

Because the tilde, wedge, and dot are functionally complete, the addition of '$\equiv$' to its vocabulary would leave the expressive power of a P-language unchanged. Nonetheless, the triple bar is almost as handy a connective as the horseshoe, and for very similar reasons: The triple bar bears to equivalence the same relation that the horseshoe bears to implication. Accordingly, we will adopt an abbreviative convention that enables us to act as if the triple bar were a primitive symbol (that is, belonged to the vocabulary) of LSP, in other words, a convention that eliminates '$\equiv$' in favor of the connectives of LSP. Specifically, we adopt the following:

Convention 6. $A \equiv B =_{Df} [A \supset B] \cdot [B \supset A]$.

Although we remarked that convention 6 eliminates the triple bar in favor of the tilde, wedge, and dot, the formulation of convention 6 suggests that '$\equiv$' is eliminated in favor of the dot and horseshoe. But we must not forget that the horseshoe is an auxiliary abbreviative symbol, not a primitive symbol of LSP. When all abbreviations are eliminated, convention 6 becomes

$A \equiv B =_{Df} [\sim A \vee B] \cdot [\sim B \vee A]$.

This latter expanded version of convention 6 makes it clear that $\ulcorner A \equiv B \urcorner$ abbreviates an equivalent wff in the tilde, wedge, and dot, that is, that '$\equiv$' is eliminated in favor of the connectives of LSP. The former version, however, puts into relief the reason why wffs of the form $\ulcorner A \equiv B \urcorner$ are called *biconditionals*.

By the *biconditional of A and B* is meant the wff that results on joining A to B by means of the triple bar, $\ulcorner A \equiv B \urcorner$. Where A and B are wffs of LSP, we will prove that A is equivalent to B if and only if their biconditional is valid, that is, if and only if $\ulcorner A \equiv B \urcorner$ is a tautology. First we show that $\ulcorner A \equiv B \urcorner$ is valid if A and B are equivalent. Suppose, then, that A is equivalent to B, and let Σ be an arbitrary value assignment to the variables of A and B. Since A and B are equivalent, they agree in truth value under Σ. Referring to the fundamental table for the triple bar, therefore, we see that $\ulcorner A \equiv B \urcorner$ comes out true under Σ. And, since Σ was an arbitrary value assignment, it follows that $\ulcorner A \equiv B \urcorner$ comes out true under every value assignment to its variables. We conclude, therefore, that $\ulcorner A \equiv B \urcorner$ is valid if A and B are equivalent. It remains to be shown that A and B are equivalent if $\ulcorner A \equiv B \urcorner$ is valid. Suppose that A and B are not equivalent. Then there is at least one value assignment Σ to the variables of A and B which confers opposite truth values on A and B. Thus the biconditional $\ulcorner A \equiv B \urcorner$ is not valid, because it comes out false under Σ. In other words, if A and B are not equivalent, then $\ulcorner A \equiv B \urcorner$ is not valid. It follows that if $\ulcorner A \equiv B \urcorner$ is valid, then A is equivalent to B.

The result just proved can be stated very succinctly: *Equivalence amounts to validity of the biconditional.* To test two wffs for equivalence, therefore, one may simply test their biconditional for validity. For example, one can establish the equivalence of '$p \supset q$' to '$\sim q \supset \sim p$' by constructing the truth table below, which shows that '$[p \supset q] \equiv [\sim q \supset \sim p]$' is valid.

p	q	$[p \supset q] \equiv [\sim q \supset \sim p]$
t	t	t
t	f	t
f	t	t
f	f	t

14.2. Implication; Consequence Relation

A wff A of LSP is said *to imply* a wff B of LSP if there is no interpretation of the class $\{A,B\}$ under which A comes out true but B comes out false.[1] For example, as the table below shows, '$\sim\sim p$' implies '$p \vee q$', because every interpretation of the two wffs which makes '$\sim\sim p$' come out true (the interpretations indicated by the first two rows of the table) also makes '$p \vee q$' come out true.

p	q	$\sim\sim p$	$p \vee q$
t	t	t	t
t	f	t	t
f	t	f	t
f	f	f	f

But '$p \vee q$' does not imply '$p \cdot q$', because there is at least one interpretation, for example, the assignment of truth to 'p' and falsehood to 'q', under which '$p \vee q$' comes out true but '$p \cdot q$' comes out false.

---

[1] See Appendix A for a brief introduction to the basic concepts and notation of set theory.

It was suggested in Section 14.1 that the horseshoe bears to implication the same relationship that the triple bar bears to equivalence. The relationship is this: A wff A implies a wff B if and only if the conditional $\ulcorner A \supset B \urcorner$ is valid. (Proof of the foregoing is left to the reader.) In other words, *implication amounts to validity of the conditional*. This epigram leads to a simple test for implication. To determine whether A implies B, merely test the conditional $\ulcorner A \supset B \urcorner$ for validity.

It was stated in Section 1.0 that a sentence A entails a sentence B if and only if it follows from the meanings of A and B that B would be true if A should be true. Just as equivalence was shown in Section 12.0 to be a sufficient condition of mutual entailment among sentences (interpreted wffs) of a P-language, it can also be readily shown that implication is a sufficient but not a necessary condition of entailment among sentences of a P-language. That is, if A and B are sentences of a P-language, then A entails B if A implies B. (Proof is obvious and left to the reader.)

We shall say that wffs $A_1, A_2, \ldots, A_n$ *jointly imply* a wff B if the conjunction $\ulcorner A_1 \cdot A_2 \cdot \ldots \cdot A_n \urcorner$ implies B. For example, the three wffs '$p \supset (q \equiv r)$', 'p', and '$\sim p$' jointly imply '$\sim r$', because the conjunction '$[p \supset (q \equiv r)] \cdot p \cdot \sim q$' implies '$\sim q$'. And we shall say that sentences $A_1, A_2, \ldots, A_n$ *jointly entail* a sentence B if the conjunction of the sentences $A_1, A_2, \ldots, A_n$ entails the sentence B. Obviously, joint implication is a sufficient but not a necessary condition of joint entailment among sentences of a P-language.

Let B be a wff of LSP and let Δ be a set of wffs of LSP. We shall say that B *is a consequence of* Δ if there is no interpretation of the set $\Delta \cup \{B\}$ under which every member of Δ comes out true but B comes out false. If Δ is finite, that is, if only finitely many wffs belong to Δ, then B is a consequence of Δ if and only if the members of Δ jointly imply B. For example, 'q' is a consequence of $\{ '\sim p', 'p \vee q' \}$, because '$\sim p$' and '$p \vee q$' jointly imply '$q$'. So if Δ is finite, the consequence relation reduces to joint implication. But what if Δ is infinite? Will there be finitely many members of Δ which jointly imply B if B is a consequence of Δ? It can be proved that this will always be the case. That is, one can prove that if B is a consequence of an infinite set Δ, then there are members $A_1, \ldots, A_n$ of Δ such that $A_1, \ldots, A_n$ jointly imply B. This result is one version of the *compactness theorem*, which is proved in Appendix D and in Section 30.4 [see also Exercises (19) and (20) of Chapter 31].

We shall say that a sentence B *follows from* a set Δ of sentences if, by virtue solely of their meanings, B would be true should every member of Δ be true. If Δ is finite, the relation of following from clearly reduces to joint entailment; that is, B follows from Δ if and only if the members of Δ jointly entail B. Furthermore, in P-languages a sentence B follows from a set Δ of sentences if B is a consequence of Δ; that is, the obtaining of the consequence relation is a sufficient condition of the obtaining of the relation of following from. It is not a necessary condition, however, as one can readily show by a counterexample.

14.3. Short-cut Test for Validity and Implication

Although the truth-table test for (joint) implication is both effective (mechanical) and simple, it quickly becomes laborious as the number of distinct variables in the table increases. Fortunately, in practice, the number of such variables rarely exceeds four. Even more fortunately, there is a short-cut procedure that usually reduces significantly the work demanded by the truth-table test for implication, not only in complicated cases but in simple ones as well. The essence of this short-cut procedure consists in reasoning backward from the structure of a (conditional) wff to a value assignment (if any) that falsifies it, that is, under which it comes out false. The wff is valid or nonvalid according as the short-cut procedure establishes, respectively, the nonexistence or existence of a falsifying value assignment to its variables. To illustrate this short-cut procedure, we test the conditional

$$[(\sim q \supset \sim p) \cdot (\sim r \equiv q) \cdot (\sim r \supset r)] \supset \sim p$$

for validity. Suppose that Σ is a value assignment to the variables of this conditional which falsifies it. Then Σ must make its antecedent true and its consequent false. Thus we have

$$[(\underset{t}{\sim q \supset \sim p}) \cdot (\underset{t}{\sim r \equiv q}) \cdot (\underset{t}{\sim r \supset r})] \supset \underset{f}{\sim p}$$

That is, Σ must give the value falsehood to the consequent '$\sim p$' and truth to the three conjuncts of the antecedent, '$\sim q \supset \sim p$', '$\sim r \equiv q$', and '$\sim r \supset r$'. As Σ makes '$\sim p$' false, Σ must assign truth to 'p'. So far, then, we have discovered that any falsifying value assignment Σ must assign truth to 'p'. Because Σ assigns truth to the first conjunct of the antecedent, '$\sim q \supset \sim p$', and falsehood to '$\sim p$', it follows that '$\sim q$' must come out false under Σ, hence that Σ assigns truth to 'q'. It remains only to determine what value Σ assigns to 'r'. The second conjunct '$\sim r \equiv q$' comes out true under Σ, and Σ assigns truth to 'q', so it is evident that '$\sim r$' must come out true under Σ, hence that Σ assigns falsehood to 'r'. Reasoning backward from the structure of the given conditional, then, we have discovered that if there is any value assignment which falsifies that conditional, it must assign truth to 'p' and 'q' and falsehood to 'r'. But, in fact, we find that the given conditional comes out true when 'p', 'q', and 'r' are assigned those values. It follows that there is no falsifying value assignment to the variables of the given conditional, that is, that the given conditional is valid. As implication amounts to validity of the conditional, we may conclude that '$\sim q \supset \sim p$', '$\sim r \equiv q$', and '$\sim r \supset r$' jointly imply '$\sim p$'.

As another illustration of the short-cut test for validity, we examine the conditional '$[(\sim p \lor q) \cdot (\sim q \supset q)] \supset p$'. Suppose Σ is a falsifying interpretation of the given wff. Then we have

$$[(\sim p \lor q) \cdot (\sim q \supset q)] \supset p$$
$$\quad\;\; t \qquad\qquad\;\; t \qquad\;\; f$$

From the fact that '$\sim p \lor q$' comes out true under Σ which assigns falsehood to 'p', we can infer nothing definite about the value Σ assigns to 'q', because either truth or falsehood would yield the required result. But for '$\sim q \supset q$' to come out true, Σ must assign truth to 'q'. Therefore, if there is any falsifying interpretation of the given conditional, it must assign falsehood to 'p' and truth to 'q'. And, indeed, we find that the given wff does come out false when 'p' and 'q' are assigned, respectively, falsehood and truth. The conditional is not valid, so the wffs '$\sim p \lor q$' and '$\sim q \supset q$' do not jointly imply 'p'.

Although we have applied it only to conditionals, the short-cut test for validity (reasoning backward from the structure of a formula to the nature of a falsifying interpretation) can be applied to any wff containing only truth-functional sentence connectives. Rather than describe it in detail, we presented the short-cut test through illustrations. We feel that such cursory treatment is warranted by the fact that in truth tables the reader already has a simple and effective test for validity. The reader who desires a more thorough treatment may consult Appendix B, in which a systematic version of the short-cut test for validity is presented in full.

14.4.   More Abbreviative Conventions

Too many abbreviative conventions are as inadvisable as too few. The purpose of abbreviation is to expose significant structure. There are two principal ways to do this: by eliminating bothersome brackets, and by supplanting complex structures with equivalent but more convenient structures (as $\ulcorner A \equiv B \urcorner$ supplants $\ulcorner [A \supset B] \cdot [B \supset A] \urcorner$ through abbreviation). But there comes a time when abbreviative devices, meant to expose significant structure, obfuscate it instead. For example, some authors use such a complicated system of dots to eliminate brackets from wffs that the net effect is to diminish perspicuity. It may also happen that a system of abbreviative conventions, though genuinely enhancing perspicuity, is so complex that the rewards of using it do not offset the effort required to master it. (This seems to be the case with some of the moderately complicated dot systems.) Aware of these pitfalls, we nonetheless propose two additional abbreviative conventions for eliminating bothersome brackets. We are convinced that the resulting increase in perspicuity offsets the little additional effort needed to master these simple conventions.

> Convention 7.   We let the horseshoe outrank the wedge, dot, and tilde.
>
> Convention 8.   We let the triple bar outrank the wedge, dot, and tilde.

Convention 7 allows us to rewrite '$[(\sim p \vee q) \cdot (\sim q \supset q)] \supset p$' as simply '$(\sim p \vee q) \cdot (\sim q \supset q) \supset p$' without introducing any ambiguity. Similarly, convention 8 permits us to rewrite

$$[(p \supset q) \cdot (q \supset p)] \equiv (p \equiv q)$$

as '$(p \supset q) \cdot (q \supset p) \equiv (p \equiv q)$'. And in virtue of the system of abbreviations 1–8, the formula '$\sim r \vee p \cdot q \equiv [r \supset p \cdot q]$' unambiguously abbreviates the wff '$\{[\sim r \vee (p \cdot q)] \equiv [r \supset (p \cdot q)]\}$'. It should be evident that the subsystem of conventions formed by 1, 2, 5–8 is formally acceptable. The total system formed by 1–8 is not formally acceptable, however, because of the tolerable ambiguities generated by 3 and 4.

14.5. Equivalence and Implication

It is easy to prove that wffs which imply one another are equivalent. For, suppose that A and B imply each other. Because implication amounts to validity of the conditional, it follows that the conditionals $\ulcorner A \supset B \urcorner$ and $\ulcorner B \supset A \urcorner$ are both valid. Clearly, then, their conjunction $\ulcorner [A \supset B] \cdot [B \supset A] \urcorner$ is valid. That is, as it merely abbreviates $\ulcorner [A \supset B] \cdot [B \supset A] \urcorner$, the biconditional $\ulcorner A \equiv B \urcorner$ is valid. And because equivalence amounts to validity of the biconditional, it follows that A is equivalent to B. We conclude, therefore, that wffs which imply one another are equivalent. It is also the case, as we now prove, that equivalent wffs imply one another. For, suppose that A and B are equivalent. Then their biconditional $\ulcorner A \equiv B \urcorner$ is valid, that is, $\ulcorner [A \supset B] \cdot [B \supset A] \urcorner$ is valid. Obviously, therefore, the conditionals $\ulcorner A \supset B \urcorner$ and $\ulcorner B \supset A \urcorner$ are valid. And, because implication amounts to validity of the conditional, it follows both that A implies B and that B implies A. We conclude, therefore, that equivalent wffs imply one another. Combining the two results just proved, we see that wffs imply one another if, and only if, they are equivalent. We express this combined result thus: *Equivalence amounts to mutual implication.*

In Section 10.1 we proved that equivalence is a reflexive, symmetrical, and transitive relation among the wffs of LSP. We will now verify that implication is also reflexive and transitive, but not symmetrical among the wffs of LSP. It is obvious from the definition of implication that any wff implies itself. So it follows that implication is reflexive among the wffs of LSP. To establish transitivity, we let A, B, and C be wffs which we assume to be so related that A implies B and B implies C. Suppose A does not imply C. Then there is at least one interpretation Σ of the set $\{A,B,C\}$ which makes A true and C false. By assumption, B implies C, so we see that B comes out false under Σ. (For, if B came out true under Σ, then Σ would give the value truth to B and falsehood to C, whence it would follow that B does not imply C.) And since Σ makes B false, it follows from the assumption that A implies B that A comes out false under Σ. But this result contradicts our other result that Σ makes A true. Thus our supposition that A does not imply C is inconsistent with our assumption that A implies B and that B implies C. We conclude, therefore, that if A implies B and B implies C, then A also implies C. Implication, therefore, is transitive among the wffs of LSP. Finally, to verify that implication is not symmetrical, we need merely to exhibit a pair of wffs only one of which implies the other. Obviously '$p \cdot q$' and '$p \vee q$' are such a pair; the former implies the latter, whereas the latter fails to imply the former. There are, of course, pairs of wffs that imply each other, for example, '$\sim p \cdot \sim q$' and '$\sim[p \vee q]$'. But to say that implication is not symmetrical is to say merely that not all pairs of wffs exhibit this feature.

15. EXERCISES

(1) Prove each of the following statements about implication among wffs of LSP:
   (a) A contradictory wff implies every wff.
   (b) A contingent wff is implied only by contradictory and contingent wffs.
   (c) No contingent wff implies a contradiction.
   (d) A valid wff is implied by every wff.
   (e) A tautology implies all and only tautologies.
   (f) A contradiction is implied by all and only contradictions.

(2) Use truth tables to determine whether
   (a) '$[p \supset q] \cdot r$' and '$q \equiv \sim r$' jointly imply '$\sim p$';
   (b) '$p \supset r$' and '$q \supset r$' jointly imply '$p \vee q \supset r$';
   (c) '$p \vee q \supset r$' implies '$[p \supset r] \cdot [q \supset r]$';
   (d) '$\sim p \supset p$' implies 'p';
   (e) '$p \cdot q \supset r$' implies '$[p \supset r] \cdot [q \supset r]$';
   (f) '$q \supset r$' implies '$p \vee q \supset p \vee r$';
   (g) '$p \supset [q \supset r]$' implies '$q \supset [p \supset r]$';
   (h) '$p \supset q$' implies '$[q \supset r] \supset [p \supset r]$';
   (i) 'p' implies '$[p \supset q] \supset q$';
   (j) '$p \supset q$' and '$\sim p \supset q$' jointly imply 'q';

(k)   '$p \vee q$' and '$\sim p$' jointly imply '$\sim q$';

(l)   '$p \supset q$' and '$p \supset \sim q$' jointly imply '$\sim p$';

(m)   '$p \equiv q$' and '$q \equiv r$' jointly imply '$\sim p \equiv \sim r$';

(n)   '$p \cdot q \supset r \cdot \sim r$' implies '$p \supset \sim q$';

(o)   '$\sim p \supset q \cdot \sim q$' implies '$p$'.

Do this exercise again, this time using the short-cut test for implication.

(3)   Prove that the expressive power of a P-language cannot be increased by the mere addition of new truth-functional sentence connectives.

(4)   Why is it somewhat misleading to speak of *the* associated conjunction of a row of a table, and of *the* characteristic wff of a table? (*Hint:* Focus on the tolerable ambiguity introduced by conventions 3 and 4.)

(5)   Prove that a set Γ of truth-functional sentence connectives is functionally complete if every truth-functional connective is definable in terms of members of Γ.

(6)   Define the ternary connective '$\odot$' of Section 13.0 in terms of the tilde, wedge, and dot. Define the horseshoe in terms of the tilde, wedge and dot.

(7)   Prove that in P-languages equivalence is not a necessary condition of mutual entailment among sentences.

[8]   Show that the system of abbreviation consisting solely of conventions 1, 2, 5, 6, 7, and 8 is formally acceptable.

(9)   Show that truth tables supply a mechanical test or algorithm for determining whether a wff B is a consequence of a *finite* set Δ of wffs of LSP. Why the proviso that Δ be finite?

(10)   Prove that implication amounts to validity of the conditional.

(11)   Prove that in a P-language implication is a sufficient, but not a necessary, condition of entailment among sentences.

(12)   Prove that $\ulcorner A \cdot B \urcorner$ is valid if and only if both A and B are valid. Is it true that $\ulcorner A \vee B \urcorner$ is valid if and only if at least one of A and B is valid? Is A invalid if and only if $\ulcorner \sim A \urcorner$ is valid? Is $\ulcorner \sim A \urcorner$ invalid if and only if A is valid?

(13)   Indicate which of the following are true for arbitrary wffs A and B of LSP:

(a)   If A is valid, then $\ulcorner A \vee B \urcorner$ is valid.

(b)   If neither A nor B is invalid, then $\ulcorner A \cdot B \urcorner$ is not invalid.

(c)   If A is invalid, then $\ulcorner A \supset B \urcorner$ is valid.

(d)   If B is valid, then $\ulcorner A \supset B \urcorner$ is valid.

(e)   If A and B are contingent, then $\ulcorner A \equiv B \urcorner$ is valid.

(f)   If both $\ulcorner A \vee B \urcorner$ and $\ulcorner A \supset B \urcorner$ are valid, then B is valid.

(g)   If $\ulcorner A \supset B \urcorner$ is invalid, then A is valid and B is invalid.

(14)   Show that all and only valid wffs are consequences of the empty set of wffs.

16.   NORMAL FORMS; DUALITY[1]

16.0.   Normal Forms

In analytic geometry $(x - a)^2 + (y - b)^2 = r^2$ is the standard form of an equation of a circle, that is, of an equation the graph of which is a circle. The center of such a circle is the point (a,b), and the radius of the circle is r. Hence, when an equation of a circle

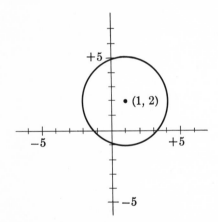

is put in standard form, complete information about its graph can be read off directly and easily from the equation. For example, the graph of $(x - 1)^2 + (y - 2)^2 = 3^2$ shown here is a circle of radius 3 centered on the point $(1,2)$.

---

[1] The reader who is in a hurry may skip directly to Chapter 20 without loss of continuity. We do not adhere very closely to the use-mention distinction in this chapter.

If an equation of a circle is not in standard form, it may be very difficult, if not impossible, to determine what its graph is from a cursory inspection of the equation. For example, it is very difficult to visualize the graph of $x^2 + y^2 - 4x - 2y + 4 = 0$ merely by inspecting that equation. Yet, if we first transform it into standard form, we get $(x - 2)^2 + (y - 1)^2 = 1^2$, off which we can readily read the information that its graph is a circle of unit radius centered on the point (2,1). Unlike other equations of circles, those in standard form wear their graphical meaning on their sleeves. One of the principal advantages of the standard form is the easy accessibility of important information.

Standard forms, or *normal forms* as we shall hereafter call them, are as useful in logic as in mathematics. Though nothing was said about it at the time, we have already encountered one important normal form for wffs of LSP, the so-called *full disjunctive normal form*. Let A be any noncontradictory wff of LSP and let $b_1, \ldots, b_n$ be in lexicographical order[2] a complete list of the distinct variables of A. Construct a truth table T for A such that the first n columns of T are headed by the variables $b_1, \ldots, b_n$, in that order. Then, as in Section 12.1, write the characteristic wff B of T. The wff B is a *full disjunctive normal form of A*. For example, if A is

$$\sim[\sim(p \cdot \sim q) \cdot (\sim p \vee \sim r)],$$

then a full disjunctive normal form B of A is the wff

$$p \cdot q \cdot \sim r \vee p \cdot \sim q \cdot r \vee p \cdot \sim q \cdot \sim r.$$

Notice that the *truth conditions* of a wff in full disjunctive normal form, that is, the interpretations under which it comes out true, can be read off directly and easily from it. For example, a brief inspection of B above reveals that B comes out true under these three interpretations:

'p' true, 'q' true, 'r' false
'p' true, 'q' false, 'r' true
'p' true, 'q' false, 'r' false

and B comes out false under all other value assignments to its variables. Because A is equivalent to B, the foregoing are also the truth conditions of A, but it would have been very difficult to see

---

[2] By the *lexicographical order* of the variables of LSP is meant the order of their introduction in the statement of the vocabulary of LSP: 'p', 'q', 'r', 's', 'p_1', and so on.

this upon brief inspection of A. So one advantage of full disjunctive normal forms is the obviousness of their truth conditions.

A second advantage of full disjunctive normal forms lies in the ease with which validity is recognizable. Let C be a wff in full disjunctive normal form and let k be the number of distinct variables which occur in C. Then C is valid if and only if C contains 2^k disjuncts. (If the reader will recall how the full disjunctive normal form of a wff is obtained from a truth table, this last claim should be obvious.) For example, because $k = 3$ for the full disjunctive normal form wff B mentioned in the last paragraph, that wff is not valid, for it has fewer than eight ($8 = 2^3$) disjuncts. But the following wff is valid, because it has four (disjuncts) and because for it $k = 2$:

$$p \cdot q \vee p \cdot \sim q \vee \sim p \cdot q \vee \sim p \cdot \sim q$$

A third and perhaps the most important advantage of full disjunctive normal forms is theoretical. Frequently a theoretical problem about all the wffs of a language system can be reduced to a similar but more easily solvable problem about wffs that are in some normal form (standard form) or other. This is an advantage that the reader will come to appreciate more and more as he gets further and further into the discipline of logic.

So far we have indicated only how to find the full disjunctive normal form of a noncontradictory wff via the special construction of a truth table, but we never gave an explicit definition of the concept. Here is the somewhat overdue definition. Let $a_1, \ldots, a_n$ be in lexicographical order a complete list of the distinct sentential variables that occur in a wff D of LSP. Then D is said to be *in full disjunctive normal form* if the following three conditions are all met:

(i) D is a continued disjunction $\ulcorner C_1 \vee C_2 \vee \ldots \vee C_r \urcorner$ of one or more disjuncts (that is, $r \geq 1$).

(ii)   No two disjuncts of D are the same.

(iii) Each disjunct C_i of D is a continued conjunction of the form $\ulcorner A_1 \cdot A_2 \cdot \ldots \cdot A_n \urcorner$, where each A_j is either a_j or $\ulcorner \sim a_j \urcorner$.

Besides the examples already given, the wff '$p \cdot \sim q \cdot r$' is in full disjunctive normal form. [This last example corresponds to the somewhat special case under clause (i) when $r = 1$.]

The reader may have noticed that only noncontradictory wffs can be in full disjunctive normal form. (See Exercise (2) of Chapter 17.) So, because it will also prove useful to have a standard or normal form for contradictory wffs, let us invent one. Where *b* is any sentential variable, we will say that the wff $\ulcorner b \cdot \sim b \urcorner$ is *in standard* (or *normal*) *contradictory form*. For example, '$q \cdot \sim q$' is in standard contradictory form, whereas the contradictory wffs '$p \cdot q \cdot \sim p$' and '$\sim p \cdot p$' are not.

16.1. Reduction to Normal Form

To reduce a wff *B* *to full disjunctive normal form* is to produce a wff in full disjunctive normal form that is equivalent to *B*, and the wff so produced is said to be a *full disjunctive normal form of B*. For example, we might reduce '$\sim[p \cdot \sim(p \vee q)]$' to full disjunctive normal form by producing the equivalent wff

$$p \cdot q \vee p \cdot \sim q \vee \sim p \cdot q \vee \sim p \cdot \sim q,$$

which is a full disjunctive normal form of the given wff. There will be infinitely many full disjunctive normal forms of a given non-contradictory wff but, by virtue of the fact that equivalence is a symmetrical and transitive relation, they will all be equivalent to one another. For example, the equivalent wffs '$p \cdot q \vee p \cdot \sim q$', '$p \cdot \sim q \vee p \cdot q$', and '$p$' are all full disjunctive normal forms of the wff '$p \vee (q \cdot \sim q)$'.

In Section 12.1 we introduced an effective method or algorithm for reducing a noncontradictory wff to full disjunctive normal form. The essence of the method lay in constructing, in a prescribed manner, a truth table for the wff, and then writing out the characteristic wff of the table. But if we are interested solely in whether the wff is valid and what its truth conditions are (that is, under what interpretations the wff comes out true), the writing of the characteristic formula, that is, the full disjunctive normal form, is rather superfluous, because that information is just as readily retrievable from the truth table itself. But there are ways to reduce a wff to full disjunctive normal form which do not involve the construction of a truth table. Some of them are not only occasionally more economical than the truth-tabular method now at hand, but also have independent theoretical interest. One such method will now be described.

The new method for reducing a wff to full disjunctive normal form will be called the *transformational method* to distinguish it from our old method, which will be called the *truth-tabular method*. The essence of the transformational method will consist in successively transforming a given wff, in accordance with certain specified rules, into a series of wffs, each equivalent to the preceding, until one reaches either a full disjunctive normal form (this will happen when the wff with which one began is noncontradictory) or a standard contradictory form (in the case when the given wff is contradictory). The permitted transformations are the following:

(i)   Continued conjunctions or continued disjunctions may be introduced in accordance with abbreviative conventions 3 and 4.

(ii)   One may reorder the conjuncts of a continued conjunction.

(iii) One may replace subformulas of the form

$$\ulcorner {\sim}[A_1 \cdot A_2 \cdot \ldots \cdot A_n] \urcorner \text{ by } \ulcorner {\sim}A_1 \vee {\sim}A_2 \vee \ldots \vee {\sim}A_n \urcorner.$$

(iv)   One may replace subformulas of the form

$$\ulcorner {\sim}[A_1 \vee A_2 \vee \ldots \vee A_n] \urcorner \text{ by } \ulcorner {\sim}A_1 \cdot {\sim}A_2 \cdot \ldots \cdot {\sim}A_n \urcorner.$$

(v)   One may replace subformulas of the form $\ulcorner {\sim}{\sim}A \urcorner$ by A.

(vi)   One may replace subformulas of the form

$$\ulcorner A \cdot (B_1 \vee B_2 \vee \ldots \vee B_n) \urcorner \text{ by } \ulcorner A \cdot B_1 \vee A \cdot B_2 \vee \ldots \vee A \cdot B_n \urcorner.$$

(vii) One may drop redundant disjuncts from continued disjunctions. (For example, one may pass from

'$p \vee q \vee r \vee q \vee p$' to '$p \vee q \vee r$'.)

(viii) One may drop redundant conjuncts from continued conjunctions.

(ix)   One may replace subformulas of the form $\ulcorner A \cdot [B \vee {\sim}B] \urcorner$ by A, or vice versa.

(x)   One may replace subformulas of the form $\ulcorner A \cdot B \cdot {\sim}B \urcorner$ by $\ulcorner B \cdot {\sim}B \urcorner$.

(xi)   One may replace subformulas of the form $\ulcorner A \vee B \cdot {\sim}B \urcorner$ by A.

The reference to *subformulas* in these transformational rules means that they can be applied to wffs which are parts of larger wffs, as well as to a whole wff (which is trivially a subformula of itself). The same holds, of course, for rules (i), (ii), (vii), and (viii). The reader should satisfy himself that whenever any of these transformational rules is used to transform a wff A into a wff B, A is equivalent to B. Thus, no matter how many successive transformations a wff undergoes, the end or last wff will be equivalent to the initial or starting wff.

Let us now see how these transformational rules can be used to reduce a wff to full disjunctive normal form, for example, '$\sim[p \cdot \sim(p \vee q)]$':

$\sim[p \cdot \sim(p \vee q)]$	Starting wff
$\sim p \vee \sim\sim(p \vee q)$	Rule (iii)
$\sim p \vee (p \vee q)$	Rule (v)
$\sim p \vee p \vee q$	Rule (i)
$\sim p \cdot [q \vee \sim q] \vee p \cdot [q \vee \sim q] \vee q \cdot [p \vee \sim p]$	Rule (ix)
$[\sim p \cdot q \vee \sim p \cdot \sim q] \vee [p \cdot q \vee p \cdot \sim q] \vee [q \cdot p \vee q \cdot \sim p]$	Rule (vi)
$\sim p \cdot q \vee \sim p \cdot \sim q \vee p \cdot q \vee p \cdot \sim q \vee q \cdot p \vee q \cdot \sim p$	Rule (i)
$\sim p \cdot q \vee \sim p \cdot \sim q \vee p \cdot q \vee p \cdot \sim q \vee p \cdot q \vee \sim p \cdot q$	Rule (ii)
$\sim p \cdot q \vee \sim p \cdot \sim q \vee p \cdot q \vee p \cdot \sim q$	Rule (vii)

Much time and labor can be saved by the simultaneous application of several rules. For example, examine the following reduction of '$\sim[p \vee \sim(\sim p \vee q)]$' to full disjunctive normal form:

$\sim[p \vee \sim(\sim p \vee q)]$	Starting wff
$\sim p \cdot (\sim p \vee q)$	Rules (iv), (v)
$\sim p \vee \sim p \cdot q$	Rules (vi), (viii)
$\sim p \cdot (q \vee \sim q) \vee \sim p \cdot q$	Rule (ix)
$\sim p \cdot q \vee \sim p \cdot \sim q$	Rules (vi), (i), (vii)

Let us see how these transformational rules can be used to reduce a contradictory wff to standard contradictory form:

$p \cdot [q \cdot \sim p \vee p \cdot \sim r \cdot \sim p]$	Starting wff
$p \cdot q \cdot \sim p \vee p \cdot \sim r \cdot \sim p$	Rules (vi), (viii)
$p \cdot \sim p$	Rules (ii), (x), (xi)

Using the transformational method, one can reduce any noncontradictory wff to full disjunctive normal form and any contradictory wff to standard contradictory form, but we have neither proved this assertion (that is left as an exercise) nor described how to go about reducing wffs, that is, what strategy to follow. We will now describe one possible strategy.

This strategy can be broken down into six steps. The *first step* is to work from the starting wff toward a wff in which tildes are attached only to sentential variables and in which no wedge occurs as part of a conjunction, that is, to work toward a wff that is a continued disjunction the disjuncts of which are continued conjunctions of sentential variables with or without tildes prefixed to them. One can accomplish this by repeatedly applying the following rules until they can no longer be applied; if at any stage several of the rules are applicable, apply the one that comes earliest in the list: (vii), (viii), (v), (i), (iii), (iv), (vi). When this first step is completed, one will have a continued disjunction D_1 of the form $\ulcorner B_1 \vee B_2 \vee \ldots \vee B_n \urcorner$ in which each disjunct B_i is a continued conjunction of variables or negations of variables.

The *second step* is to eliminate any B_i that is contradictory. To do this, inspect each B_i (beginning, say, at the left of D_1) to determine whether it contains both a sentential variable b and its negation $\ulcorner \sim b \urcorner$. If so, use rule (ii) to move $\ulcorner b \cdot \sim b \urcorner$ to the extreme right end of the disjunct, and then use rule (x) to replace the whole disjunct by just $\ulcorner b \cdot \sim b \urcorner$. Then use rule (xi) to drop $\ulcorner b \cdot \sim b \urcorner$ out of the formula altogether. When this second step is completed, one will either have a standard contradictory form (this will happen when each B_i is contradictory) or else a continued disjunction D_2 of the form $\ulcorner C_1 \vee C_2 \vee \ldots \vee C_m \urcorner$ in which each C_i is a noncontradictory continued conjunction of sentential variables or negations of sentential variables.

The *third step* consists in successively introducing "missing" sentential variables. Let $b_1, b_2, \ldots, b_k$ be a complete list of the distinct sentential variables that occur in D_2. Let C_j be the first disjunct of D_2 which is "missing" any variable in the list $b_1, b_2, \ldots, b_k$, and let b be any one of the missing variables. Use rule (ix) to replace C_j by $\ulcorner C_j \cdot (b \vee \sim b) \urcorner$, then use rule (vi) to replace this formula by $\ulcorner C_j \cdot b \vee C_j \cdot \sim b \urcorner$, and then apply rule (i) to get a new continued disjunction. If any of the disjuncts of this new continued disjunction are missing variables in the list $b_1, b_2, \ldots, b_k$, repeat the process just described until you get a continued disjunction D_3 each disjunct of which contains every variable in the list $b_1, b_2, \ldots, b_k$.

The *fourth step* consists in subjecting D_3 to step one. Let D_4 be the result of this step. Clearly D_4 will have the form

$$\ulcorner A_1 \vee A_2 \vee \ldots \vee A_r \urcorner,$$

where each A_i is a noncontradictory continued conjunction of sentential variables or negations of such. The *fifth step* is to order the sentential variables in each disjunct A_i lexicographically by applying rule (ii). Let D_5 be the result. The *sixth* and *last step* is to get rid of redundant disjuncts by applying rule (viii) to D_5. The result D_6 will be a full disjunctive normal form of the starting wff.

The detailed description just given of one strategy for using the transformational method to reduce wffs to full disjunctive normal form (or standard contradictory form) probably makes the method seem much more complicated than it really is. A little practice at reducing wffs should remove that false impression.

16.2.   Simple Disjunctive Normal Form

Notice that it is even more easy to read off the truth conditions of 'p v $\sim q$ v $\sim p \cdot r$' than to read off the truth conditions of its full disjunctive normal form

$$p \cdot q \cdot r \text{ v } p \cdot q \cdot \sim r \text{ v } p \cdot \sim q \cdot r \text{ v } p \cdot \sim q \cdot \sim r \text{ v}$$
$$\sim p \cdot q \cdot r \text{ v } \sim p \cdot \sim q \cdot r \text{ v } \sim p \cdot \sim q \cdot \sim r.$$

So, if it is exclusively truth conditions that interest us, formulas such as the former (which are said to be in simple disjunctive normal form) are even more useful than full disjunctive normal forms.

We shall say that a formula D is *in simple disjunctive normal form* if D satisfies these three conditions:

(i) D is a continued disjunction $\ulcorner C_1 \text{ v } \ldots \text{ v } C_r \urcorner$ of one or more disjuncts.

(ii)   No two disjuncts of D are equivalent.

(iii)   Each disjunct C_i of D is a noncontradictory nonredundant continued conjunction of sentential variables or negations of sentential variables.

For example, the following wffs are in simple disjunctive normal form:

$$p \text{ v } q \text{ v } \sim r, \qquad p \cdot q \text{ v } p \cdot \sim r,$$

and

$$p \cdot q \text{ v } p \cdot \sim q \text{ v } \sim p \cdot q \text{ v } \sim p \cdot \sim q.$$

Surprisingly, a transformational method for reducing wffs to simple disjunctive normal form is almost at hand. If we terminate the six-step strategy of Section 16.1 at the end of the second step and drop from the formula so obtained any disjunct equivalent to an earlier disjunct, the wff that results will be a simple disjunctive normal form of the starting wff (provided only that the starting wff is noncontradictory). For example, using this two-step strategy we can reduce '$\sim\sim\sim[\sim q \cdot \sim(p \cdot r)]$' to the simple disjunctive normal form '$q \vee p \cdot r$' as follows:

$\sim\sim\sim[\sim q \cdot \sim(p \cdot r)]$	Starting wff
$\sim[\sim q \cdot (\sim p \vee \sim r)]$	Rules (v), (iii)
$q \vee \sim(\sim p \vee \sim r)$	Rules (iii), (v)
$q \vee p \cdot r$	Rules (iv), (v)

Similarly, '$p \cdot q \vee q \cdot (p \vee r)$' reduces to the simple disjunctive normal form '$p \cdot q \vee q \cdot r$':

$p \cdot q \vee q \cdot (p \vee r)$	Starting wff
$p \cdot q \vee q \cdot p \vee q \cdot r$	Rules (vi), (i)
$p \cdot q \vee q \cdot r$	Dropping equivalent disjuncts

16.3. Duality

The mathematically trained reader is probably familiar with so-called "duality principles" from his acquaintance with subjects like projective geometry and Boolean algebra. Roughly speaking, the duality principle for the former discipline states that thoroughgoing interchange of the words 'point' and 'line' will convert a theorem of projective geometry into still another theorem. For example, such interchange converts the theorem 'Two points determine a line' into the theorem 'Two lines determine a point'. Similarly, in Boolean algebra the duality principle affirms (roughly) that thoroughgoing interchange of '$\cup$' and '$\cap$' (called 'cup' and 'cap', these symbols signify, respectively, class union and class intersection[3]) converts a theorem into another theorem.[4] For example, such interchange converts the Boolean theorem

$$[x \cup (y \cap z)] = [(x \cup y) \cap (x \cup z)]$$

into the Boolean theorem '$[x \cap (y \cup z)] = [(x \cap y) \cup (x \cap z)]$'.

---

[3] For an elementary introduction to set or class concepts, see Appendix A.

[4] More exactly, not only must the cup and cap be interchanged, but the symbols 'Λ' and 'V' must also be interchanged. (The symbols 'Λ' and 'V' denote, respectively, the null or empty class and the universal class.)

(In these Boolean formulas the letters 'x', 'y', and 'z' are used as class variables, that is, variables whose values are classes.) The economy that such duality principles afford lend them some practical interest, because to prove a pair of "dual" theorems it suffices to establish only one of them; the other then follows from the duality principle. Although logicians have been much less concerned with duality than have mathematicians, we are including a brief treatment of duality in truth-functional logic for the sake of comprehensive coverage.

Henceforth, truth and falsehood will be said to be *opposite to* one another. Let Σ_1 and Σ_2 be interpretations that make value assignments to the same set Δ of sentential variables. Then we will say that Σ_1 and Σ_2 are *opposite to* one another if, for each variable b of Δ, Σ_1 and Σ_2 assign opposite truth values to b. To have a convenient notation, we symbolize by 'Σ^*' the interpretation opposite to a given interpretation Σ. For example, if Σ is the interpretation which assigns t to 'p' and f to 'q', then Σ^* is the interpretation which assigns f to 'p' and t to 'q'. Let A and B be wffs of LSP. Then A will be said to be *dual to B* if, for every interpretation Σ of the set $\{A,B\}$, the value of A under Σ is opposite to the value of B under Σ^*. For example, the following table shows that '$\sim(p \vee q)$' is dual to '$\sim(p \cdot q)$':

Σ				Σ^*	
p	q	$\sim(p \vee q)$	$\sim(p \cdot q)$	p	q
t	t	f	t	f	f
t	f	f	t	f	t
f	t	f	t	t	f
f	f	t	f	t	t

Many of the most important facts about duality follow almost immediately from the definitions just given. Here are some of them:

(i)   Duality is a symmetrical relation among the wffs of LSP.
(ii) The duals of a given wff are equivalent to one another; that is, if both B and C are dual to A, then B and C are equivalent.
(iii) A wff is valid if and only if its duals are contradictory.
(iv) A wff is contradictory if and only if its duals are valid.
(v)   A wff is contingent if and only if its duals are contingent.

(vi)   Let the wff B result from the wff A by first prefixing a tilde
to each occurrence of every sentential variable in A and then
prefixing a tilde to the entire result. Then B is dual to A. For
example, '$\sim[\sim p \vee (\sim q \cdot \sim\sim r)]$' is dual to '$p \vee (q \cdot \sim r)$'.

(vii) Let C and D be, respectively, dual to A and B. Then A
implies B if and only if D implies C.

(viii) Two wffs are equivalent if and only if their duals are
equivalent.

(ix)   Let A be a wff of LSP (containing no abbreviations) and let
B result from A by thoroughgoing interchange of dots and
wedges. Then B is dual to A. For example, '$[\sim(\sim p \vee \sim q) \cdot r]$'
is dual to '$[\sim(\sim p \cdot \sim q) \vee r]$'. (This is the only fact about
duality in our list that is not immediately evident from
the definition of duality. Although its proof is quite simple,
it requires mathematical induction and will therefore be
deferred until proof by mathematical induction has been
discussed, namely until Chapter 22.)

17.   EXERCISES

(1)   Why is it somewhat misleading but nonetheless innocuous to
speak of *the* full disjunctive normal form of a given wff? Reduce '$\sim[p \cdot \sim(p \vee \sim q)]$' to a wff in full disjunctive normal
form that contains occurrences of the three variables 'p',
'q', and 'r' but no other variables. How many full disjunctive
normal forms of a given noncontradictory wff are there?

(2)   Prove that, if A is a wff in full disjunctive normal form, then
A is noncontradictory. Let A be a wff in full disjunctive
normal form and let k be the number of distinct sentential
variables that occur in A. Prove that A is valid if and only
if A is a continued disjunction with 2^k disjuncts.

(3)   On the basis of the definition of full disjunctive normal form,
prove that the truth-tabular method of reducing wffs to full
disjunctive normal form, as described in the third paragraph
of Section 16.0, works.

[4] Prove that any noncontradictory wff of LSP can be reduced to full disjunctive normal form by the transformational method. Prove that any contradictory wff of LSP can be reduced to standard contradictory form by the transformational method.

(5) Reduce to full disjunctive normal form by the transformational method every wff reduced to full disjunctive normal form by the truth-tabular method in Section 16.0. (Where possible, telescope the application of several transformational rules.)

(6) Prove that every wff in full disjunctive normal form is also in simple disjunctive normal form.

(7) Rewrite Exercise (1) by substituting 'simple' for every occurrence of 'full', and do the resulting exercise.

[8] Prove that any noncontradictory wff of LSP can be reduced to simple disjunctive normal form by the two-step transformational procedure described in Section 16.2.

(9) Rewrite Exercise (5) by substituting 'simple' for 'full', and do the resulting exercise.

(10) Prove that there is exactly one value assignment opposite to a given value assignment.

(11) Determine whether duality is reflexive, symmetrical, or transitive among the wffs of LSP.

(12) Prove each of the claims (i)–(viii) made at the end of Section 16.3.

(13) Produce a dual of each of the following wffs:

$\sim p \qquad q \cdot (p \vee r)$

$p \vee q \qquad \sim[\sim(p \vee \sim q) \vee (q \cdot r)]$

[14] Let $\otimes$ and $\ominus$ be n-ary truth-functional sentence connectives. Then $\otimes$ will be called *a dual connective to* $\ominus$ if the wff $\ulcorner\otimes(p_1, \ldots, p_n)\urcorner$ is dual to the wff $\ulcorner\ominus(p_1, \ldots, p_n)\urcorner$. Prove that there is exactly one connective dual to a given connective. Which are the connectives dual to the tilde, the dot, the wedge, the horseshoe, and the triple bar?

18.   BOOLEAN EQUATIONS; ELECTRICAL CIRCUITS

18.0.   Boolean Equations

Boolean algebra is an elementary branch of mathematics which deals with the unions, intersections, and complements of the subclasses of an arbitrary nonempty class which is called the *universal class* or simply the *universe*. (By the *complement of* a class x *in* V is meant the class of objects, if any, which belong to V but not to x. The complement of x in V is sometimes symbolized as '$-x$', and it is customary to speak simply of *the complement of x* rather than to say *the complement of x in* V.[1]) As Boolean algebra is closely related to sentential (truth-functional) logic, in our introduction to the latter we have included a cursory treatment of the former.

We begin our treatment of Boolean algebra with a careful statement of the syntax and semantics of what we will call the *system of Boolean equations* (SBE):

Vocabulary
 (i)   An infinite supply of class variables:
       'w', 'x', 'y', 'z', 'w_1', 'x_1', and so on.
 (ii)   Two class constants (class names): 'V' and 'Λ'.
 (iii)   One singulary operator: '$-$'.
 (iv)   Two binary operators: '$\cup$' and '$\cap$'.
 (v)   Two grouping indicators: '[' and ']'.
 (vi)   One binary predicate: '$=$', called the *equality* or *identity sign*.

Grammatical Rules
 (i)   A class variable or a class constant is a *class term*.
 (ii)   If T is a class term, so is $\ulcorner -T \urcorner$.

---

[1] It is customary to denote the complement of a class x by '$\bar{x}$' rather than by '$-x$'. Thus '$\bar{x}$', '$\overline{(x \cup y)}$', and '$\overline{(\bar{x} \cap y)}$' are mere variant but rather common forms of our expressions '$--x$', '$-(x \cup y)$', and '$-(-x \cap y)$'.

(iii)   If T_1 and T_2 are class terms, then $\ulcorner(T_1 \cup T_2)\urcorner$ and $\ulcorner(T_1 \cap T_2)\urcorner$ are also class terms.[2]

(iv)   A formula is a class term if and only if it can be constructed by a finite number of applications of the preceding rules.

(v)   If T_1 and T_2 are class terms, then $\ulcorner(T_1 = T_2)\urcorner$ is an (atomic) wff. (We will call these atomic wffs *Boolean equations*.)

For example, all the following are Boolean equations, that is, atomic wffs of SBE:

$[-(x \cup y) = -(-x \cap -y)]$ $[--y = (V \cap y)]$ $(x = \Lambda)$
$[(w \cup (x \cup y)) = ((w \cup x) \cup y)]$ $[-V = (x \cap y)]$

But none of the following are Boolean equations:

$[(x \cup y) \cup z]$ $(x = y = z)$ $[x \cup y \cup z = x \cup y \cup z]$

Semantics.   Let ϕ be a class term or wff (Boolean equation) of SBE. By an *interpretation of ϕ* is meant the selection of some *non-empty* class, thereafter called the *universal class*, as the value of 'V', and of the empty class as the value of 'Λ', together with an assignment of some subclass or other of the universal class to each class variable in ϕ. (For example, if ϕ were '$[(x \cup y) = -V]$', the selection of the set of positive integers as the universal class together with the assignment of the set of prime integers to 'x' and the set of even primes greater than two to 'y' would constitute an interpretation of ϕ.) The following semantical rules define the value of a class term or wff (Boolean equation) ϕ under an interpretation Σ:

(i)   If ϕ is 'V', then the value of ϕ under Σ is the universal class.

(ii)   If ϕ is 'Λ', then the value of ϕ under Σ is the empty class.

(iii)   If ϕ is $\ulcorner-T\urcorner$, then the value of ϕ under Σ is the class that is the complement (in the universal class) of the class that is the value of T under Σ. (In other words, Σ assigns to $\ulcorner-T\urcorner$ the complement of the class that it assigns to T.)

(iv)   If ϕ is $\ulcorner(T_1 \cup T_2)\urcorner$, then the value of ϕ under Σ is the union of the classes Δ_1 and Δ_2, where Δ_1 and Δ_2 are, respectively, the values of T_1 and T_2 under Σ. [In other words, Σ assigns to $\ulcorner(T_1 \cup T_2)\urcorner$ the union of the classes that it assigns to T_1 and T_2.]

---

[2] What informal (unofficial) convention about writing brackets is being used here?

(v)   If ϕ is $\ulcorner(T_1 \cap T_2)\urcorner$, then the value of ϕ under Σ is the intersection of the classes Δ_1 and Δ_2, where Δ_1 and Δ_2 are, respectively, the values of T_1 and T_2 under Σ. [In other words, Σ assigns to $\ulcorner(T_1 \cap T_2)\urcorner$ the intersection of the classes that it assigns to T_1 and T_2.]

(vi) If ϕ is $\ulcorner(T_1 = T_2)\urcorner$, then the value of ϕ under Σ is truth if the value of T_1 under ϕ is the same as the value of T_2 under ϕ; otherwise, the value of ϕ under Σ is falsehood. [In other words, Σ assigns truth to $\ulcorner(T_1 = T_2)\urcorner$ if Σ assigns the same class to T_1 and T_2; and otherwise Σ assigns falsehood to $\ulcorner(T_1 = T_2)\urcorner$.]

Inspection of the above semantical rules will disclose that under an interpretation a class term will have a class as its value, whereas a wff (Boolean equation) will have a truth value as its value. Now, as a rule the mathematician is no more interested in Boolean equations that happen to come out true under a particular interpretation than the logician is interested in truth-functional wffs which happen to come out true under a particular interpretation. Rather the mathematician is principally interested in the *valid* Boolean equations, that is, in those Boolean equations (atomic wffs) which come out true under every interpretation. And it turns out that the valid Boolean equations are as easily recognized as are the valid truth-functional wffs. In fact, there is a "truth-tabular" decision procedure for determining atomic Boolean validity (that is, the validity of Boolean equations) which is almost exactly like our familiar truth-tabular technique for determining truth-functional validity (that is, the validity of wffs of LSP).

Consider the following fundamental "truth table" for the complement operator '$-$':

T	$-T$
$\in$	$\notin$
$\notin$	$\in$

The above table is to be understood thus. The symbol 'T' stands for any interpreted class term and the table shows whether or not an arbitrary member α of the universal class belongs to the complement of the class assigned to T in the following way. The first row shows that, if the object α belongs to the class (denoted by) T, then α does not belong to its complement, that is, the class denoted by $\ulcorner - T \urcorner$. (Thus '$\in$' and '$\notin$' mean 'belongs to' and 'does not belong to', respectively.) The second row shows that, if α does not belong to the class denoted by T, then α does belong to the complement of that class. The fundamental tables for '$\cup$' and '$\cap$' are to be understood in a similar way:

T_1	T_2	$(T_1 \cup T_2)$
$\in$	$\in$	$\in$
$\in$	$\notin$	$\in$
$\notin$	$\in$	$\in$
$\notin$	$\notin$	$\notin$

T_1	T_2	$(T_1 \cap T_2)$
$\in$	$\in$	$\in$
$\in$	$\notin$	$\notin$
$\notin$	$\in$	$\notin$
$\notin$	$\notin$	$\notin$

The last fundamental table, the one for the identity predicate '$=$', calls for additional comment:[3]

T_1	T_2	$T_1 = T_2$
$\in$	$\in$	t
$\in$	$\notin$	f
$\notin$	$\in$	f
$\notin$	$\notin$	t

The idea behind this table is a little more difficult to grasp, although it is just as easy to work with this table as with the others. On the supposition that a member of the universe (that is, of the universal class) belongs to both T_1 and T_2, there is a presumption raised that the classes T_1 and T_2 are identical, hence the entry 't' in the first row. Similarly, the supposition that a member of the universe belongs to neither class raises the presumption that they are identical classes, hence the entry 't' in the fourth row. But if a member of the universe is assumed to belong to the class designated by T_1 but not to the class designated by T_2, then those classes cannot be the same if the assumption is true, hence the entry 'f' in the second row. Similar reasoning justifies the entry 'f' in row three. Accordingly, if in a completely filled in table for a Boolean equation there

[3] When the practice will not mislead, we will drop outermost brackets.

occur only 't's under the identity sign, that means that the classes designated by the left-hand and right-hand terms of the Boolean equation must be identical, because the presumption of identity is established for every possible supposition about the membership or nonmembership of an arbitrary element in all the classes out of which the left-hand and right-hand members are composed. For example, the following table shows that under any interpretation of the given Boolean equation, the class designated by the left-hand class term is the same as the class designated by the right-hand class term. Or, put otherwise, the table shows that the given Boolean equation is valid.

x	y	$-(x \cup y)$	$=$	$(-x \cap -y)$
$\in$	$\in$	$\notin$	t	$\notin$
$\in$	$\notin$	$\notin$	t	$\notin$
$\notin$	$\in$	$\notin$	t	$\notin$
$\notin$	$\notin$	$\in$	t	$\in$

(The reader should fill in all the '$\in$'s and '$\notin$'s missing from the above table, remembering that '$\notin$' is *not* a scratched-out '$\in$'.) Similarly, the table below establishes the validity of the given Boolean equation.

y	$(y \cup -y)$	$=$	V
$\in$	$\in$	t	$\in$
$\notin$	$\in$	t	$\in$

(Why was an '$\in$' put beneath 'V' in every row of the table? Why should '$\notin$' be put beneath 'Λ' in every row of any table? Why should '$\in$' be put beneath 'V' in every row of any table?) The following table, however, shows that the given Boolean equation is not valid, because there are suppositions about membership of an arbitrary element α in the ultimate component classes x, y, and z under which α would belong to the class $[(x \cap y) \cap z]$ but not to the class Λ: the supposition (indicated by the first row) that α is a member of each of the three classes x, y, and z.

x	y	z	$[(x \cap y) \cap z] = \Lambda$		
$\in$	$\in$	$\in$	$\in$	f	$\notin$
$\in$	$\in$	$\notin$	$\notin$	t	$\notin$
$\in$	$\notin$	$\in$	$\notin$	t	$\notin$
$\in$	$\notin$	$\notin$	$\notin$	t	$\notin$
$\notin$	$\in$	$\in$	$\notin$	t	$\notin$
$\notin$	$\in$	$\notin$	$\notin$	t	$\notin$
$\notin$	$\notin$	$\in$	$\notin$	t	$\notin$
$\notin$	$\notin$	$\notin$	$\notin$	t	$\notin$

The obvious parallel between the truth-tabular techniques for determining the validity of truth-functional wffs and those for deciding the validity of atomic Boolean wffs (Boolean equations) suggests an alternative method for dealing with Boolean equations, a method we will call the *translational method*. It consists in "translating" a Boolean equation into a truth-functional wff that is valid if and only if the Boolean equation is valid, and then testing (by any of our several methods) the truth-functional translation for validity. The "dictionary" needed to make such translations is given below:

Boolean symbol	w x y z w_1 ... [ ] $-$ $\cap$ $\cup$	V	Λ	$=$
Translation	p q r s p_1 ... [ ] $\sim$ $\cdot$ $\vee$	$(p \vee \sim p)$	$(p \cdot \sim p)$	$\equiv$

For example, the Boolean equation tested in the last table above translates via this dictionary into the wff '$[(q \cdot r) \cdot s] \equiv (p \cdot \sim p)$', which is valid if and only if the Boolean original is valid. Note that our claim about this translational method is simply that valid Boolean equations translate into valid truth-functional wffs and that nonvalid Boolean equations translate into nonvalid truth-functional wffs. No stronger relation than the one just described was claimed to hold between a Boolean equation and its truth-functional translation.

18.1. Design of Electrical Circuits

We expected truth-tabular methods to be useful in dealing with such logical matters as implication, equivalence, validity, and so on, because they were invented for just such purposes. It was a pleasant surprise, however, to find them useful in dealing with Boolean equations. Even so, we are a long way from exhausting the fruitfulness of truth-tabular techniques. In this section we illustrate their utility in an entirely different direction—in the design of electrical switching circuits.

Consider the switching circuit shown. In the diagram, switches *p*, *q*, and *r* are *open* and switch *s* is *closed*. For our purposes, all we

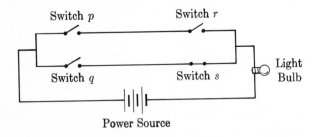

need understand about the behavior of electricity is that the light bulb will glow if and only if there is an unbroken path from one side of the power source to the other. So, when the circuit is in the state depicted above, the bulb will not glow, because there is then no unbroken path. But if both switch *q* and switch *s* were closed, the bulb would glow; similarly, the bulb would glow if switches *p* and *r* were both closed; under all other circumstances, the bulb would fail to glow. Let '*p*' mean 'switch *p* is closed', let '*q*' mean 'switch *q* is closed', and so on. Then the wff '*p·r* v *q·s*' completely describes the behavior of the circuit depicted above in the sense that the bulb will glow when and only when the switches are in a state that makes '*p·r* v *q·s*' true. For example, when the switches are in the state depicted by the diagram, the bulb will not glow, as '*p·r* v *q·s*' will then be false.

By mechanical or electrical linkages, two or more switches can be made to operate as a unit. We will regard switches linked to operate together as a unit as a *single complex switch* and we will therefore use the same label for each of its component switches. Suppose, for example, that in the circuit depicted we linked switches *p* and *q* so that they open and close together as a unit. Then we could produce a new circuit diagram, as shown. Clearly,

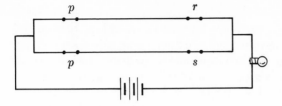

the wff '$p \cdot r \vee p \cdot s$' or the equivalent wff '$p \cdot (r \vee s)$' both completely describe the behavior of the circuit just depicted. (In the circuit state depicted, the bulb will glow, for '$p \cdot (r \vee s)$' is obviously true.)

Linkages can also be used to make several switches operate in opposition, that is, to so link them that when some are closed, the others are open, and vice versa. We shall also regard switches linked to operate in opposition as a single complex switch, labeling those of its components that open and close together by the same letter, using the same letter with a bar over it for those components that work oppositely to those labeled by the plain letter. Suppose, for example, that in the above-described circuit we linked switches r and s to operate in opposition. Then we could produce the diagram shown for the resulting circuit. Clearly, the wff '$p \cdot (r \vee \sim r)$' com-

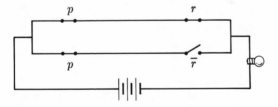

pletely describes this circuit. (We regard a complex switch as closed when its components whose labels lack bars are closed. Note, then, that when complex switch r is open, the component switch $\bar{r}$ is closed.) But, because '$p \cdot (r \vee \sim r)$' is equivalent to just 'p', the wff 'p' itself completely describes the circuit. It follows that the complex switch r is superfluous in the sense that one could never turn the bulb on or off by throwing it. Money could obviously be saved by eliminating the complex r switch without affecting the properties of the circuit.

Suppose a homeowner commissioned us to design an electrical circuit for a garage light which he wants to be able to turn on and off from two locations, inside his garage and inside his house. By using two complex switches, we can easily design such a circuit. All that is needed is a circuit in which the bulb glows when and only when both switches are closed or both open, that is, a circuit described by the wff '$p \cdot q \vee \sim p \cdot \sim q$'. Such a circuit design is readily produced, as shown.

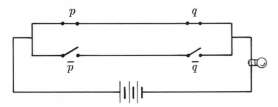

The design of "voting circuits" poses a similar problem and is as easily handled. Suppose we are to design a voting circuit for a three-man committee, so that a light comes on when and only when a majority of the committee vote *yes* (closing his switch is a member's way of voting *yes*; leaving it open, his way of voting *no*). The eight possible states of the switches are described by the following eight wffs:

(1) $p \cdot q \cdot r$ (5) $\sim p \cdot q \cdot r$

(2) $p \cdot q \cdot \sim r$ (6) $\sim p \cdot q \cdot \sim r$

(3) $p \cdot \sim q \cdot r$ (7) $\sim p \cdot \sim q \cdot r$

(4) $p \cdot \sim q \cdot \sim r$ (8) $\sim p \cdot \sim q \cdot \sim r$

Because only wffs (1), (2), (3), and (5) correspond to a majority vote, we want a circuit whose behavior is described by the wff

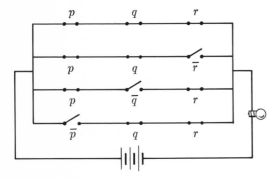

'$(p \cdot q \cdot r) \vee (p \cdot q \cdot \sim r) \vee (p \cdot \sim q \cdot r) \vee (\sim p \cdot q \cdot r)$', and such a circuit is readily designed, as shown. By blindly following the procedure illustrated, one will always come up with a design for a circuit that has the required properties. But a little ingenuity might yield a design for a *simpler circuit*, that is, *one with fewer switch components* (a complex switch with four components being counted as four). For example, shown here is a much simpler design for the above-described voting circuit:

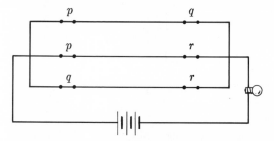

And here is an even simpler one:

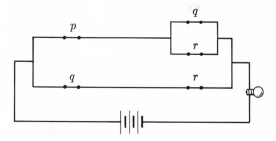

Switches arranged as depicted below are said to be *in series:*

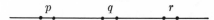

Note that the *conjunction* '$p \cdot q \cdot r$' describes the above-depicted portion of a circuit. When arranged as depicted below, switches are said to be *in parallel:*

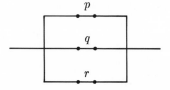

Note that the disjunction '$p \vee q \vee r$' describes the above-depicted portion of a circuit. From these observations we can see that a wff in full or simple disjunctive normal form corresponds to a parallel arrangement of switches in series. For example, the simple disjunctive normal form wff '$p \vee {\sim}p \cdot q \vee q \cdot r$' corresponds to the following circuit:

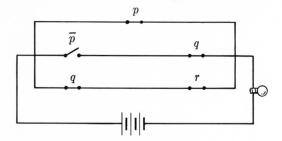

So, when a description of a proposed circuit is reduced to (simple or full) disjunctive normal form, it is child's play to produce a design for a circuit with the requisite properties.

19.   EXERCISES

(1)   Formulate abbreviative conventions analogous to conventions 1–4 to make Boolean equations more readable.

(2)   Determine via the truth-tabular method which of the following Boolean equations are valid:

(a) $(x \cap y) = (y \cap x)$

(b) $(x \cup y) = (y \cup x)$

(c) $[x \cap (y \cap z)] = [(x \cap y) \cap z]$

(d) $[x \cup (y \cup z)] = [(x \cup y) \cup z]$

(e) $[x \cap (x \cup y)] = x$

(f) $[x \cup (x \cap y)] = x$

(g) $[x \cap (y \cup z)] = [(x \cap y) \cup (x \cap z)]$

(h) $[x \cup (y \cap z)] = [(x \cup y) \cap (x \cup z)]$

(i) $(x \cap -x) = \Lambda$

(j) $(x \cup -x) = V$
(k) $(x \cap \Lambda) = x$
(l) $(x \cup \Lambda) = x$
(m) $(x \cap y) = (-x \cup -y)$
(n) $(x \cup -y) = -(-x \cap y)$

(3) Rework Exercise (2) using the translational method.

[4] Prove that a Boolean equation is valid if and only if its truth-functional translation is valid.

⟨5⟩ Consider the following system, which shall be called the *system of truth functions of Boolean equations* (TFBE).

Vocabulary of TFBE: Vocabulary of SBE supplemented by the tilde, wedge, and dot.

Formation rules of TFBE:

(i)–(v): Same as rules (i)–(v) of SBE.
  (vi) If A is a wff, so is $\ulcorner {\sim} A \urcorner$.
  (vii) If A and B are wffs, so are $\ulcorner [A \cdot B] \urcorner$ and $\ulcorner [A \vee B] \urcorner$.
  (viii) A formula is a wff if and only if it can be constructed by a finite number of applications of rules (v)–(vii).

Semantical rules of TFBE:

(i)–(vi): Same as (i)–(vi) of SBE. (Same notion of interpretation.)
(vii)–(ix): Statement of the semantical rules governing negations, conjunctions, and disjunctions are left to the reader.

Now the separate success of truth-tabular techniques as applied to truth-functional wffs and as applied to Boolean equations suggests that combining the two techniques will yield a decision procedure for validity for wffs of TFBE. This suggestion is reinforced when the combined method is applied to wffs such as the following:

x	y	$[(x \cup y) = y] \supset [(x \cap y) = x]$					
$\in$	$\in$	$\in$	t	$\in$ t	$\in$	t	$\in$
$\in$	$\notin$	$\in$	f	$\notin$ t	$\notin$	f	$\in$
$\notin$	$\in$	$\in$	t	$\in$ t	$\notin$	t	$\notin$
$\notin$	$\notin$	$\notin$	t	$\notin$ t	$\notin$	t	$\notin$

x	y	$[(x \cup y) = \text{V}] \supset [y = (x \cap y)]$		
$\in$	$\in$	t	t	t
$\in$	$\notin$	t	t	t
$\notin$	$\in$	t	f	f
$\notin$	$\notin$	f	t	t

But, unfortunately, the suggestion is false, as the reader may demonstrate by applying the combined method to the non-valid wff '$(x = \Lambda) \supset [(y = \text{V}) \vee (x = y)]$', which the combined method will "show" to be valid. Find an interpretation of the wff just mentioned under which it comes out false. Explain why the combined method breaks down. (*Hint:* It has to do with the peculiarities of the fundamental table for '=' in SBE.) A bonafide decision procedure for TFBE will be the concern of Exercise [12] of Chapter 37.)

[6]   State and prove the duality principle for SBE (see Section 16.3).

(7)   Prove that the garage-light circuit designed in Section 18.1 will work in the manner required.

(8)   Explain in detail how to convert a disjunctive normal form wff into a design for an electrical circuit completely described by the given wff.

(9)   Design a four-switch (they may be complex switches) electrical circuit whose behavior is completely described by the wff '$p \supset [\sim q \equiv (r \vee \sim s)]$'. Make your design as simple as possible. (*Hint:* Reduce to simple disjunctive normal form.)

(10) Would the following circuit satisfy the requirements for the three-man committee voting circuit described at the end of Section 18.1? Write a wff that completely describes the depicted circuit.

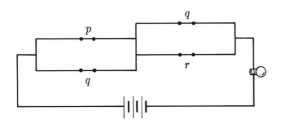

(11) Design a voting circuit for a six-man committee, one of whom is chairman, such that a measure is carried (light comes on) either by a majority vote or by a tie vote in which the chairman votes for the measure.

(12) Design as simple a circuit as you can for the voting circuit described in Exercise (11).

(13) Design a circuit for a garage light that is to be operable from three locations. Do the same for a light that can be controlled from four locations.

[14] Devise an algorithm which, applied to any given switching circuit, yields the "simplest" circuit(s) "equivalent" to the given circuit. (To solve this problem, you must first make precise the intuitive notions of "equivalent" circuits and "simplest" circuits. *Hint:* Reduce the "equivalence" of circuits to the equivalence of wffs which completely describe them.)

(15) Prove that if a Boolean equation is not valid, then there is a false interpretation of it (that is, an interpretation under which it has the value falsehood) whose universal class has only one member.

20. APPLICATION OF FORMALIZED LANGUAGES TO THE LOGICAL ANALYSIS OF NATURAL LANGUAGES

20.0. Proving Correctness of Arguments

It is one thing to recognize whether an argument of a natural language is correct and quite another to prove it.[1] Symbolic logic can contribute significantly to the former task, that is, recognition or discovery, but its greater contribution is to the latter, that is,

[1] With regard to the correctness and soundness of arguments, see Section 12.0.

justification or proof. To illustrate, we examine a simple English-language argument whose correctness is manifest:

(24)   Plato or Aristotle wrote the *Laws*.
(25)   Plato didn't.

Therefore,

(26)   Aristotle did.

(The argument happens to be unsound; Plato wrote the *Laws*.) The correctness of the foregoing argument clearly turns on nothing more than the truth-functional structure of the sentences involved. To prove the argument correct, we must do two things. First, we must render the relevant structures fully explicit; then we must subsume them under the logical theory of truth functions which we have already developed. To render the relevant truth-functional structures explicit, we utilize a P-language in which 'p' means, by stipulation, that Plato wrote the *Laws*, and in which 'q' means that Aristotle wrote the *Laws*. Our grasp of their meanings enables us to assert that (24) means '$p \vee q$', that (25) means '$\sim p$', and that (26) means 'q'.[2] Having thus rendered explicit or overt the relevant logical structures, we are in a position to bring the original argument vicariously under our logical theory. Now the following argument of the P-language under consideration,

$$p \vee q$$
$$\underline{\sim p}$$
$$q$$

is correct, because its premises jointly entail its conclusion. We know that the premises jointly entail the conclusion because they jointly imply the conclusion, and in P-languages joint implication is a sufficient condition of joint entailment among sentences. And as the above argument is correct, so is the original English argument, in virtue of the interchangeability of mutually entailing sentences that was discussed in Section 12.0.

Although we have been talking about arguments for some time, we have never stated precisely what they are. For our purposes, it is perhaps best to understand an *argument* as merely an ordered

---

[2] We shall say that one sentence *means* another not only when the two are synonymous but also when they are merely mutually entailing.

pair $\langle \Delta, S \rangle$ consisting of a set Δ of sentences (known as the *premisses* of the argument) together with a sentence S (known as the *conclusion* of the argument).[3] As we have already remarked in Section 12.0, an argument $\langle \Delta, S \rangle$ is said to be *correct* if S follows from Δ.[4] And an argument is said to be *sound* if it is correct and its premisses are all true. For example, in the illustration above, the set

$$\{ \text{`}p \vee q\text{'}, \text{`}{\sim}p\text{'} \}$$

is the set of premisses of the argument, 'q' is the conclusion, and the argument is correct because the conclusion does follow from the premisses, but it is unsound because one of the premisses is false. When giving examples of arguments, we will usually indicate the sentence to be taken as conclusion by means of expressions such as 'therefore' or 'thus', or by drawing a line between it and the sentences to be taken as premisses.

Let α_1 and α_2 be arguments, and let $\alpha_1 = \langle \Delta_1, S_1 \rangle$ and $\alpha_2 = \langle \Delta_2, S_2 \rangle$. We shall say that α_1 *mirrors* α_2 if S_1 and S_2 are mutually entailing and, in addition, there is a one-to-one mapping ϕ of Δ_1 onto Δ_2 such that the sentences mapped with one another by ϕ are mutually entailing. In view of the interchangeability of mutually entailing sentences within the context of an argument (see Section 12.0), it should be evident that if α_1 mirrors α_2, then α_1 is correct if and only if α_2 is correct. This last observation suggests a way to apply our logical theory to proving that certain English-language arguments are correct. The strategy is this. To show that an English-language argument is correct, we try to adduce a P-language argument whose correctness can be established by our logical methods and which mirrors the given English-language argument. In fact, we used this very strategy in the first part of the present section. We proved there that the given English-language argument was correct by establishing the correctness of a P-language argument that mirrored it. Part of our proof rested on logical theory, and part did not. The latter is the part where insight into meaning came in, namely the determination that '$p \vee q$' means (24), and so on, that is, the part where we established that the one argument mirrored the other. The remainder of the proof was wholly a matter of logical theory.

[3] Note that it is not excluded that Δ be the empty set of sentences or that Δ be infinite.

[4] Concerning the relation of following from; see Section 14.2.

Symbolic logic, we claimed above, can contribute significantly to the process of recognition or discovery. To document the heuristic value of symbolic logic, we examine a fairly complex argument whose correctness is by no means apparent:

(27)   Although knowledge is virtue only if the will is predetermined, decision making is morally relevant nonetheless.

(28)   There is no responsibility unless the will is free.

(29)   Decision making is morally irrelevant if and only if there is no responsibility.

---

(30)   Whatever else it might be, knowledge is surely not virtue.

To convince himself that the correctness of this argument is not manifest, the reader should try on the basis of his grasp of the meaning of the sentences to decide whether or not the argument is correct. If the above argument is correct, it would seem to be so in virtue of truth-functional aspects of the structures of the sentences involved. Accordingly, a good heuristic strategy to follow is to make explicit as much of the truth-functional logical structure of these sentences as our grasp of their meanings will allow. To this end we introduce a P-language in which 'p' means that knowledge is virtue, 'q' means that the will is predetermined, 'r' means that decision making is morally relevant, and 's' means that there is no responsibility. Thanks to our grasp of their meanings, we see that (27) means '$(p \supset q) \cdot r$', that (28) means '$s \lor \sim q$', that (29) means '$\sim r \equiv s$', and that (30) means '$\sim p$'. Having thus rendered explicit as much of the truth-functional structure of the given English language argument as we could discern, we go on to test for correctness the corresponding argument of the given P-language,

$$(p \supset q) \cdot r$$
$$s \lor \sim q$$
$$\underline{\sim r \equiv s}$$
$$\sim p$$

Our truth-tabular methods reveal the correctness of the above argument. And because it mirrors this correct argument, the given English-language argument is also seen to be correct. The foregoing demonstration of the correctness of the English argument will, of course, convince only someone whose comprehension of the sentences involved agrees with our own, that is, someone who thinks that (27) means '$(p \supset q) \cdot r$', that (28) means '$s \lor \sim q$', and so on. In other words, it will convince only someone who concedes that the one argument mirrors the other.

20.1. Proving Incorrectness of Arguments

There is a marked asymmetry between proving that (joint) entailment obtains among sentences of a P-language and disproving it. The root of this asymmetry lies in the fact that (joint) implication is only a sufficient condition of (joint) entailment, not also a necessary one. To prove that entailment obtains, therefore, we need only establish that implication obtains, a task made simple by our truth-tabular methods. But how can we prove that entailment does not obtain? Proof that implication does not obtain is no proof that entailment also fails to obtain, because implication is not a necessary condition of entailment.

One way to show that sentences S_1, ..., S_n of a formalized language L do not jointly entail a sentence S of L consists in showing that S is false, whereas each S_i is true. In those circumstances in which the foregoing tactic is possible, proof of nonentailment poses no special problem. Rather the problem is just that such circumstances are rare. Usually when we are concerned about whether or not (joint) entailment obtains, either ascertainment of (joint) entailment is an essential factor in our assessment of the truth values of at least some of the sentences involved, or else we are antecedently persuaded of the truth of all the sentences in question or of the falsity of some of the premises. In any of these circumstances, the tactic of showing that S is false but that each S_i is true is obviously inapplicable.

There just is no general way of disproving correctness which has equal cogency with our strategy for proving correctness (of arguments that have a finite number of premises). When it comes to disproving correctness, we usually have to fall back on our ability to conceive possible situations in which all the premises would be true but the conclusion false. Consider, for example, the following proof that the argument given below is not correct:

(31) If the porch light is on, then the front door is unlocked.
(32) The front door is locked only if Mary is at the movies.

(33) The porch light is off unless Mary is at the movies.

From the meaning of the premisses and conclusion, it appears that the correctness of the argument turns on the truth-functional structure of its sentences. Let us make that structure as explicit as possible. To do so, we construct a mirror argument in a P-language wherein 'p' means that the porch light is off, 'q' means that the front door is unlocked, and 'r' means that Mary is at the movies. The mirror argument is

$$\sim p \supset q$$
$$\underline{\sim q \supset r}$$
$$p \vee r$$

Truth-tabular methods show that these premisses do not jointly imply the conclusion, because there is one interpretation of the wffs under which the premiss wffs all come out true but the conclusion wff comes out false: falsehood assigned to 'p' and 'r' with truth assigned to 'q'. And in view of the meanings that 'p', 'q', and 'r' have in this P-language, we can easily conceive of possible circumstances in which 'p' and 'r' would be false but 'q' would be true: the circumstance of the porch light being on, Mary not being at the movies, and the front door being unlocked. Hence we judge the above argument to be incorrect. And, because the above argument mirrors the original one, we also judge the latter to be incorrect.

This reliance on conceivability is somewhat undesirable, but it is often the only method available for proving incorrectness, that is, for disproving correctness. Even when we are forced to fall back on it, our formal methods can still play an important role in pinpointing the nature of the circumstances whose possibility we must conceive. That is, our formal methods enable us to enumerate those value assignments to the sentential variables of an argument which make all its premisses true but its conclusion false. The sought-after circumstances, therefore, will be ones in which the variables (under the meaning given them in the P-language) have the truth values assigned to them in the aforementioned value assignments.

20.2.   Rendering Logical Structure Explicit

The characteristic method of symbolic logic, the *modus operandi* that distinguishes it from its forebears, is the thoroughgoing reduction of logical structure to grammatical structure effected by means of formalized languages. Another name for this reduction is *explicitation*. For example, in Section 20.0 we made explicit the disjunctive form of sentence (24) 'Plato or Aristotle wrote the *Laws*' by remarking that it meant the same as the disjunctive sentence '*p* v *q*' of a certain formalized language. Now one might protest that the disjunctive expression ⌜(either) ... or ___⌝ already makes explicit the disjunctive structure of (24). And so it would, if it were an infallible index of such form, not merely a reliable guide.[5] But that it is no more than a reliable guide can be gathered from an analysis of sentence

(34)   Either Jack Dempsey or Joe Louis could whip Cassius Clay.

Consider a P-language in which '*p*' and '*q*' mean, respectively, that Dempsey could whip Clay and that Louis could whip Clay. If used normally, (34) would mean '*p* · *q*'; it would not mean '*p* v *q*' as the presence of ⌜either ... or ___⌝ might suggest. Thus the rule that the expression ⌜either ... or ___⌝ indicates a disjunction is just a rule of thumb, useful but not inviolable.

The process of explicitation depends on insight into meaning. Clearly, one cannot make explicit the logical form or structure of an English sentence without first understanding that sentence. Explicitation also depends on available formalized linguistic resources. The latter dependence is twofold. First, we obviously cannot make explicit a form or structure that has no correlate in the formalized languages at our disposal. For example, were only P-languages available to us, we could not render explicit the universal affirmative structure of 'All proofs are fallacious'. And, second, we cannot render explicit even a structure for which we have a formalized correlate when that structure is buried beneath a structure for which a formalized correlate is lacking. For example, consider sentence

(35)   If anything is missing, it is probably valuable.

In sentence (35) there is a universalized cross-reference from antecedent to consequent which is brought out by the following paraphrase: 'Whatever it might be, if it is missing, then it is probably

---

[5] See Section 1.1 for more discussion of this topic.

valuable'. Lacking at present a device for universalized cross-reference, we are unable to make explicit the underlying conditional structure of (35). To convince himself of this, the reader should try to invent a P-language that boasts a sentence of the form ⌜$A \supset B$⌝, where A and B mean, respectively, the same as the "antecedent" and "consequent" of (35).

To help the reader render truth-functional logical form explicit, we advance a few rules of thumb for recognizing certain logical structures. When using them, the reader should keep firmly in mind their rough-and-ready status *qua* rules of thumb. *They are not meant as substitutes for, but rather as aids to, insight into intended meaning.* We have already touched upon one of these rules of thumb—that 'or' is a sign of weak disjunction. So far as rules of thumb go, canvassing exceptions seems more illuminating than discussing paradigms. One exception to the 'or' rule has already been noted; the word 'or' sometimes has conjunctive force. Another and less surprising exception is that 'or' occasionally signals exclusive disjunction. Consider, for example, sentence

(36)   For your prize you may have the television set or the stereo system.

Consider a P-language in which 'p' means that you may have the television set as your prize, and in which 'q' means that you may have the stereo system as your prize. Then, in normal use, (36) would not mean '$p \lor q$', but it would rather mean '$(p \lor q) \cdot \sim(p \cdot q)$'. That is, the force of 'or' in (36) is exclusive rather than inclusive. It hardly needs saying that the word 'and' usually indicates conjunction. What makes this rule worth mentioning are the exceptions to it. Consider, for example, sentence

(37)   Smith and Brown are lawyers.

The word 'and' marks a conjunction in (37), as is evident from the paraphrase 'Smith is a lawyer, and Brown is a lawyer'. But, although it closely resembles (37), sentence

(38)   Smith and Brown are partners.

is not a conjunction at all. Clearly, (38) does not mean 'Smith is a partner, and Brown is a partner'. It is rather the affirmation that Smith stands in the partnership relation to Brown. Besides 'and', the connectives 'but', 'although', 'however', 'still', 'while', 'yet', 'albeit', 'notwithstanding', and the like also usually express conjunction. For example, consider a P-language in which '*p*' and '*q*' mean the same as the sentences 'Smith is a lawyer' and 'Brown is an acrobat', respectively. Then sentence

(39)   Smith is a lawyer while Brown is an acrobat.

would ordinarily mean '*p* · *q*'; that is, 'while' would have conjunctive force. Of course, 'while' does more than conjoin the components 'Smith is a lawyer' and 'Brown is an acrobat'; it also contrasts them. Still the contrast does not void the fact that (39) and '*p* · *q*' are mutually entailing.

The rule that 'while' expresses conjunction is merely a rule of thumb. For an exception, consider sentence

(40)   Jones ran off with Smith's wife while Smith was away on business.

Here 'while' does not have conjunctive force; (40) does not mean 'Jones ran off with Smith's wife, and Smith was away on business', though (40) does entail that sentence. Rather, the expression 'while Smith was away on business' specifies the time or circumstance under which Jones is said to have run off with Smith's wife.

In Section 20.1 we understood sentence (33) 'The porch light is off unless Mary is at the movies' to mean the same as the sentence '*p* ∨ *r*' of a certain P-language. (But since '∼*p* ⊃ *r*' is equivalent to '*p* ∨ *r*', we could just as well have translated (33) as '∼*p* ⊃ *r*'.) For the word 'unless' commonly has the force of the inclusive disjunctive 'or', appearances to the contrary notwithstanding. As a rule of thumb, a sentence of the form ⌜*A* unless *B*⌝ can be paraphrased as ⌜*A* or *B*⌝, meaning ⌜*A* or *B*, or both⌝. For another example, consider

(41)   Unless his grade report is erroneous, Smith failed calculus.

In a P-language in which '*p*' and '*q*' mean, respectively, that Smith's grade report is erroneous and that Smith failed calculus, we would ordinarily understand (41) to mean '∼*q* ⊃ *p*' or, what comes to the same, to mean '*q* ∨ *p*'. There is, however, a regrettable tendency to take (41) to mean '∼*q* ≡ *p*', and hence to entail '*p* ⊃ ∼*q*'. But (41) does not claim that Smith passed calculus if his grade report is erroneous; it simply leaves open that possibility.

Perhaps the best way to check this tendency is to develop the habit of reading 'unless' as 'or', except where context clearly demands some other reading. Other connectives which, like 'unless', commonly have inclusive disjunctive force are 'except', 'save', 'barring', and the like. For example, we would usually interpret the sentence 'Barring an erroneous grade report, Smith failed calculus' to mean '$p \vee q$'.

English luxuriates in ways to form the negation of a sentence. All the following, for example, are negations of the sentence 'The porch light is off': 'The porch light is on', 'The porch light is not off', 'It is false that the porch light is off'. Generally speaking, negative particles, negative adjectives, negative adverbs, and negative nouns indicate negation. But care must be taken to distinguish the exception from the rule. For example, when prefixed to an adjective, the particle 'in-' usually expresses negation. Thus the sentence 'Jones is incapable of feeling great emotion' would usually be understood as the negation of 'Jones is capable of feeling great emotion', that is, to mean 'It is not the case that Jones is capable of feeling great emotion'. It could be disastrous, however, to interpret the sentence 'This gas is inflammable' to be the negation of 'This gas is flammable', that is, to mean 'This gas is not flammable'. The prefix 'in-' in 'inflammable' is not, as our grasp of its meaning reveals, a negative particle at all. The word 'inflammable' does not derive from the adjective 'flammable' via a negative prefix; it comes from the verb 'inflame' via the suffix 'able'.

Care must also be taken to fix the scope of a negation, that is, to determine exactly what is negated. For example, the negative particle 'in-' in sentence

(42)   Jones wrote ten incorrect answers on the exam.

does not negate the sentence 'Jones wrote ten correct answers on the exam'. For, clearly, the sentence 'It is false that Jones wrote ten correct answers on the exam' means something quite different from (42). Or, for example, sentence

(43)   Jones committed an inexcusable blunder.

does not, unluckily for Jones, mean merely

(44)   It is false that Jones committed an excusable blunder.

Indeed, unlike (43), sentence (44) would be true if Jones committed no blunder at all. Rather, (43) means

(45)   Jones committed a blunder, and it was not excusable.

With only P-languages at our command, we cannot do much about making explicit even the truth-functional structure of (43). For, as its paraphrase (45) brings out, the implicit conjunction in (43) is buried beneath an ineluctable cross-reference.

There are many ways to express a conditional in English. For example, a sentence of the form ⌜If A, then B⌝ would·commonly mean the same as any of the following: ⌜A only if B⌝, ⌜B if A⌝, ⌜B on condition that A⌝, ⌜B provided that A⌝. There is a regrettable tendency to be misled by the occurrence of 'if' in ⌜A only if B⌝ so as to take B to be the antecedent of a conditional having A as consequent. Remember: ⌜A only if B⌝ means ⌜If A, then B⌝. In ⌜B if A⌝, on the other hand, the occurrence of 'if' precedes the antecedent; ⌜B if A⌝ means ⌜If A, then B⌝. But the word 'if' does not invariably signal a conditional; witness sentence

(46)   Jones wants to know if Smith is coming along.

It would be ludicrous to understand (46) as 'Smith is coming along only if Jones wants to know', that is, to treat 'Jones wants to know' as the consequent of a conditional whose antecedent is 'Smith is coming'. In sentences such as (46), the word 'if' has the interrogative sense of 'whether'. Surprisingly, the word 'whether' can be used to express two conditionals. For example, sentence

(47)   Whether she marries Tom, Rose will be unhappy.

means 'If she marries Tom Rose will be unhappy, and if she doesn't marry him she will also be unhappy'. In a P-language wherein 'p' and 'q' mean, respectively, that Rose marries Tom and that Rose will be unhappy, sentence (47) could be understood to mean '$(p \supset q) \cdot (\sim p \supset q)$'. And this wff is equivalent to just plain 'q', so (47) could be interpreted to mean simply 'q'.

Some uses of 'if' are obviously not truth functional. Consider, for example, the *counterfactual* conditional

(48)   If Hitler had not attacked Russia, the Nazis would still be in power.

That Hitler did attack Russia surely is not enough to guarantee the truth of (48); an expert on German military history who knows that Hitler did attack Russia might seriously question (48). But if (48) were a truth-functional conditional, the falsehood of its antecedent would suffice to make it true. Counterfactuals are a species of so-called *subjunctive conditionals*, which differ from counterfactuals in not necessarily presupposing the falsehood of their antecedents but resemble counterfactuals in not being truth functional. The sentence 'If an iron bar should be heated, it would expand' is an example of a subjunctive conditional. Many lawlike statements, although not explicitly subjunctive, have the logical form of subjunctive conditionals. For example, the lawlike sentence 'If an iron bar is heated, it expands' means the same as the subjunctive conditional 'If an iron bar should be heated, it would expand'.

To round out this section with a few miscellaneous remarks, we note that the biconditional of A and B can be expressed as $\ulcorner A$ if and only if $B \urcorner$ or $\ulcorner A$ when and only when $B \urcorner$ or the like. The jargon of necessary and sufficient conditions can also be used to express the biconditional. For example, 'The light being on is a necessary and sufficient condition of the door being locked' means the same as 'The light is on if and only if the door is locked'. *Neither-nor* expressions, on the other hand, have the force of conjunctions with negated components. For example, in a P-language in which 'p' and 'q' mean, respectively, 'Smith is a lawyer' and 'Brown is a lawyer', one might translate the sentence 'Neither Brown nor Smith is a lawyer' as '$\sim p \cdot \sim q$' or equivalently as '$\sim(p \vee q)$'.

English Constructions	*Formalized Correlate*
A and B; A but B; A however B; A yet B; A although B; A albeit B	$A \cdot B$
A or B; A unless B; B unless A	$A \vee B$
If A, then B; B if A; A only if B; B provided that A; B on condition that A	$A \supset B$
A if and only if B; A when and only when B; If A, and only if A, then B	$A \equiv B$
Neither A nor B	$\sim A \cdot \sim B$ $\sim(A \vee B)$

Similarly, the sentence 'Neither Dempsey nor Louis could whip Clay' means 'Dempsey could not whip Clay, and Louis could not whip Clay'. To help the reader keep the above rules of thumb in mind, we supply the accompanying table. In the left column '*A*' and '*B*' stand for arbitrary English sentences; in the right column, they stand for sentences of a P-language which mean the same as the respective English sentences.

As a forceful reminder that the above rules are only rules of thumb, consider sentence

> (49)   Charlie doesn't drink unless he is alone or with somebody.

If we mechanically applied the above rules to the analysis of (49), we would understand it to mean 'Charlie doesn't drink, or he is alone or with somebody' which is analytically true. That is, whatever Charlie's drinking habits might be, (49) would be true. But as it is ordinarily used, sentence (49) means that Charlie drinks when he is alone and when he is with someone.

20.3.   Bringing Logical Form to the Surface

Consider sentence

> (50)   Either Notre Dame won or Michigan State lost and Princeton upset Yale.

and a P-language in which the variables 'p', 'q', and 'r' mean, respectively, that Notre Dame won, that Michigan State lost, and that Princeton upset Yale. Clearly (50) means either '$p \lor q \cdot r$' or '$(p \lor q) \cdot r$', but which? Although punctuation can relieve much perplexity over intended grouping, it cannot relieve all. Determination of the intended grouping of an English sentence is sometimes a delicate task calling for sympathetic understanding and sensitivity to context. For example, the comma in 'Either Notre Dame won, or Michigan State lost and Princeton upset Yale' makes it fairly clear that that sentence means '$p \lor q \cdot r$'. But how punctuate sentence

> (51)   Notre Dame won or Princeton upset Yale and Michigan State lost unless Notre Dame won and Princeton did not upset Yale.

to signify that '$p \vee (r \cdot q \vee p) \cdot \sim r$' is meant? So far as unearthing the intended grouping of (51) is concerned, there is no getting away from sympathetic understanding and attention to context.

To render explicit as much of the truth-functional form of a sentence as possible, it is good practice to begin with the most over-lying structures and proceed gradually to structures buried further and further beneath them. Consider, for example, sentence

   (52)   If Notre Dame or California won then Princeton upset Yale, unless Michigan State lost while neither Purdue nor Wisconsin tied.

The most overlying structure of (52) is a disjunction, because 'unless' joins together the two components 'If Notre Dame. . .Yale' and 'Michigan State. . .tied'. Our first step, then, is to supplant 'unless' by its symbolic correlate '$\vee$' so as to get

   (53)   If Notre Dame or California won then Princeton upset Yale $\vee$ Michigan State lost while neither Purdue nor Wisconsin tied.

Notice that, unlike (52), the expression (53) belongs neither to English nor to any P-language; it is merely a hybrid schema of transitory value.

Next we look to the most overlying structures of the two un-analyzed components of (53). The left component then becomes 'Notre Dame or California won $\supset$ Princeton upset Yale', while the right component resolves into 'Michigan State lost $\cdot$ neither Purdue nor Wisconsin tied'. Being careful to preserve the intended grouping of (52), we supplant the unanalyzed components of (53) by their schematic counterparts so as to obtain schema

   (54)   [Notre Dame or California won $\supset$ Princeton upset Yale] $\vee$ [Michigan State lost $\cdot$ neither Purdue nor Wisconsin tied].

Applying the same procedure now to the unanalyzed components of (54), we get schema

   (55)   [(Notre Dame won $\vee$ California won) $\supset$ Princeton upset Yale] $\vee$ [Michigan State lost $\cdot$ ($\sim$Purdue tied $\cdot$ $\sim$Wisconsin tied)].

Here our procedure comes to a halt, for we see no way to resolve any of the unanalyzed components of (55) into truth functions of still other components. To render explicit in a P-language the logical structure schematized by (55), we obviously require a P-language that contains atomic sentences answering to each of the unanalyzed components of (55). Therefore, with respect to the P-language utilized in the first paragraph of this section, let us stipulate that 's' means that California won, that 'p_1' means that Purdue tied, and that 'q_1' means that Wisconsin tied. Then the truth-functional form of sentence (52), so far as (55) schematizes it, is given by the sentence '$[(p \vee s \supset r] \vee q \cdot [\sim p_1 \cdot \sim q_1]$'. Notice that this last sentence comes from (55) on replacement of unanalyzed components by corresponding atomic sentences (variables).

For the sake of another illustration, let us make as explicit as possible the truth-functional form of sentence

(56)   If anyone escapes both the guards and trustees will be reprimanded unless the warden changes his standing orders.

Unlike the intended grouping of (52), that of (56) is somewhat ambiguous, so we do the best we can to reproduce the intended grouping of (56) on the basis of our understanding of it. The following sequence represents the successive stages of our analysis of (56):

(57)   Someone escapes $\supset$ the guards and trustees will be reprimanded unless the warden changes his standing orders.

(58)   Someone escapes $\supset$ [the guards and trustees will be reprimanded $\vee$ the warden will change his standing orders].

(59)   Someone escapes $\supset$ [(the guards will be reprimanded $\cdot$ the trustees will be reprimanded) $\vee$ the warden will change his standing orders].

Unable to resolve further any of the unanalyzed components of (59), we introduce a P-language in which 'p' means that someone escapes, 'q' means that the guards will be reprimanded, 'r' means that the trustees will be reprimanded, and 's' means that the warden will change his standing orders. Then the truth-functional form of (56) which is schematized by (59) is rendered explicit by the sentence '$p \supset q \cdot r \vee s$'.

20.4.   The Semantics of Atomic Sentences

Our way of endowing sentential variables with meaning has been pretty cavalier. For example, to confer meaning on 'p' in the P-language of Section 20.3, we contented ourselves with the remark that 'p' was to mean that Notre Dame won. Now the logical theory of P-languages has been openly predicated on the assumption that *interpreted wffs are sentences unambiguously possessing reference (truth value)*. Let us call this assumption the *truth-value assumption* and let us see whether, as interpreted above, 'p' satisfies it.

Notice that sentence

(60)   Notre Dame won.

is quite ambiguous. There are many institutions called *Notre Dame*; to which of them does (60) refer? Furthermore, what sort of a contest is meant, football, basketball, debating, or something else? The determination that, as we have used it, (60) means that the varsity football squad of the University of Notre Dame at South Bend, Indiana won is not even sufficient to remove all ambiguity; it is also necessary to specify dates. Had we said that 'p' was to mean

(61)   The varsity football squad of the University of Notre Dame at South Bend won its football game on Saturday, October 8, 1966.

the atomic sentence 'p' would have come much closer to satisfying the truth-value assumption.

The semantical rules for the truth-functional sentence connectives guarantee that a truth-functional compound satisfies the truth-value assumption provided that its atomic components satisfy that assumption. We have already seen one way in which an atomic sentence can fail to meet the truth-value assumption, through ambiguity of the specification of its meaning, as with (60) and 'p'. Another way lies in the *vagueness* of such specification. Suppose, for example, that we said that in some P-language the atomic sentence 'q' is to mean that it is raining in East Lansing, Michigan. Now, there are many possible states of the world that would make it true to say that it is raining there, and many that would make it false. But there are also some possible states, for example, when it is misting in East Lansing, in which it would be neither true nor false to say it is raining there. What counts as raining is just not definite enough to guarantee that 'q' has a truth value. Although our logical theory certifies '$q \supset q$' as a logical truth, that "sentence" has no truth value if it is misting in East Lansing, that is, if it is neither true nor false that it is raining there. For, in virtue of the semantical rules for the truth-functional connectives, a truth value accrues to a truth-functional compound when and only when all its atomic components possess truth values. Our logical theory breaks down, therefore, when the truth-value assumption is not satisfied. That is what we meant by saying that our logical theory is predicated on the truth-value assumption.

English sentences typically do not possess their truth values unqualifiedly. Rather, they have their truth values qualifiedly, that is, relative to such factors as time, place, speaker, and so on. For example, the vagueness of the concept *rain* aside, the truth value of the sentence 'It is raining in East Lansing' is relative to time, the sentence being true at certain times and false at others. And the truth value of 'I love you' is relative not only to time but also to speaker and addressee. What makes possession of truth value relative is the presence of *indexical* or *token-reflexive* expressions, expressions which are so to speak systematically ambiguous or ambiguous by design, the ambiguity being resolved by the production of tokens of the expressions. Tensed expressions are indexical, and so are such words as 'I', 'you', 'now', 'here', 'this', and so on. Typically, speakers of English employ utterances or tokens of a sentence to indicate relative to which factors the truth of the sentence is being asserted. For example, by uttering 'It is now raining', I intend to signify that the sentence 'It is now raining' is true at the time and place of my utterance. In marked contrast to English statements, the sentences of the formalized languages developed in the body of this book[1] are intended to have their truth values unqualifiedly. That is, these statements are intended to be true or false *simpliciter*, not true or false relative to this or that. In consequence, utterances of one of these formalized statements are quite on a par with one another; they do not serve to indicate relative to which factors the truth of the statement is being asserted, because there are no factors to which its truth value is relative.

All this raises a serious practical problem: how properly to endow

[1] In Appendix H tensed formalized languages are developed in which the truth values of sentences are relative to time. Thus the sentences of these tensed formalized languages do not possess truth values unqualifiedly.

sentential variables with meaning when setting up a P-language? Ideally, perhaps, one should spell out in complete detail the meaning to be given to a sentential variable by equating it with a sentence such as (61). For most purposes, however, it suffices to let the context of assignation determine the meaning assigned. For example, we might say that the variable '*r*' is to mean that I feel wonderful. Although we used the inherently ambiguous sentence 'I feel wonderful' to endow '*r*' with meaning, the context of assignation confers immediately on that utterance and hence mediately on '*r*' a definite meaning. The advantage which the first course offers over the second is this obvious one: to discover the meaning of the atomic components, one does not have to delve into the context of assignation. But, as it is by far the more economical, we will usually follow the second course. Thus, in examples and exercises, the reader should assume or pretend that, were the context of assignation made manifest, the atomic sentences of the relevant P-language would be found not only to satisfy the truth-value assumption but also to possess their truth values unqualifiedly. For example, if we say that '*s*' means that 'Brown and Smith are lawyers', the reader should pretend that the context of assignation would make it definite which Brown and Smith are meant and what time span is the relevant one.

It would be unethical to close this section without mentioning a skeleton in the closet. Lack of truth value cannot always be traced to vagueness and ambiguity. Consider sentence

(62)   Sentence (62) is false.

To see that (62) has no truth value, suppose that it does. If true, sentence (62) must be false, because it affirms that (62) is false. And if false, (62) must likewise be true. It cannot, therefore, be either true or false. Sentence (62) is one version of the famous Liar Antinomy of Epimenides,[6] which has vexed logicians from antiquity. Though neither vague nor ambiguous, (62) cannot consistently be supposed to possess a truth value. Therefore, to equate an atomic sentence with (62) would violate the truth-value assumption, just as a vague or ambiguous assignation of meaning does. The treatment and resolution of antinomies such as the Liar is beyond the scope of this book, so we can offer the reader no advice

---

[6] Epimenides, himself a Cretan, asserted that all Cretans always lie.

on how to avoid them. Fortunately, antinomies such as (62) crop up only in rare and rather queer circumstances. The elementary applications of symbolic logic are far removed from them.

21. EXERCISES

(1) Render explicit as much of the truth-functional structure of the following sentences as you can: [That is, for each sentence below, write a sentence (wff) of an appropriate P-language which means the same as it, and whose grammatical form makes explicit as much of the truth-functional structure of the given sentence as you can discern.]

(a) Although Smith and Brown are heavy smokers, neither of them seems especially nervous.

(b) Unless he falls ill, Jones will graduate this year if he passes mathematics and philosophy.

(c) Like Jimmy Foxx, Willie Mays is a right-handed slugger.

(d) Of Mantle, Maris, and Mays, only the latter has a chance to hit as many home runs as Babe Ruth.

(e) Unless her family disapproves, Catherine will spend her vacation in Florida or perhaps California.

(f) It is unlikely that Smith will be acquitted unless the judge is too permissive and the jury is dazzled by the defense counsel.

(g) True to the old adage, Smith is neither a borrower nor a lender.

(h) Romeo loved no one but Juliet.

(i) But for the grace of God there go I.

(j) Babe Ruth was not only a great hitter, he was a good pitcher as well.

(k) Unless the Chinese Communists committed troops, the American forces would surely defeat the Viet Cong if the South Vietnamese people would only rally around their political leaders.

(l)   Your leave request is denied; every able-bodied soldier is needed at the front.

(m)   If Rock n' Roll is music, then I'm a monkey's uncle.

(n)   When you are here, and only then, my heart feels like singing.

(o)   The French insist that they will use their nuclear weapons if and only if they are victims of aggression.

(p)   Get out of here and don't ever come back!

(q)   However you meant it, an insult is still an insult.

(r)   If taxes go up while income remains steady, then there will be a recession unless cuts are made in federal spending.

(s)   If I had noticed that you were wearing glasses, I wouldn't have struck you on the nose.

(t)   Though Peter likes Claire and Eileen, he is in love with Veronica.

(2)   Prove that the following arguments are correct:

(a)   It is unlikely that Smith will be acquitted unless the judge is permissive and the jury is dazzled by the defense counsel. But, as fate would have it, Smith drew a strict judge. Therefore, Smith will probably be convicted, regardless of how the defense counsel impresses the jurors.

(b)   Although Smith and Brown are heavy smokers, neither of them is particularly nervous. But one of the two is especially nervous if both are heavy smokers. Therefore, smoking is injurious to health.

(c)   Unless he falls ill, Jones will graduate this year if he passes mathematics and philosophy. If Jones does not fall ill, he will pass philosophy, and conversely. Surprisingly, Jones passes both philosophy and mathematics. Thus he will graduate this year.

(d)   Unless her family disapproves, Catherine will spend her vacation in Florida or perhaps California. If her family disapproves, Catherine will be incensed, and Catherine is foolish when incensed. Catherine will spend her vacation in California only if she is not foolish. Therefore, if her family does not disapprove, Catherine will spend her vacation in Florida, provided she is incensed.

(e)   The senses are deceived if things are not what they seem to be. But if a straight stick half-immersed in water looks bent, then things are indeed not what they seem to be. Thus a straight stick half-immersed in water does not look bent unless the senses are deceived.

(f)   If taxes go up while income holds steady, then there will be a recession unless federal spending is reduced. But there will be neither a recession nor a reduction in federal spending. Therefore, either taxes will not go up or income will fluctuate.

(3)   Show that none of the following arguments are correct:

(a)   The argument whose premises are the same as those of (2)(a) but whose conclusion is 'Smith will probably not be convicted if the defense counsel dazzles the jury'.

(b)   The argument from the premises of (2)(c) to the conclusion 'Jones will not graduate this year'.

(c)   The argument from the premises of (2)(d) to the conclusion 'Catherine will spend her vacation in Florida if her family does not disapprove'.

(4)   How does our technical use of the word 'argument', as defined in Section 20.0, differ from the various ordinary uses of that word?

(5)   Show that mirroring is an equivalence relation among arguments.

22. FUNCTIONAL INCOMPLETENESS

22.0. Mathematical Induction

We proved in Section 13.1 that either the dot or the wedge could be dropped from a P-language without any loss of expressive power; in either event the remaining connectives would be functionally complete. We will now show that, unlike the dot and wedge, the tilde cannot be dropped without risk of reducing expressive power.

In other words, we will show that the dot and wedge form a functionally incomplete set of connectives. We will prove this metatheorem by means of mathematical induction, which is a very common and useful way of proving metatheorems. The so-called *(weak) principle of mathematical induction* can be stated as a rule of inference from two premisses to a conclusion—*from the two premisses*

> The number 0 has the property ϕ.   *(Basis)*
> If any (natural) number has the property   *(Induction step)*
> ϕ, so does its immediate successor.[1]

one may infer the conclusion

> All the (natural) numbers have the prop-   *(Conclusion)*
> erty ϕ.

The first premiss is called the *basis of the induction*, and the second premiss is called the *induction step*.

The word 'induction' might suggest that the principle of mathematical induction is not absolutely trustworthy, that in perhaps a small minority of cases it authorizes one to draw a false conclusion from true premisses. But the principle gets its name, not from any supposed unreliability, but rather from its outward resemblance to veritable inductive principles such as the principle of induction by simple enumeration,[2] which are in fact not absolutely trustworthy. Unlike these inductive principles, the principle of mathematical induction is absolutely reliable in the sense that it cannot lead to a false conclusion from true premisses. Principles of inference which are absolutely reliable in the sense just explained are said to be *deductive principles*.

To make it plausible that (the principle of) mathematical induction is a deductive principle, we will argue that the supposition that it leads from true premisses to a false conclusion is contradictory. Suppose, then, that for some property ϕ the basis and induction step are true but the conclusion is false. For the conclusion to be

---

[1] When n is any natural number, its immediate successor is $n + 1$. The natural numbers are the numbers 0, 1, 2, ...

[2] Suppose the members of a class Δ of objects are arranged at random in a certain order, say $a_1, a_2, a_3, \ldots$. The principle of induction by simple enumeration authorizes the inference to the conclusion that all the members of Δ have the property ϕ from the two premisses that $a_1, a_2, \ldots, a_n$ all have ϕ, where n is large, and that no member of Δ is known not to have the property ϕ.

false, at least one natural number must lack the property ϕ. Let k, therefore, be a number that lacks ϕ. From the basis, we know that 0 has ϕ. So it follows by the induction step that 1 has ϕ. And since 1 has ϕ, it also follows from the induction step that 2 has ϕ. Simply repeating this reasoning, we eventually conclude that $k - 1$ has ϕ, from which it follows by the induction step that k has ϕ. But this last contradicts the assumption that k lacks ϕ. Since the assumption that mathematical induction leads from true premises to a false conclusion is contradictory, we conclude that it is a veritable deductive principle, its name notwithstanding.[3]

Before using mathematical induction to prove metatheorems of symbolic logic, we will illustrate its use within mathematics by proving that, for every (natural) number n, the sum of the numbers up to n inclusive equals half the product of n and its immediate successor, that is, that $0 + 1 + \ldots + n = [n \cdot (n + 1)]/2$. That is, we will prove that every number has the property ϕ, where a number n has ϕ if and only if $0 + 1 + \ldots + n = [n \cdot (n + 1)]/2$. Clearly 0 has ϕ, since $0 = [0 \cdot 1]/2$. The basis of the induction, therefore, is true. On the supposition that any number k has ϕ, let us show that its immediate successor $k + 1$ also has it, that is, that $0 + 1 + \ldots + k + (k + 1) = [(k + 1) \cdot (k + 2)]/2$. Assume, then, that k possesses ϕ, that is, that $0 + 1 + \ldots + k = [k \cdot (k + 1)]/2$. Adding $k + 1$ to both sides of this equation yields

$$0 + 1 + \ldots + k + (k + 1) = [k \cdot (k + 1)]/2 + (k + 1).$$

But

$$[k \cdot (k + 1)]/2 + (k + 1) = [k \cdot (k + 1) + 2 \cdot (k + 1)]/2$$
$$= [(k + 1) \cdot (k + 2)]/2.$$

Therefore, $0 + 1 + \ldots + k + (k + 1) = [(k + 1) \cdot (k + 2)]/2$. We have shown, then, that for any number k, if k has ϕ, so does its immediate successor $k + 1$. That is, we have shown that the induction step is also true. From the basis and induction step we infer by mathematical induction the conclusion that all numbers possess ϕ, that is, that for every number n,

$$0 + 1 + \ldots + n = [n \cdot (n + 1)]/2.$$

The basis and induction steps have been shown to be true, so we

---

[3] This argument turns on a principle that is equivalent to mathematical induction, so it can hardly be considered a proof that mathematical induction is a deductive principle.

know that the conclusion is also true because mathematical induction is a deductive principle of inference.

22.1.   Strong Mathematical Induction

The so-called *principle of (strong) mathematical induction* is the rule of inference that authorizes one to infer from the two premises

> The number 0 has the property ϕ.   (*Basis*)
> If all the predecessors of any number have   (*Induction step*)
> the property ϕ, then so does the number
> itself.[4]

to the conclusion

> All the (natural) numbers have the prop-   (*Conclusion*)
> erty ϕ.

More often than not we will use strong rather than weak mathematical induction to prove metatheorems about our logical systems. The difference between the two principles is more apparent than real, as the following consideration shows. Let ψ be the property that a number has if both it and all its predecessors have the property ϕ. Then weak induction on ψ is tantamount to strong induction on ϕ. Both principles, therefore, are deductive principles of reasoning.

A little reflection reveals that what makes mathematical induction a deductive principle is simply the type of ordering which the natural numbers have when arranged in order of magnitude. Whenever any objects exhibit the same ordering, there are weak and strong mathematical induction principles which hold for them, that is, which are deductive principles of proof. Consider, for example, this enumeration of the wffs of LSP: wffs with 0 occurrences of connectives, wffs with 1 occurrence of connectives, wffs with 2 occurrences of connectives, and so on. Corresponding to this enumeration is a strong principle of mathematical induction—*from the two premises*

---

[4] By a *predecessor of* a number is meant any number that comes before it in the usual ordering of the natural numbers, that is, 0, 1, 2, 3, ... Thus the predecessors of 4 are 3, 2, 1, and 0.

Wffs with zero occurrences of connectives   *(Basis)*
have the property ϕ.

Wffs with a given number of occurrences   *(Induction step)*
of connectives have the property ϕ if all
wffs with fewer occurrences of connectives
have ϕ.

one may infer the conclusion

All wffs have the property ϕ. (That is, wffs   *(Conclusion)*
with any number of connectives have ϕ.)

To illustrate the use of mathematical induction to prove logical metatheorems, we will prove a metatheorem about LSP which we have tacitly assumed on several occasions, the so-called *principle of interchange of equivalents*, to wit: If C is equivalent to B and if A_C results from A_B by replacing zero or more (not necessarily all) occurrences of B in A_B by occurrences of C, then A_C is equivalent to A_B.[5] A wff A_B that satisfies this principle for all choices of B and C will be said to have the property ϕ. It is evident that any wff A_B with zero occurrences of connectives has ϕ, for such a wff must consist of a sentential variable standing alone. Thus we have established the basis of the induction. Suppose now that all wffs with n or fewer occurrences of connectives have ϕ. Let A_B be any wff containing $n + 1$ occurrences of connectives, and let A_C result from A_B by replacing zero or more occurrences of B in A_B by occurrences of a wff C equivalent to B. If the replacement is made at zero occurrences of B, then A_C is clearly equivalent to A_B because A_C and A_B are then the same wff. Similarly, if A_B and B happen to be the same wff, A_C is also clearly equivalent to A_B. But suppose neither of these two special cases obtains. Then A_B will have one of these three forms: $\ulcorner{\sim}D_B\urcorner$, $\ulcorner D_B \vee E_B\urcorner$, or $\ulcorner D_B \cdot E_B\urcorner$. If A_B is $\ulcorner{\sim}D_B\urcorner$ and neither special case obtains, then the replacement which converts A_B into A_C is made wholly within D_B, converting D_B into D_C. D_B contains n occurrences of connectives, so our assumption that all wffs with n or fewer occurrences of connectives have ϕ applies to it. So D_C is equivalent to D_B. Obviously, then, $\ulcorner{\sim}D_C\urcorner$ is equivalent to $\ulcorner{\sim}D_B\urcorner$, that is, A_C is equivalent to A_B. If, however, A_B is

[5] As a mnemonic aid we here use capital letters instead of numerals as subscripts on capital letters. Frequent use will be made of this mnemonic artifice in Part Four.

$\ulcorner D_B \lor E_B \urcorner$ and neither special case obtains, then the replacement which converts A_B into A_C is made wholly within D_B and within E_B, converting D_B into D_C and E_B into E_C. D_B and E_B each have n or fewer occurrences of connectives, so it follows from our overriding assumption that each has ϕ. Thus D_C is equivalent to D_B, and E_C is equivalent to E_B. It follows that A_C, that is, $\ulcorner D_C \lor E_C \urcorner$, is equivalent to A_B, that is, $\ulcorner D_B \lor E_B \urcorner$. The third case where A_B is $\ulcorner D_B \cdot E_B \urcorner$ is left to the reader. The foregoing reasoning establishes the induction step. By strong mathematical induction, therefore, we conclude that all wffs have ϕ, that is, that the principle of interchange of equivalents is true.

The strategy just used to establish the truth of the induction step is quite standard: to assume for an arbitrary number n that all wffs with n or fewer occurrences of connectives have ϕ, and then to show that this assumption entails that wffs with $n + 1$ occurrences of connectives have ϕ. The assumption is even given a name; it is called the *hypothesis of induction*.

Although perhaps the most common, the ordering of (classes of) wffs by the number of occurrences of connectives in them is not the only ordering that gives rise to proofs by mathematical induction. For example, though none are presented in the body of this text, structural metatheorems about well-formedness are frequently proved by mathematical induction on the number of occurrences of symbols in wffs. As mentioned above, orderings of the kind exhibited by the natural numbers supply the warrant for proofs by mathematical induction. Roughly speaking, whenever a set Δ of cases are so arranged that

(i)   there is a first case, a second case, a third case, and so on;
(ii) every member of Δ occurs exactly once in the enumeration in (i),

proofs of theorems about members of Δ can proceed by mathematical induction. The basis of the induction affirms that the *first case* has the property ϕ. The induction step of (weak) induction affirms that, if *any case* has the property ϕ, so does the *next case*. And the conclusion of the induction states that *all the cases* have ϕ. It is just coincidental that the number zero is frequently associated with the basis of proofs by mathematical induction. For example, in the proof by mathematical induction given in Section 22.3, the first case, that is, the case relevant to the induction basis, concerns wffs that contain not zero but rather one occurrence of certain connectives.

22.2. Functional Incompleteness of the Dot and Wedge

To prove that the set of connectives formed by the dot and wedge is functionally incomplete it suffices to exhibit a truth table that is satisfied by no wff in those connectives. We will show, accordingly, that there is no wff A_p written in 'p', brackets, the dot, and the wedge which satisfies the following table T[6]:

p	A_p
t	f
f	t

To this end we argue that any such wff A_p comes out true for the value truth of 'p', and therefore does not satisfy T. Let ϕ be the property of coming out true when 'p' is given the value truth. First we notice that, if it contains zero occurrences of connectives, A_p has the property ϕ, because A_p is then the wff 'p' itself. So the basis of the induction is established. As our hypothesis of induction, we assume that all wffs (in 'p', brackets, dot, and wedge) with n or fewer occurrences of connectives have ϕ. Let A_p contain $n + 1$ occurrences of connectives. Then A_p has one of these two forms $\ulcorner B_p \cdot C_p \urcorner$ or $\ulcorner B_p \vee C_p \urcorner$. Suppose A_p is $\ulcorner B_p \cdot C_p \urcorner$. Since both B_p and C_p have n or fewer occurrences of connectives, both fall under the hypothesis of induction. It follows that both B_p and C_p come out true when 'p' is assigned truth. By the semantics of the dot, therefore, the wff A_p, that is, $\ulcorner B_p \cdot C_p \urcorner$, also comes out true when 'p' is given the value truth. Thus A_p has ϕ. The proof that A_p has ϕ when A_p is $\ulcorner B_p \vee C_p \urcorner$ is exactly like the preceding and is left to the reader. Thus we have established the induction step. By strong mathematical induction, we conclude that all wffs A_p have the property ϕ. We conclude, therefore, that the dot and wedge are functionally incomplete.

[6] As a mnemonic device we here use lowercase letters as subscripts.

Does the functional incompleteness of a set of connectives necessarily result in a deficiency of expressive power? Put otherwise, can the expressive power of a formalized language with a functionally incomplete set of connectives always be augmented by appropriately enlarging its set of truth-functional connectives? The answer is *no!* Even though its connectives be functionally incomplete, a formalized language *might* nonetheless have the same expressive power as it would if its connectives were functionally complete. To see this, let L be a formalized language with '⊃' as sole connective and which contains an analytically false sentence '*p*'. We define $\ulcorner \sim A \urcorner$ as $\ulcorner A \supset p \urcorner$. Then it is easy to see that $\ulcorner \sim A \urcorner$ and $\ulcorner A \supset p \urcorner$ are mutually entailing. The tilde and horseshoe together are functionally complete, and the tilde can be defined in L, so it follows that no addition of truth-functional connectives to L would enhance its expressive power even though its set of connectives is functionally incomplete. Why, then, so much insistence on functionally complete sets of connectives? One reason is to avoid the *risk* of loss of expressive power. This risk is perhaps negligible in the case of a formalized language containing the horseshoe; all that is needed is a single analytical falsehood. But the risk is appreciable in a language that contains just the dot and wedge. If such a language boasts a modest number of atomic sentences that do not entail one another, it must meet rather stringent conditions to enjoy the same expressive power that it would enjoy if it also contained the tilde. Another reason for the insistence on functional completeness of connectives is practical. It is sometimes very difficult to show that the functional incompleteness of its connectives does not impair the expressive power of a given formalized language.

To prove the functional completeness or incompleteness of a set of connectives in the manner in which such proofs have been presented in this text requires ingenuity. There do exist, however, algorithms or effective methods for deciding whether a finite set of connectives is functionally complete. Although these algorithms dispense with the need for ingenuity, we have not introduced them for the following reason. These algorithms are quite impractical in that their application to even relatively simple sets of connectives demands that one perform an astronomically large number of operations. (Though humanly impractical, these algorithms could sometimes be efficiently applied by a high-speed computing machine.) Theoretically, therefore, no ingenuity is needed to decide functional completeness; practically, ingenuity is indispensable unless one has a computer at his call.

23. EXERCISES

(1) Prove that the set of connectives consisting of the horseshoe alone is functionally incomplete.

⟨2⟩ Show that the statement that every nonempty set of natural numbers has a least member entails and is entailed by the statement that, for any property ϕ, if zero has ϕ and if the immediate successor of any number has ϕ provided the number itself has ϕ, then all the natural numbers have ϕ. (You may assume the following about natural numbers: Zero is the immediate successor of no natural number. Every natural number is either identical with zero or else is the immediate successor of some natural number. For any natural numbers x, y, and z, if z is the immediate successor of y and if x is less than z, then x is either less than or identical with y.)

(3) Prove that the principle of induction by simple enumeration is not a deductive principle of inference.

[4] Make explicit those features of the usual ordering of the natural numbers which ground proof by mathematical induction.

⟨5⟩ Let L be a formalized language whose connectives consist of the dot and wedge only, and suppose that L contains a moderate number of atomic sentences which do not entail one another. What conditions must L satisfy to be as expressively powerful as it would be if it also contained the tilde?

(6) Prove that the ternary connective '⊗' forms by itself a functionally incomplete set of connectives, where '⊗' has the following fundamental truth table.

A	B	C	$\otimes[A,B,C]$
t	t	t	f
t	f	t	t
f	t	t	t
f	f	t	t
t	t	f	t
t	f	f	t
f	t	f	t
f	f	f	f

⟨7⟩   Prove that the set of connectives consisting of the tilde and triple bar is not functionally complete. (*Hint:* Show by strong mathematical induction that every wff that can be written using only 'p', 'q', '$\sim$', '$\equiv$', '[', and ']' comes out true under zero or an even number of value assignments to the *two* variables 'p' and 'q'.)

⟨8⟩   Let Δ be an arbitrary finite set of truth-functional connectives whose fundamental truth tables are known. Develop an algorithm for determining whether or not Δ is functionally complete.

(9)   Prove by strong mathematical induction the claim made about duality in clause (ix) of Section 16.3.

24.   ALTERNATIVE NOTATIONS

24.0.   Trivial Alternatives

That the dot has been used to symbolize conjunction was largely a matter of free choice. Had we been so inclined, we might have used some other symbol, such as '&' or '∧' or '$\otimes$', in lieu of the dot. In fact, there are authors who use the ampersand '&' and the inverted wedge '∧' to express conjunction. What symbol one chooses to express conjunction is obviously inconsequential as far as logical theory is concerned. There are good practical reasons, however, for adopting as standard a notation as possible; at the level of notation, innovation is usually just idiosyncrasy. The notation adopted in this text seems to us to be the most widely used. But there are other fairly common notations and, if he wishes to read with facility works by other authors, the reader would do well to become familiar with these alternatives. To help the reader achieve such familiarity, a table of some common alternative symbols is supplied below:

Truth Function	Symbol Adopted	Common Alternatives
Conjunction[1]	·	&, ∧
Disjunction	∨	No common alternative
Negation	∼	¯, ¬
Conditional	⊃	→
Biconditional	≡	↔

[1] Occasionally mere juxtaposition is used to express conjunction, the conjunction of 'p' and 'q' being written 'pq'.

24.1. Nontrivial Alternative: Polish Notation

The so-called *Polish notation*, invented by the Polish logician Jan Łukasiewicz, differs from our notation by more than inconsequential changes of particular symbols. Also called the *parenthesis-free* notation, the Polish notation dispenses with grouping indicators altogether, thus effecting a notable economy. One feature of the Polish notation, however, is trivial. Instead of the symbols '∼', '∨', and so on, it employs capital letters as sentence connectives. The accompanying table matches our connectives with their Polish counterparts:

	Nega-tion	Alterna-tion	Conjunc-tion	Condi-tional	Bicondi-tional
Standard connective,	∼	∨	·	⊃	≡
Polish connective,	N	A	K	C	E

The use of capitals as connectives has the advantage that formulas can be typed on an ordinary typewriter.

Placing binary connectives *between* the components they join is what necessitated indicators to keep our groupings straight. The Polish notation places all connectives *in front of* the components they join, thus eliminating the need for grouping indicators. The following are formation rules for a Polish formalized language whose vocabulary consists of an infinite stock of sentential variables 'p', 'q', 'r', 's', 'p_1', and so on, and the connectives 'N', 'A', 'K', 'C', and 'E':

(i)   A sentential variable is a wff.

(ii) If ϕ is a wff, so is $\ulcorner N\phi \urcorner$.

(iii) If ϕ and ψ are wffs, so are $\ulcorner A\phi\psi \urcorner$, $\ulcorner K\phi\psi \urcorner$, $\ulcorner C\phi\psi \urcorner$, and $\ulcorner E\phi\psi \urcorner$.

(iv) A formula is a wff if and only if it can be constructed by a finite number of applications of the above rules.

(The reader will have noticed that we just used Greek letters as metalinguistic variables having formulas as values, rather than italicized English capitals as we have customarily done. The shift was made to avoid confusing Polish connectives with metalinguistic variables, for example, the Polish binary connective 'A' with the metalinguistic variable 'A'.) The following table exhibits some Polish wffs together with the corresponding wffs of the standard notation.

Polish	ANpq	NApq	AAqrNKpp	ENCpqr
Standard	$[\sim p \vee q]$	$\sim[p \vee q]$	$[(q \vee r) \vee \sim(p \cdot p)]$	$[\sim(p \supset q) \equiv r]$

At first blush the groupings of Polish wffs might seem to be ambiguous. But it can be proved by mathematical induction that the grouping of a Polish wff is perfectly unambiguous. Notice that the first symbol of a molecular Polish wff is always its main connective. Thus alternations always begin with 'A', conjunctions with 'K', and so on. The foregoing makes for one additional advantage of the Polish over the standard notation: It is easier to pick out the main connective in a Polish wff than in a standard wff.

There is a rather simple technique for recognizing which are the components joined by a connective in a Polish wff. If the connective is a singulary connective, its component consists of the shortest consecutive well-formed string of symbols beginning with the first symbol to the right of the connective and running from left to right. For example, the underlined portion is the component "joined" by the second occurrence of 'N' in the wff 'NECqrNKpNp'. If the connective is one of the four binary ones, its left component consists of the shortest consecutive well-formed string of symbols beginning with the first symbol to the right of the connective and running left to right; its right component consists of the shortest consecutive well-formed string of symbols beginning with the first symbol to the right of its left component and running left to right. For example, the underlined and overlined portions are, respectively, the left and right components joined by the first occurrence of 'A' in the wff NAKqrNApq.

The chart above pairs Polish wffs with the *corresponding* wffs of the standard notation. For example, ' $\sim[p \lor q]$ ' is paired with 'NApq'. The sense of correspondence is doubtless intuitively obvious; quite evidently, 'NApq' and ' $\sim[p \lor q]$ ' are merely *transliterations* of one another. Many authors have adopted the Polish notation, so it is important that the reader learn to transliterate the Polish into the standard notation, and vice versa. So rather than leave the concept of transliteration to the vagaries of intuition, we provide an inductive characterization of the notion:

(i) If ϕ and ψ are the same sentential variable, then ϕ and ψ are transliterations of one another.

(ii) If a Polish wff ϕ is a transliteration of a standard wff ψ, then $\ulcorner N\phi \urcorner$ and $\ulcorner \sim\psi \urcorner$ are transliterations of one another.

(iii) If Polish wffs ϕ_1 and ϕ_2 are, respectively, transliterations of standard wffs ψ_1 and ψ_2, then

    (a) $\ulcorner A\phi_1\phi_2 \urcorner$ and $\ulcorner [\psi_1 \lor \psi_2] \urcorner$ are transliterations of one another;

    (b) $\ulcorner K\phi_1\phi_2 \urcorner$ and $\ulcorner [\psi_1 \cdot \psi_2] \urcorner$ are transliterations of one another;

    (c) $\ulcorner C\phi_1\phi_2 \urcorner$ and $\ulcorner [\psi_1 \supset \psi_2] \urcorner$ are transliterations of one another;

    (d) $\ulcorner E\phi_1\phi_2 \urcorner$ and $\ulcorner [\psi_1 \equiv \psi_2] \urcorner$ are transliterations of one another.

(iv) A Polish wff and a standard wff are transliterations of one another if and only if their being so follows from the above rules.

Because of the advantages and economies of the Polish notation, our decision to adopt the standard notation may appear capricious. But there are good reasons for that decision. First, the interior groupings of a wff seem more perspicuous in the standard notation. Second, as the standard notation conforms to that ordinarily used in mathematics, it is more familiar to the beginning student of symbolic logic than the Polish notation would be.

25.   EXERCISES

[1]   Prove, by mathematical induction on the number of occurrences of symbols it contains, that the grouping of a Polish wff is unambiguous. (*Hint:* First prove by mathematical induction that, if ϕ is a Polish wff, no initial portion of ϕ that is not ϕ itself is a wff, and no wff can result by adding symbols at the right of ϕ.)

(2)   Formulate the semantics of the Polish system by constructing fundamental truth tables for its connectives.

(3)   Show that the three-step evaluational procedure of Section 6.1 applies also to Polish wffs.

(4)   Determine which of the formulas below are well formed:

NNA*p*NNNN*q*   CAKE*ppppp*   ENE*pq*   K*p*K*p*K*pq*
ANN*p*NNNN*q*   CAKE*pqrp*   N*p*NK*pr*   A*r*K*r*E*r*C*r*N*pq*

(5)   Find the standard-notation transliteration of each wff exhibited in Exercise (4).

(6)   For each occurrence of a connective in the wffs of Exercise (4), indicate which component or components it joins.

PART TWO[1]
Axiomatization of Truth-Functional Logic

[1] The reader who is not particularly interested in axiomatics may skip either to Part Three (if he is curious about modal logic) or directly to Part Four (if he is eager to move on to quantification theory). Neither move will result in any loss of continuity.

26. AXIOMATIC SYSTEM OF TRUTH-FUNCTIONAL LOGIC

26.0. Primitive Basis of System P

From a logical point of view the most important wffs of LSP are the valid wffs. Truth tables provide a mechanical routine for specifying or isolating the valid wffs. By means of a truth table we can effectively recognize or decide whether a given wff is valid, that is, whether it has the property of validity. An effective method or algorithm for recognizing or deciding whether an object possesses a certain property is called a *decision procedure for* that property. Truth tables, then, constitute a decision procedure for validity with respect to wffs of LSP. Now, one way to isolate or specify the objects that exhibit a certain property is to supply a decision procedure for that property. That is how we isolated the valid wffs in Part One. Some properties of great importance in logic and mathematics do not admit of decision procedures, so it is fortunate that there are other ways to isolate or specify the objects that possess a certain property. One very important way is the axiomatic method, used informally but very successfully by Euclid and perfected by latter-day mathematicians and logicians.

To illustrate the axiomatic method, we will employ it to specify the valid wffs of LSP. To this end, we lay down an axiomatic system that will be called system P. System P has the following vocabulary, formation rules, axioms, and rules of inference:[1]

Vocabulary

(i) An infinite supply of sentential variables: 'p', 'q', 'r', 's', 'p_1', ...

(ii) Grouping indicators: '[' and ']'.

(iii) The singulary connective '$\sim$' and the binary connective '$\supset$'.

Formation rules

(i) A sentential variable is a wff.

(ii) If A is a wff, so is $\ulcorner \sim A \urcorner$.

---

[1] Except for inconsequential changes of variables, this system is the system P_2 of Alonzo Church, *Introduction to Mathematical Logic*, vol. I, Princeton University Press, Princeton, N.J., 1956, as adapted from Lukasiewicz.

(iii)   If A and B are wffs, so is $\ulcorner[A \supset B]\urcorner$.
(iv)   A formula is a wff if and only if it can be constructed by a finite number of applications of the preceding rules.

Axioms

These three wffs are the sole axioms of system P:

Axiom 1. $p \supset [q \supset p]$ (law of affirmation of the consequent).

Axiom 2. $[p \supset (q \supset r)] \supset [(p \supset q) \supset (p \supset r)]$ (self-distributive law of the horseshoe).

Axiom 3. $[\sim p \supset \sim q] \supset [q \supset p]$ (converse law of contraposition).[2]

Rules of Inference

Rule 1.   From A and $\ulcorner[A \supset B]\urcorner$, one may infer B (*modus ponens*).

Rule 2.   From A, one may infer the result of substituting a wff B for a sentential variable c throughout A (*substitution*).

In the rule of substitution, it is, of course, understood that B replaces c at every occurrence of c in A. Thus the rule of substitution authorizes the inference from '$p \supset [q \supset p]$' to

$$[\sim q \supset \sim p] \supset [q \supset [\sim q \supset \sim p]]$$

but not to '$[\sim q \supset \sim p] \supset [q \supset p]$'. In an application of substitution, the wff A is referred to as the *premiss*, and the wff that results through the substitution is called the *conclusion of* the application of substitution. Similarly, A and $\ulcorner[A \supset B]\urcorner$ are referred to as the *premisses*, and B as the *conclusion*, of an application of *modus ponens*.

The vocabulary, formation rules, axioms, and rules of inference together constitute the *primitive basis* of an axiomatic system. In strict rigor, the axiomatic method requires that the primitive basis of an axiomatic system be presented effectively and in full. That is, the primitive basis should be presented in such a way that it is a purely mechanical matter to recognize whether an arbitrary object belongs to the vocabulary of the system, whether it is a wff of the system, and whether it is an axiom of the system. More-

---

[2] The reader will notice that in exhibiting these axioms we have used the abbreviative convention of dropping outermost brackets. Hereafter we shall employ obvious abbreviations without pausing to formulate them or to announce our intention to use them.

over, the rules of inference must be effective in the sense that, given any putative application of any of the rules of inference, it is a mechanical matter to determine whether or not the rule has been properly applied. When followed thus rigorously, the axiomatic method is known as the *formal axiomatic method*, and the system presented is called a *formal axiomatic system* or a *logistic system*. System P, for example, is a logistic system. Although widely used in mathematics, the axiomatic method is seldom followed so rigorously as to produce a logistic system. Usually only the axioms are carefully stated. Recognition of wffs is left to the student's grasp of the meaning of the symbols employed, and "the laws of logic" are tacitly assumed as the rules of inference. For example, this is the customary way in which Euclidean geometry is developed. When followed thus informally, the axiomatic method is known as the *informal axiomatic method*, and the system presented is called an *informal axiomatic system*.

26.1. Basic Concepts of Axiomatics

By a *proof in* a logistic system is meant any finite sequence of wffs, each member of which is either an axiom of the system or can be inferred from earlier members of the sequence by means of a rule of inference of the system. In the case of system P, therefore, a proof is any finite sequence of wffs of system P, each member of which is one of the three axioms of system P or can be inferred from two earlier members by *modus ponens* or from one earlier member by substitution. Notice that the notion of proof in a logistic system is effective in the sense that proofs are mechanically recognizable. To determine whether a given finite sequence of wffs is a proof, one has merely to inspect each member to ascertain whether it is an axiom or inferable by a rule of inference from earlier members of the sequence. Proceeding thus, the reader should verify that the following finite sequence of wffs is a proof in system P:

$[p \supset (q \supset r)] \supset [(p \supset q) \supset (p \supset r)]$

$[p \supset (q \supset p)] \supset [(p \supset q) \supset (p \supset p)]$

$p \supset [q \supset p]$

$[p \supset q] \supset [p \supset p]$

$[p \supset (q \supset p)] \supset [p \supset p]$

$p \supset p$

Proper annotation can greatly reduce the time and labor of verifying that a putative proof is really a proof. Consider, for example, this annotated version of the above proof:

(1) $[p \supset (q \supset r)] \supset [(p \supset q) \supset (p \supset r)]$ Axiom 2

(2) $[p \supset (q \supset p)] \supset [(p \supset q) \supset (p \supset p)]$ Sub. of 'p' for 'r' in (1)

(3) $p \supset [q \supset p]$ Axiom 1

(4) $[p \supset q] \supset [p \supset p]$ *Modus ponens* from (2) and (3)

(5) $[p \supset (q \supset p)] \supset [p \supset p]$ Sub. of '$[q \supset p]$' for 'q' in (4)

(6) $p \supset p$ *Modus ponens* from (5) and (3)

Although such annotation is extremely convenient, we must emphasize its superfluity. Even without annotation, proofs are mechanically recognizable.

A proof is said to be a *proof of* its last line. The above sequence, for example, is a proof of the wff '$p \supset p$'. And by a *theorem of* a logistic system is meant any wff of which there is a proof in that system. Thus '$p \supset p$' is a theorem of system P. Notice that, trivially, the axioms of a logistic system are theorems of it, because the one-member-long sequence consisting of an axiom by itself is a proof of itself. Notice, too, that every member (or, as we shall sometimes say, every *line*) of a proof is itself a theorem, because any initial (unbroken) subsequence of a proof is also a proof. For example, '$[p \supset q] \supset [p \supset p]$' is a theorem of system P, because the sequence of the first four lines of the above proof of '$p \supset p$' is itself a proof. Later we will use this feature of proofs to distinguish logistic systems from so-called *natural deduction systems*.

The theorems are the wffs specified or isolated by a logistic system. The theorems, that is, the wffs generated from the axioms via the rules of inference, are thus marked off from the nontheorems, which cannot be reached or obtained from the axioms via those rules. It is essential to distinguish the wffs that a system *actually* specifies from those it is *meant* or *intended* to specify. Logistic systems are commonly designed or constructed to specify or isolate the wffs that possess a certain property. If a logistic system L is designed to specify those of its wffs that have the property ϕ, we will refer to the set of those wffs of L which possess ϕ as the *intended output of* L. By the *actual output of* L is meant the set of the theorems of L. For example, system P was, in fact, designed to specify or isolate those of its wffs which are valid under the ordinary interpretation of the tilde and horseshoe. The intended output of system P, therefore, is the set of its valid wffs. The actual output of system P, its theorems, is completely determined by its primitive basis, irrespective of how its wffs are interpreted. A logistic system L is said to be *complete with respect to* a property ϕ if its theorems include all its wffs that possess ϕ, that is, if every wff that has ϕ is a theorem. And a logistic system is said to be *consistent with respect to* a property ϕ if all its theorems possess ϕ, that is, if its theorems form a subset of the wffs that possess ϕ. It follows from these definitions that L is both consistent and complete with respect to ϕ if and only if the theorems of L happen to be exactly the wffs of L that possess ϕ.

The design of a logistic system is called *successful* if its actual output is the same as its intended output. Therefore, if a system L is designed to specify those of its wffs that have ϕ, its design is successful if and only if L is both consistent and complete with respect to ϕ. There are two ways for the design of a logistic system to miscarry. If L is inconsistent with respect to ϕ, L generates theorems it was designed not to generate. If, on the other hand, L is incomplete with respect to ϕ, L fails to generate as theorems some wffs it was designed to generate. Notice that it is quite possible for the design of a system to miscarry in both ways at the same time. Usually miscarriages of design are due to insufficient skill or ingenuity on the part of the designer, but not always. The gist of Gödel's celebrated (first) incompleteness theorem is that no possible logistic system is both consistent and complete with respect to the property of being an arithmetic truth.[3] According to Gödel's incompleteness theorem, even God could not design a logistic system whose actual output is the set of arithmetic truths! By contrast, as we will prove shortly, the design of system P is successful; that is, system P is both consistent and complete with respect to validity.

[3] See Section 61.2 for a statement and proof of Gödel's (first) incompleteness theorem.

27.   EXERCISES

(1)   Construct a logistic system that has the same vocabulary and formation rules as system P but which is both inconsistent and incomplete with respect to validity, that is, give the primitive basis of such a system.

(2)   Explain carefully the difference between a proof in a logistic system and a proof of some true statement about the logistic system.

(3)   Prove that if there is one proof of a wff in system P, then there are infinitely many. Prove also that there is no upper bound on the length of proofs in system P.

(4)   Prove that there is no upper bound on the length of theorems in system P; that is, show that for any positive integer n, there are theorems of system P which are more than n symbols long. Is there a lower bound on the length of theorems in system P?

{5}   Although very useful for many purposes in mathematics, there are situations in mathematics where the informal axiomatic method breaks down, where the formal axiomatic method must be employed. Describe several of these situations and explain why the breakdown occurs.

(6)   Annotate the following proof:

$p \supset [q \supset p]$

$p \supset [[q \supset r] \supset p]$

$[[p \supset [q \supset r]] \supset [[p \supset q] \supset [p \supset r]]] \supset$
$\quad [[q \supset r] \supset [[p \supset [q \supset r]] \supset [[p \supset q] \supset [p \supset r]]]]$

$[p \supset [q \supset r]] \supset [[p \supset q] \supset [p \supset r]]$

$[q \supset r] \supset [[p \supset [q \supset r]] \supset [[p \supset q] \supset [p \supset r]]]$

$[p \supset [q_1 \supset r]] \supset [[p \supset q_1] \supset [p \supset r]]$

$[p \supset [q_1 \supset r_1]] \supset [[p \supset q_1] \supset [p \supset r_1]]$

$[p_1 \supset [q_1 \supset r_1]] \supset [[p_1 \supset q_1] \supset [p_1 \supset r_1]]$

$[p_1 \supset [q_1 \supset [[p \supset q] \supset [p \supset r]]]] \supset$
$\quad [[p_1 \supset q_1] \supset [p_1 \supset [[p \supset q] \supset [p \supset r]]]]$

$[p_1 \supset [[p \supset [q \supset r]] \supset [[p \supset q] \supset [p \supset r]]]] \supset$
$\quad [[p_1 \supset [p \supset [q \supset r]]] \supset [p_1 \supset [[p \supset q] \supset [p \supset r]]]]$

$[[q \supset r] \supset [[p \supset [q \supset r]] \supset [[p \supset q] \supset [p \supset r]]]] \supset$
$\quad [[[q \supset r] \supset [p \supset [q \supset r]]] \supset [[q \supset r] \supset [[p \supset q] \supset [p \supset r]]]]$
$[[q \supset r] \supset [p \supset [q \supset r]]] \supset [[q \supset r] \supset [[p \supset q] \supset [p \supset r]]]$
$p \supset [q_1 \supset p]$
$[q \supset r] \supset [q_1 \supset [q \supset r]]$
$[q \supset r] \supset [p \supset [q \supset r]]$
$[q \supset r] \supset [[p \supset q] \supset [p \supset r]]$

(7) Try to devise abbreviative conventions that make the groupings of wffs of system P more perspicuous.

(8) Give the primitive basis of a Polish-notation transliteration of system P.

(9) Consider the inane logistic system that has the same vocabulary and formation rules as system P, one rule of inference which is substitution, and the two axioms '$\sim p$' and '$[p \supset p]$'. Prove that this system is complete but not consistent with respect to the property of being a negation. (By a *negation* is meant a wff whose main connective is a tilde.) Prove that it is neither consistent nor complete with respect to the property of being a conditional.

[10] Consider the logistic system that has the same vocabulary, formation rules, and rules of inference as system P, but which has just one axiom, '$[p \supset (p \supset q)]$'. Prove that every wff of this system is a theorem of it.

(11) The rule of substitution permits substitution for only one variable at a time. The so-called *rule of simultaneous substitution* permits substitution for any number of variables at the same time. For example, it allows one to infer '$q \supset (p \supset q)$' from '$p \supset (q \supset p)$' by the simultaneous substitution of 'p' for 'q' and of 'q' for 'p'. For another example, it allows one to infer '$(q \supset q) \supset (r \supset p)$' from '$p \supset (q \supset r)$'. Formulate precisely the rule of simultaneous substitution.

(12) Consider a system exactly like system P except for having the rule of simultaneous substitution in place of the rule of substitution. Show that the actual output of this system is the same as the actual output of system P.

28. METATHEORY OF SYSTEM P (I)

28.0. Consistency of System P

By a *metatheorem of* a logistic system L is meant any significantly true statement about L. Metatheorems of L should not be confused with theorems of L, which are the wffs of L that can be generated from its axioms via its rules of inference. Metatheorems belong to the metalanguage in which L is studied; theorems belong to the object language L itself. When there is no danger of confusion, the prefix 'meta-' is sometimes dropped from the word 'metatheorem'. For example, one usually speaks of the completeness or consistency *theorems* rather than of the completeness or consistency *metatheorems*.

The fundamental truth tables for the tilde and horseshoe supply the intended semantics of system P. The semantical notions of valid wff, contradiction, contingent wff, and so on, are all to be understood with reference to these truth tables. We shall now prove that system P is consistent with respect to the semantical property of validity. Or, what comes to the same thing, we will prove the following metatheorem:

> M1.   Every theorem of system P is valid (consistency theorem).

To prove M1, we will show that

(i)   the axioms of system P are all valid;

(ii)   the rules of inference of system P *preserve* validity in the sense that if the premises of an application of a rule are all valid, then so is the conclusion.

It follows from (i), (ii), and the definitions of theorem and proof that every theorem of system P is valid. It is left to the reader to verify that the axioms of system P are all valid. To see that *modus ponens* preserves validity, suppose that A and $\ulcorner A \supset B \urcorner$ are both valid but that B is not. Let $a_1, a_2, \ldots, a_n$ be a complete list of the distinct variables of $\ulcorner A \supset B \urcorner$. B is not valid, so there is some value assignment Σ to $a_1, a_2, \ldots, a_n$ which gives B the value falsehood. But A is valid, so A comes out true under Σ. By the semantics of the horseshoe, therefore, $\ulcorner A \supset B \urcorner$ comes out false under Σ, which contradicts our initial assumption that both A and $\ulcorner A \supset B \urcorner$ are valid. We conclude, therefore, that B is valid if both A and $\ulcorner A \supset B \urcorner$ are valid, which is to say that *modus ponens* preserves validity.

To show that substitution preserves validity, we first prove the following lemma:

> Lemma.   Let the wff A_B be the result of substituting the wff B for the sentential variable b in the wff A_b, let $a_1, \ldots, a_n$ be a list of distinct variables which includes b and any variable that occurs in A_b or B, and let Σ be a value assignment to the variables $a_1, \ldots, a_n$. Then, if the value of B under Σ is the same as the value which Σ assigns to b, the value of A_B under Σ is the same as the value of A_b under Σ (substitution lemma).

We begin our proof of the substitution lemma by considering the special case in which b does not occur in A_b. In this special case, the lemma holds trivially because A_B is the same wff as A_b. Suppose, however, that b does occur in A_b. If A_b contains zero occurrences of sentence connectives, A_b is the same wff as b itself, and it is evident that the lemma holds. Assume, then, that the lemma holds for any wff A_b^* with k or fewer occurrences of sentence connectives such that b occurs in A_b^*, and let A_b contain $k + 1$ occurrences of sentence connectives and also contain at least one occurrence of b. Then A_b has the form $\ulcorner \sim C_b \urcorner$ or $\ulcorner D_b \supset E_b \urcorner$. Suppose A_b is $\ulcorner \sim C_b \urcorner$. C_b falls under the hypothesis of induction, so the lemma holds for C_b and thus also for A_b, because A_B is the same wff as $\ulcorner \sim C_B \urcorner$. But suppose A_b is $\ulcorner D_b \supset E_b \urcorner$. Then D_b either falls under the hypothesis of induction (if it contains at least one occurrence of b) or under the special case (if it contains no occurrences of b). In either event the lemma holds for D_b. Similarly, E_b falls either under the hypothesis of induction or under the special case, and the lemma thus holds also for E_b. It follows, then, that the lemma holds for $\ulcorner D_b \supset E_b \urcorner$, that is, for A_b, because A_B is the same wff as $\ulcorner D_B \supset E_B \urcorner$. By strong mathematical induction, therefore, we infer that the lemma holds for any wff A_b in which b occurs. And if b does not occur in A_b, we know that the lemma holds for A_b, which then falls under the special case. This completes the proof of the substitution lemma. It follows as a corollary of the substitution lemma that substitution preserves validity (details are left to the reader).

28.1. Independence of Axioms and Rules

Other things being equal, elegance is preferable to inelegance. Accordingly, in logic and mathematics some emphasis is put on the creation of elegant primitive bases for axiomatic systems. One feature that contributes to the elegance of a primitive basis is the independence of its axioms and rules of inference. An axiom or rule of inference of a system L is *dependent in* L if the system that results by dropping the given axiom or rule from the primitive basis of L has the same set of theorems (actual output) that L has. So, if an axiom of a logistic system L is independent in L, then its omission from the primitive basis would diminish the set of theorems of L. The same holds for an independent rule of inference.

We will show that all the axioms and rules of system P are independent (in system P). Hence none of the axioms or rules of system P could be dropped from its primitive basis except on pain of denying theoremhood to some of the theorems (the valid wffs) of system P. First, the rules of inference. If the rule of substitution were dropped from the primitive basis of system P, no theorem of the resulting system would be longer than its longest axiom, axiom 2. The reason is that the conclusion of an application of *modus ponens* is always shorter than the longer premiss. But there are theorems of system P longer than axiom 2. So it follows from the definition of dependence that substitution is an independent rule in system P.

Just as substitution is needed in system P to obtain theorems longer than the longest axiom, so *modus ponens* is needed to obtain theorems shorter than the shortest axiom. (Full details are left to the reader.) There are theorems of system P shorter than its shortest axiom, for example, '$[p \supset p]$', so it follows that *modus ponens* is an independent rule in system P.

To prove that an axiom of a logistic system L is independent (in L), it suffices to find some property which the given axiom lacks but which is possessed by the remaining axioms and preserved by the rules of inference. If there is such a property ϕ, then the theorems of the system that results on dropping the given axiom all have ϕ. But this entails that the given axiom is not a theorem of the resulting system, which means that the axiom is independent in L. We will employ the strategy just described to prove that the axioms of system P are all independent (in P). To get the requisite properties ϕ, we introduce several *secondary interpretations* of system P.

Disregard for the moment the principal or intended semantics of system P and consider the following secondary interpretation. We let the range of values of the variables of system P be the three numbers 0, 1, and 2. That is, we let the variables take on any of the three "truth values" 0, 1, and 2.[1] And we introduce these fundamental "truth tables" for the tilde and horseshoe.

A	$\sim A$
0	1
1	1
2	1

A	B	$A \supset B$
0	0	0
0	1	2
0	2	2
1	0	2
1	1	2
1	2	0
2	0	0
2	1	0
2	2	0

We call 0 the *designated* truth value, and we refer to 1 and 2 as *undesignated* truth values. By a *valid wff* we now understand a wff that has a designated truth value under every assignment of values to its variables. For example, as the tables below show, axiom 2 and axiom 3 are valid in the sense just defined.

[1] Any three objects would have done just as well as the numbers 0, 1, and 2.

p	q	$[\sim p \supset \sim q] \supset [q \supset p]$				
0	0	1	2	1	0	0
0	1	1	2	1	0	2
0	2	1	2	1	0	0
1	0	1	2	1	0	2
1	1	1	2	1	0	2
1	2	1	2	1	0	0
2	0	1	2	1	0	2
2	1	1	2	1	0	0
2	2	1	2	1	0	0

p	q	r	$[p \supset [q \supset r]] \supset [[p \supset q] \supset [p \supset r]]$		
0	0	0	0	0	0
0	0	1	2	0	2
0	0	2	2	0	2
0	1	0	2	0	0
0	1	1	2	0	0
0	1	2	0	0	0
0	2	0	0	0	0
0	2	1	0	0	0
0	2	2	0	0	0
1	0	0	2	0	0
1	0	1	0	0	0
1	0	2	0	0	0
1	1	0	0	0	0
1	1	1	0	0	0
1	1	2	2	0	0
1	2	0	2	0	2
1	2	1	2	0	2
1	2	2	2	0	0
2	0	0	0	0	0
2	0	1	0	0	0
2	0	2	0	0	0
2	1	0	0	0	0
2	1	1	0	0	0
2	1	2	0	0	0
2	2	0	0	0	0
2	2	1	0	0	0
2	2	2	0	0	0

Axiom 1, however, is not valid in this sense, as shown by the table below.

p	q	$p \supset [q \supset p]$		
0	0	0̸	0	0̸
0	1	0̸	2	2̸
0	2	0̸	0	0̸
1	0	1̸	0	2̸
1	1	1̸	0	2̸
1	2	1̸	2	0̸
2	0	2̸	0	2̸
2	1	2̸	0	0̸
2	2	2̸	0	0̸

That *modus ponens* preserves validity (in the present sense) is evident from the truth table for the horseshoe. For suppose that A and $\ulcorner A \supset B \urcorner$ are valid and let Σ be a value assignment to the variables of $\ulcorner A \supset B \urcorner$. Clearly, both A and $\ulcorner A \supset B \urcorner$ have the value 0 under Σ. But, referring to the fundamental table for the horseshoe, we see that A and $\ulcorner A \supset B \urcorner$ can both have the value 0 only when B also has the value 0. Σ was an arbitrary value assignment, so it follows that B comes out 0 under every value assignment to its variables, that is, that B is valid. We conclude, therefore, that *modus ponens* preserves validity. As the proof that substitution preserves validity (in the sense just defined) parallels exactly the proof given in Section 28.0 that substitution preserves validity (in the familiar sense), details of this proof are left to the reader. Validity (defined with reference to the above secondary interpretation), therefore, is a property preserved by the two rules of inference, possessed by the second and third axioms but not possessed by axiom 1. It follows that axiom 1 is an independent axiom in system P.

To show that axiom 2 is independent, we use another three-valued secondary interpretation of system P, with 0 again as the sole designated truth value, in which the following are taken as the fundamental truth tables for the tilde and horseshoe.

A	$\sim A$
0	2
1	1
2	0

A	B	$A \supset B$
0	0	0
0	1	1
0	2	2
1	0	0
1	1	0
1	2	1
2	0	0
2	1	0
2	2	0

It is left to the reader to verify that under the interpretation of system P determined by the above tables axiom 1 and axiom 3 are valid, axiom 2 is not, and both *modus ponens* and substitution preserve validity. Such verification establishes the independence of axiom 2 in system P.

Similarly, it is left to the reader to prove that axiom 3 is independent by appealing to still another secondary three-valued interpretation, with 0 again as sole designated truth value, determined by the following fundamental truth tables for the tilde and horseshoe:

A	$\sim A$
0	2
1	2
2	2

A	B	$A \supset B$
0	0	0
0	1	1
0	2	2
1	0	0
1	1	0
1	2	2
2	0	0
2	1	0
2	2	0

Although we have used secondary three-valued interpretations to establish the independence of the three axioms of system P, the reader should not infer that all independence proofs make use of secondary three-valued interpretations. There are many ways to show independence. For example, we could have shown that axiom 3 is independent in system P by appealing to the ordinary truth table for the horseshoe coupled with the following table for the tilde:

A	$\sim A$
t	t
f	f

With respect to these tables, all the axioms except axiom 3 are obviously valid (because we have not changed the table for the horseshoe), axiom 3 is not valid, and the rules of inference preserve validity. It follows, then, that axiom 3 is independent in system P.

That independence is only one factor which contributes to the elegance of a logistic system is strikingly illustrated by the system P_1, which has the following primitive basis:

Vocabulary: same as system P.
Formation rules: same as system P.
Axioms: all and only valid wffs are axioms.
Rules of inference: none.

Both system P and system P_1 have the same set of theorems, the valid wffs. Furthermore, every axiom of system P_1 is independent in system P_1. Nevertheless, system P_1 is exceedingly inelegant because it is wholly deficient in *systematicity*. Unlike the axioms and rules of system P, those of system P_1 do not organize or interrelate its theorems in an economical or interesting way. It would be a mistake to attribute this lack of systematicity, with its resulting inelegance, to the fact that system P_1 contains infinitely many axioms. There are logistic systems of sentential logic with infinitely many axioms which are just as economical, systematic, and elegant as system P. For example, there is the system P_2 with the following primitive basis:

Vocabulary: same as system P.
Formation rules: same as system P.
Axioms: any wff that has any of these three forms is an axiom:
   Schema 1: $A \supset [B \supset A]$.

Schema 2: $[A \supset [B \supset C]] \supset [[A \supset B] \supset [A \supset C]]$.
Schema 3: $[\sim A \supset \sim B] \supset [B \supset A]$.
Rules of inference: *modus ponens*.

The schemata 1, 2, and 3 are known as *axiom schemata*. An axiom schema singles out infinitely many wffs as axioms. For example, schema 1 confers axiomhood on '$p \supset [q \supset p]$', '$r \supset [p \supset r]$', '$r \supset [[p \supset q] \supset r]$', and so on. System P_2, therefore, has infinitely many axioms. Moreover, it can be proved that system P and system P_2 have exactly the same theorems, the tautologies. Yet, with respect to economy, systematicity, and elegance, the two systems seem quite comparable.

28.2. Independence and Consistency

But, after all, elegance is only the icing on the systematic cake. If independence were relevant only to elegance, it would surely not merit the considerable attention paid it by logicians and mathematicians. But independence is germane to, among other things, problems of consistency. Of a host of consistency concepts, we have so far dealt with just one, consistency with respect to a property. Another fundamental consistency concept is absolute consistency. A logistic system is said to be *absolutely consistent* if at least one of its wffs is not a theorem. Clearly, the three systems we have just examined are all absolutely consistent. But suppose we formed a new logistic system by adding '$p \supset q$' as an axiom to the primitive basis of system P. This new system would not only be inconsistent with respect to validity, which is obvious, but would also be absolutely inconsistent, which is not quite so evident.

Independence bears a close relationship to absolute consistency. A logistic system L is absolutely consistent if and only if it contains at least one nonaxiom A which is independent in the system L^+ that results on adding A as an axiom to the primitive basis of L. The principal goal of the famous Hilbert program in mathematics was to prove the absolute consistency of a logistic system of ordinary arithmetic. To realize this goal, it would have sufficed to adduce a single wff A such that A was independent in the system that resulted on adding A as an axiom to the given logistic system of arithmetic. (Hilbert put rather severe restrictions on the methods of proof permissible in proving that a given wff was independent in a system.) Because of the intimate connection between independence and consistency, methods for establishing independence become valuable techniques for proving consistency, and conversely. It is this relationship that accounts for much of the emphasis placed on independence in logic and mathematics.

29. EXERCISES

(1)   Prove that each axiom of system P_2 is valid.

(2)   Prove that, if *modus tollens* were added to system P as a rule of inference, the resulting system would still be consistent with respect to validity, by showing that *modus tollens* preserves validity. *Modus tollens* is the rule that authorizes the inference from the premises $\ulcorner A \supset B \urcorner$ and $\ulcorner \sim B \urcorner$ to the conclusion $\ulcorner \sim A \urcorner$.

(3)   Prove that the rule of simultaneous substitution preserves validity. This rule authorizes the inference from a wff A to any wff B that results from A by the simultaneous substitution of wffs B_1, B_2, ..., B_n for *distinct* variables b_1, b_2, ..., b_n throughout A. [See Exercises (11) and (12) of Chapter 27.]

{4}   What factors besides independence contribute to the elegance of a formal axiomatic or logistic system?

(5)   Formulate a precise definition of the concept of an independent rule of inference.

{6}   Rather than use the pseudo truth values 0, 1, 2 in our secondary interpretations, might we have not used instead truth, falsehood, and a third bonafide truth value on a par with truth and falsehood? That is, is there such a third truth value?

(7)   Prove that the system which results from system P on adding '$p \supset q$' as an axiom is absolutely inconsistent.

(8)   Prove that a logistic system L is absolutely consistent if and only if L contains at least one nonaxiom A which is independent in the system L^+ which results on adding A as an axiom to the primitive basis of L.

[9]   Prove that systems P and P_2 have the same set of theorems. [*Hint:* Use the result of Exercise (12) of Chapter 27.]

⟨10⟩   Corresponding to every consistency concept is a related completeness concept. For one can say that a logistic system L is *complete in a given sense* if the system L^+, formed by adding an arbitrary nontheorem to L as an axiom, is inconsistent in the given sense. For example, we may say that a logistic system L is *absolutely complete* if it becomes absolutely inconsistent whenever a nontheorem is added to it as an axiom. Prove that system P is absolutely complete. (You may assume that system P is both consistent and complete with respect to validity.)

(11)   Given that the intended output of system P is the set of valid wffs, mention several properties with respect to which it would be undesirable that system P be either consistent or complete.

{12}   Try to devise a criterion of significance which can be used to demarcate the significantly true statements about a logistic system (the metatheorems) from the other true statements about it.

(13)   Let T be the following trivial formal axiomatic system:
       Vocabulary: the symbols '0' and '1'.
       Formation rules: any formula (finite sequence of symbols) that contains an equal number of occurrences of '0' and '1' is well formed.
       Axioms: the wffs '01' and '10' are the axioms.
       Rules of inference:
       R1.   If A is a wff that begins with an occurrence of '1', from A one may infer ⌜$1A0$⌝.
       R2.   If A is a wff that begins with an occurrence of '0', from A one may infer ⌜$0A1$⌝.
       Prove that T is absolutely consistent but not absolutely complete. Prove that each axiom and each rule of T is independent in T. Develop a decision procedure (algorithm) for recognizing the theorems of T.

⟨14⟩   Let L be a logistic system whose vocabulary consists exclusively of sentential variables, sentence connectives, and grouping indicators. By *a characteristic matrix for* L we mean an ordered triple ⟨$\Delta, \Delta^*, \mathbf{M}$⟩, where Δ is a set of objects called *truth values*, Δ^* is a proper nonempty subset of Δ the members of which are said to be *designated*, and **M** is a set of fundamental "truth tables" that indicate which member (truth value) of Δ is the value of a compound for every possible assignment of members (truth values) of Δ as values of its components, such that the theorems of L are the same as the valid wffs (wffs that take on only designated values under interpretation). If Δ is finite, the characteristic matrix is said to be *finite*. Notice that a finite characteristic matrix for L is a decision procedure for L. But a system for which there is no finite characteristic matrix may nonetheless have a decision procedure. For example, consider the following system L*. The vocabulary of L* contains every symbol of system P except the tilde; the formation rules of L* consist of the first, third, and fourth formation rules of system P; the wff '[p ⊃ p]' is the sole axiom of L*, and substitution is the sole rule of inference of L*. Develop a decision procedure (algorithm for recognizing theorems) for L*. Prove that there is no finite characteristic matrix for L*. (*Hint:* Suppose that there is a finite characteristic matrix ⟨Δ,Δ*,**M**⟩ for L*. Let n be the number of members of Δ, and let A_1, A_2, ..., A_{n^n+1} be an enumeration of $n^n + 1$ mutually distinct wffs of L* in which no variable except 'p' occurs. Show that this enumeration contains at least two wffs A_i, A_j, $i \neq j$, which are "equivalent" to one another in the sense that, for any interpretation Σ of the two wffs, A_i and A_j have the same value under Σ. Then show that $\ulcorner A_i \supset A_j \urcorner$ is valid by appealing to the fact that '$p \supset p$' comes out with a designated value regardless what truth value is assigned to 'p'. Then show that $\ulcorner A_i \supset A_j \urcorner$ is not a theorem, contrary to the supposition that ⟨Δ,Δ*,**M**⟩ is a characteristic matrix for L*.)

(15) Let L** be like L* of Exercise ⟨14⟩ except that *modus ponens* is also a rule of inference of L**. Show that *modus ponens* is not independent in L**.

(16) Derive the metatheorem that substitution preserves validity as a corollary of the substitution lemma of Section 28.0.

30.   METATHEORY OF SYSTEM P (II)

30.0.   The Deduction Theorem

A metatheorem important both in itself and as a tool for finding proofs of object language theorems is the so-called *deduction theorem*. Its succinct formulation calls for some special terminology. By a *variant of* a wff A is meant a wff that differs from A by at most alphabetical changes of variables. More precisely, let $a_1, \ldots, a_n$ be a complete list of the distinct variables in A and let $b_1, \ldots, b_n$ be any list of distinct variables. Then B is a *variant of A* if B results from A by the simultaneous substitution of $b_1, \ldots, b_n$ for $a_1, \ldots, a_n$, respectively. For example, '$p \supset (r \supset p)$', '$q \supset (p \supset q)$', and '$s \supset (q \supset s)$' are all variants of axiom 1 of system P, but neither '$p \supset (q \supset q)$' nor '$p \supset (p \supset p)$' is a variant of axiom 1. Notice that, trivially, every wff is a variant of itself. A finite sequence $B_1, B_2, \ldots, B_k$ of wffs of system P is said to be a *proof of B_k from the hypotheses $A_1, A_2, \ldots, A_n$* if each B_i is either an axiom or a variant of an axiom of system P, or one of the hypotheses A_j, or inferable by *modus ponens* from two earlier wffs in the sequence, or inferable from one earlier wff in the sequence by a substitution in which the variable substituted for does not occur in any of the hypotheses. For example, the following is an (annotated) proof of '$p \supset q$' from the single hypothesis '$\sim p$':

(1)	$r \supset [q \supset r]$	Variant axiom 1
(2)	$\sim p \supset [q \supset \sim p]$	Sub. in (1) for 'r'
(3)	$\sim p \supset [\sim q \supset \sim p]$	Sub. in (2) for 'q'
(4)	$\sim p$	Hypothesis
(5)	$[\sim q \supset \sim p] \supset [p \supset q]$	Variant axiom 3
(6)	$[\sim q \supset \sim p]$	*Modus ponens* (3) and (4)
(7)	$p \supset q$	*Modus ponens* (5) and (6)

Notice that in neither application of substitution was substitution made for a variable that occurs in the hypothesis '$\sim p$'.

For convenience, we write '$A_1, A_2, \ldots, A_n \vdash B$' to mean 'there is a proof of B from the hypotheses $A_1, A_2, \ldots, A_n$'. Thus '$\vdash B$' means 'there is a proof of B from no hypotheses'. Notice that a proof of B from no hypotheses is not quite the same thing as a proof of B, because the former may contain variants of axioms in lieu of the axioms themselves. We will, however, prove a lemma to the effect that there is a proof of B from no hypotheses if and only if there is a proof of B. (A *lemma* is a useful true statement about a logistic system that interests us less for itself than for what we can do with it.) First we show that there is a simple proof of any variant axiom. Let B be a variant of an axiom A of system P. Then B results from A by the *simultaneous* substitution of distinct variables a_1, a_2, a_3 for 'p', 'q', 'r', respectively. Let b_1, b_2, b_3 be distinct variables different from all of a_1, a_2, a_3, 'p', 'q', and 'r'. Then the following is a proof of B:

(1)	A	Axiom
(2)	A_1	Sub. of 'b_1' for 'p' in (1)
(3)	A_2	Sub. of 'b_2' for 'q' in (2)
(4)	A_3	Sub. of 'b_3' for 'r' in (3)
(5)	A_5	Sub. of 'a_1' for 'b_1' in (4)
(6)	A_6	Sub. of 'a_2' for 'b_2' in (5)
(7)	B	Sub. of 'a_3' for 'b_3' in (6)

Now we are in a position to prove:

L1. $\vdash B$ if and only if B is a theorem of system P.

Clearly, if B is a theorem of system P, then $\vdash B$ by the definition of proof and of proof from hypotheses. Now suppose $\vdash B$. Let $B_1, B_2, \ldots, B_k$ be a proof of B from no hypotheses. If $B_1, B_2, \ldots, B_k$ is not already a proof of B, it is because it contains variant axioms whose presence is not otherwise warranted in a proof. In the given sequence, replace each of these variant axioms B_i by a sequence $C_1, C_2, \ldots, C_m$ of wffs which is a proof of B_i. The resulting sequence is clearly a proof of B.

M2. If $A_1, A_2, \ldots, A_n \vdash B$, then $A_1, A_2, \ldots, A_{n-1} \vdash \ulcorner A_n \supset B \urcorner$ (deduction theorem).

Before proving the deduction theorem, we illustrate its value for establishing theoremhood. We showed above that '$\sim p$' $\vdash$ '$p \supset q$'.

Whence, by the deduction theorem, $\vdash$ '$\sim p \supset [p \supset q]$'. Whence, by L1, we have that '$\sim p \supset [p \supset q]$' is a theorem of system P.

We now prove the deduction theorem. Suppose that $A_1, A_2, \ldots,$ $A_n \vdash B$. Then there is a sequence $B_1, B_2, \ldots, B_k$, where $B_k = B$, which is a proof of B from the hypotheses $A_1, A_2, \ldots, A_n$. We first form the sequence $\ulcorner A_n \supset B_1 \urcorner$, $\ulcorner A_n \supset B_2 \urcorner$, $\ldots$, $\ulcorner A_n \supset B_k \urcorner$ and show how, by appropriate insertions, to convert it into a proof of $\ulcorner A_n \supset B_k \urcorner$ from the hypotheses $A_1, A_2, \ldots, A_{n-1}$. But the existence of such a sequence entails that $A_1, A_2, \ldots, A_{n-1} \vdash \ulcorner A_n \supset B \urcorner$, which is what we want to show. Different insertions are made before each $\ulcorner A_n \supset B_i \urcorner$ depending on how B_i got into the original proof from hypotheses. If B_i is an axiom or variant of an axiom or one of the hypotheses $A_1, A_2, \ldots, A_{n-1}$, let a_1 and a_2 be distinct variables that do not occur in any of the hypotheses or anywhere in the original proof from hypotheses, and insert immediately before $\ulcorner A_n \supset B_i \urcorner$ the following four-membered sequence:

(1)	$a_1 \supset [a_2 \supset a_1]$	Variant axiom
(2)	$B_i \supset [a_2 \supset B_i]$	Sub. in (1)
(3)	$B_i \supset [A_n \supset B_i]$	Sub. in (2)
(4)	B_i	Axiom, variant axiom, or hypothesis
	$\overline{ A_n \supset B_i }$	*Modus ponens* (3) and (4)

If B_i is the hypothesis A_n, then $\ulcorner A_n \supset B_i \urcorner$ is $\ulcorner A_n \supset A_n \urcorner$. So insert the following sequence immediately before $\ulcorner A_n \supset B_i \urcorner$, where a_1, a_2, a_3 are distinct variables that occur in none of the hypotheses nor anywhere in the original proof from hypotheses:

(1)	$[a_1 \supset (a_2 \supset a_3)] \supset [(a_1 \supset a_2) \supset (a_1 \supset a_3)]$	Variant axiom
(2)	$[a_1 \supset (a_2 \supset a_1)] \supset [(a_1 \supset a_2) \supset (a_1 \supset a_1)]$	Sub. in (1)
(3)	$[a_1 \supset (a_2 \supset a_1)]$	Variant axiom
(4)	$[a_1 \supset a_2] \supset [a_1 \supset a_1]$	*Modus ponens* (2) and (3)
(5)	$[a_1 \supset (a_2 \supset a_1)] \supset [a_1 \supset a_1]$	Sub. in (4)
(6)	$a_1 \supset a_1$	*Modus ponens* (5) and (3)
	$A_n \supset B_i$, i.e., $A_n \supset A_n$	Sub. in (6)

Suppose B_i results from an earlier line B_e by substitution of a wff C for a variable b. Let $\ulcorner D \supset B_i \urcorner$ be the result of substituting C for b in $\ulcorner A_n \supset B_e \urcorner$. From the restriction on substitution in proofs from hypotheses, it follows that b does not occur in A_n. Hence $\ulcorner D \supset B_i \urcorner$

is the same as $\ulcorner A_n \supset B_i \urcorner$. So there is no need to insert any wffs in front of $\ulcorner A_n \supset B_i \urcorner$, because that wff comes from the earlier wff $\ulcorner A_n \supset B_e \urcorner$ in the new sequence by substitution of C for b.

But suppose B_i results from earlier wffs $\ulcorner B_e \supset B_i \urcorner$ and B_e by *modus ponens*. Then the new sequence already contains $\ulcorner A_n \supset [B_e \supset B_i] \urcorner$ and $\ulcorner A_n \supset B_e \urcorner$. So insert immediately before $\ulcorner A_n \supset B_i \urcorner$ the following five-membered sequence, where a_1, a_2, a_3 are distinct variables chosen as above:

(1)	$[a_1 \supset (a_2 \supset a_3)] \supset [(a_1 \supset a_2) \supset (a_1 \supset a_3)]$	Variant axiom
(2)	$[A_n \supset (a_2 \supset a_3)] \supset [(A_n \supset a_2) \supset (A_n \supset a_3)]$	Sub. in (1)
(3)	$[A_n \supset (B_e \supset a_3)] \supset [(A_n \supset B_e) \supset (A_n \supset a_3)]$	Sub. in (2)
(4)	$[A_n \supset (B_e \supset B_i)] \supset [(A_n \supset B_e) \supset (A_n \supset B_i)]$	Sub. in (3)
(5)	$[A_n \supset B_e] \supset [A_n \supset B_i]$	*Modus ponens* (4) and earlier wff
	$A_n \supset B_i$	*Modus ponens* (5) and earlier wff

The relevant insertions having been made in front of each member of $\ulcorner A_n \supset B_1 \urcorner$, $\ulcorner A_n \supset B_2 \urcorner$, ..., $\ulcorner A_n \supset B_k \urcorner$, the resulting sequence becomes a proof of $\ulcorner A_n \supset B \urcorner$ from the hypotheses A_1, A_2, ..., A_{n-1}. (The reader should check carefully to see that the restriction on substitution in proofs from hypotheses is not violated). This completes our proof of the deduction theorem.

30.1. Some Key Theorem Schemata

Just as an axiom schema gathers together infinitely many axioms under one form, so also a *theorem schema* represents infinitely many theorems. By the same method used in Section 30.0 to show that there is a proof of a variant axiom, it can be readily shown that any wff which results from a theorem by simultaneous substitution is itself a theorem. (Details are left to the reader.) Therefore, not only is '$\sim p \supset [p \supset q]$' a theorem of system P as we proved above, but so is every wff of the form $\ulcorner \sim A \supset [A \supset B] \urcorner$. We call an expression such as '$\sim A \supset [A \supset B]$' a *theorem schema*. For convenient reference, we will label as 'T1', 'T2', and so on, certain theorem schemata to which we will appeal in our proof that system P is complete with respect to validity. And we let the first of these be:

T1. $\sim A \supset [A \supset B]$ (law of denial of the antecedent).

We now proceed to establish:

T2. $\sim\sim A \supset A$ (law of double negation).

Proof.   For convenience, we will write $\ulcorner \vDash A \urcorner$ for $\ulcorner A$ is a theorem of system P$\urcorner$.

(1)	$\vDash \; \sim\sim p \supset [\sim p \supset q]$	Instance of T1
(2)	$\vDash \; \sim\sim p \supset [\sim p \supset \sim\sim\sim p]$	From (1) by sub.
(3)	$\sim\sim p \vDash \; \sim p \supset \sim\sim\sim p$	From (2)
(4)	$\sim\sim p \vDash [\sim p \supset \sim\sim\sim p] \supset [\sim\sim p \supset p]$	By axiom 3
(5)	$\sim\sim p \vDash \; \sim\sim p \supset p$	From (3) and (4)
(6)	$\sim\sim p \vDash p$	From (5)
(7)	$\vDash \; \sim\sim p \supset p$	Ded. th. on (6)
(8)	$\vDash \; \sim\sim A \supset A$	From (7) by L1

T3. $A \supset \sim\sim A$ (converse law of double negation).

(1)	$\vDash \; \sim\sim\sim p \supset \sim p$	Instance of T2
(2)	$\vDash [\sim\sim\sim p \supset \sim p] \supset [p \supset \sim\sim p]$	From axiom 3
(3)	$\vDash p \supset \sim\sim p$	From (1) and (2)
(4)	$\vDash A \supset \sim\sim A$	From (3)

T4. $[A \supset B] \supset [\sim B \supset \sim A]$ (law of contraposition).

(1)	$p \supset q, \; \sim\sim p \vDash p$	From T2
(2)	$p \supset q, \; \sim\sim p \vDash q$	From (1)
(3)	$p \supset q, \; \sim\sim p \vDash \; \sim\sim q$	From (2) and T3
(4)	$p \supset q \vDash \; \sim\sim p \supset \sim\sim q$	Ded. th. on (3)
(5)	$p \supset q \vDash \; \sim q \supset \sim p$	From (4) and ax. 3
(6)	$\vDash [p \supset q] \supset [\sim q \supset \sim p]$	Ded. th. on (5)
(7)	$\vDash [A \supset B] \supset [\sim B \supset \sim A]$	From (6) by L1

When inspecting the above metalinguistic proofs that T2–T4 are theorem schemata of system P, the reader should carefully check to see that the restriction on substitution in proofs from hypotheses is nowhere violated. For example, in line (1) of the proof of T4 it is claimed that there is a proof of 'p' from the two hypotheses '$p \supset q$' and '$\sim\sim p$', and T2 is cited as justification. Let $B_1, B_2, \ldots, B_k$ be a proof of '$\sim\sim p \supset p$'; we know from T2 that such a proof exists. Let $a_1, a_2, \ldots, a_n$ be a complete list of the distinct variables in B_1, B_2, ..., B_k. Let b_1, b_2, ..., b_n be distinct variables different from any of 'q', a_1, a_2, ..., a_n. Let C_1, C_2, ..., C_k result from B_1, B_2, ..., B_k by the simultaneous substitution of b_1, b_2, ..., b_n for a_1, a_2, ..., a_n, respectively. Then the sequence C_1, C_2, ..., C_k, '$\sim\sim p \supset p$', '$\sim\sim p$', 'p' is a proof of 'p' from the two hypotheses '$p \supset q$' and '$\sim\sim p$'. The reader should verify that the sequence C_1, C_2, ..., C_k is a variant proof of $\ulcorner \sim\sim b_i \supset b_i \urcorner$, which sequence contains neither 'p' nor 'q'. Hence '$\sim\sim p \supset p$' comes from C_k by substitution of 'p' for 'b_i', '$\sim\sim p$' is one of the hypotheses, and 'p' is inferable by *modus ponens* from '$\sim\sim p \supset p$' and '$\sim\sim p$'.

30.2. Maximal Consistent Classes

A class Γ of wffs of system P will be said to be *inconsistent* if it contains finitely many members A_1, A_2, ..., A_n such that, for some wff B of system P, both A_1, A_2, ..., $A_n \vdash B$ and A_1, A_2, ..., $A_n \vdash \ulcorner \sim B \urcorner$. If not inconsistent, Γ is said to be *consistent*. A class Γ of wffs of system P is said to be *maximal* if each class that results by adding to Γ any wff of system P that is not a member of Γ is *inconsistent*.[1] The intuitive idea is this: A consistent class is maximal if and only if it contains all the wffs it can contain without lapsing into inconsistency. The principal aim of this section is to prove that every consistent class (of wffs of system P) can be extended to a maximal consistent class, but we first prove an intermediate lemma.

L2. If Γ is maximal and consistent, and A_1, A_2, ..., A_n all belong to Γ, and A_1, A_2, ..., $A_n \vdash B$, then B also belongs to Γ.

To prove L2, we begin by supposing that Γ is maximal and consistent, that A_1, A_2, ..., A_n all belong to Γ, that A_1, A_2, ..., $A_n \vdash B$, but that B does not belong to Γ. B does not belong to Γ, so it follows from the definition of a maximal class that the class that results on adding B to Γ is inconsistent. Accordingly, there is some wff D and members C_1, C_2, ..., C_k of Γ such that C_1, C_2, ..., C_k, $B \vdash D$ and C_1, C_2, ..., C_k, $B \vdash \ulcorner \sim D \urcorner$. Whence by the deduction theorem we have both A_1, A_2, ..., A_n, C_1, C_2, ..., $C_k \vdash \ulcorner B \supset D \urcorner$, and A_1, A_2, ..., A_n, C_1, C_2, ..., $C_k \vdash \ulcorner B \supset \sim D \urcorner$. But, by supposi-

---

[1] Trivially, then, any inconsistent class of wffs is maximal.

tion, A_1, A_2, ..., A_n, C_1, C_2, ..., $C_k \vdash B$. Therefore, A_1, A_2, ..., A_n, C_1, C_2, ..., $C_k \vdash D$ and A_1, A_2, ..., A_n, C_1, C_2, ..., $C_k \vdash \ulcorner \sim D \urcorner$. All these hypotheses belong to Γ, so it follows that Γ is not consistent, which contradicts our initial supposition. L2 follows from the contradictoriness of our initial assumption. (In the foregoing proof we made use of the lemma, assigned to the reader as an exercise, that if A_1, A_2, ..., $A_n \vdash B$, then A_1, A_2, ..., A_n, B_1, B_2, ..., $B_k \vdash B$ for all wffs A_1, A_2, ..., A_n, B_1, B_2, ..., B_k, B. The import of this lemma is that the addition of wffs to a set of hypotheses never diminishes what can be proved from those hypotheses.)

L3. Every consistent class can be extended to a maximal consistent class.

To say that a consistent class Γ *can be extended to a maximal consistent class* is to say that there exists a maximal consistent class $\bar{\Gamma}$ such that Γ is a subset of $\bar{\Gamma}$, that is, $\Gamma \subseteq \bar{\Gamma}$. To prove L3, we let Γ be a consistent class of wffs of system P and we consider an enumeration A_1, A_2, A_3, ... of all the wffs of system P without exception or repetition. First we define an infinite sequence Γ_0, Γ_1, Γ_2, ... of classes as follows. We let $\Gamma_0 = \Gamma$. And we let $\Gamma_{i+1} = \Gamma_i \cup \{A_{i+1}\}$, if $\Gamma_i \cup \{A_{i+1}\}$ is consistent; otherwise we let $\Gamma_{i+1} = \Gamma_i$. For example, Γ_1 is the class that results on adding A_1 to Γ_0 if that class is consistent, and otherwise $\Gamma_1 = \Gamma_0$. And, finally, we let $\bar{\Gamma}$ be the union of all the classes in the enumeration Γ_0, Γ_1, Γ_2, ... That is, we let $\bar{\Gamma}$ be the set of wffs that belong to any class in the enumeration Γ_0, Γ_1, Γ_2, ... We now show that $\bar{\Gamma}$ is a maximal consistent extension of Γ. That $\bar{\Gamma}$ is an extension of Γ, that is, that $\Gamma \subseteq \bar{\Gamma}$, is evident from the construction of $\bar{\Gamma}$, because $\Gamma_0 = \Gamma$. To prove that $\bar{\Gamma}$ is consistent, we begin by supposing that $\bar{\Gamma}$ is not consistent. By definition of class inconsistency, then, there are members B_1, B_2, ..., B_k of $\bar{\Gamma}$ and some wff B such that both B_1, B_2, ..., $B_k \vdash B$ and B_1, B_2, ..., $B_k \vdash \ulcorner \sim B \urcorner$. We claim that B_1, B_2, ..., B_k all belong to some class Γ_m. From the construction of the sequence Γ_0, Γ_1, Γ_2, ..., it is evident that if a wff belongs to any member of that sequence, that wff also belongs to all later members. Furthermore, as B_1, B_2, ..., B_k all belong to $\bar{\Gamma}$, each must belong to some member or other of Γ_0, Γ_1, Γ_2, ... It follows from these two considerations that B_1, B_2, ..., B_k all belong to some class Γ_m. The class Γ_m, therefore, is inconsistent. But notice, by the way the sequence Γ_0, Γ_1, Γ_2, ... is constructed, that Γ_{i+1} is consistent if Γ_i is consistent. Moreover, the first class Γ_0 is consistent by assumption. It follows that all the classes Γ_0, Γ_1, Γ_2, ... are consistent, which contradicts the result that Γ_m is inconsistent. By indirect proof, therefore, we conclude that $\bar{\Gamma}$ is consistent.

To prove that $\bar{\Gamma}$ is also maximal, we begin by supposing that it is not. Then there is some wff B, not a member of $\bar{\Gamma}$, which is such that its addition to $\bar{\Gamma}$ yields a consistent class; that is, $\bar{\Gamma} \cup \{B\}$ is consistent. But B is one of the wffs in the enumeration A_1, A_2, A_3, ..., say A_{j+1}. Consider how Γ_{j+1} is formed from Γ_j, which is a consistent subclass of $\bar{\Gamma}$. If the addition of A_{j+1}, that is, B, to Γ_j yields a consistent class, then $\Gamma_{j+1} = \Gamma_j \cup \{A_{j+1}\}$. But clearly $\Gamma_j \cup \{A_{j+1}\}$ is consistent, because $\bar{\Gamma} \cup \{A_{j+1}\}$ is consistent (remember $A_{j+1} = B$ and $\Gamma_j \subseteq \bar{\Gamma}$). So $\Gamma_{j+1} = \Gamma_j \cup \{B\}$, that is, B belongs to Γ_{j+1}. B belongs to Γ_{j+1}, so B also belongs to $\bar{\Gamma}$, which contradicts the supposition that B is not a member of $\bar{\Gamma}$. It follows by indirect proof that $\bar{\Gamma}$ is a maximal class.

To conclude this section, we establish one more lemma:

L4.   If A_1, A_2, ..., $A_n \vdash B$ and A_1, A_2, ..., $A_n \vdash \ulcorner {\sim} B \urcorner$, then A_1, A_2, ..., $A_{n-1} \vdash \ulcorner {\sim} A_n \urcorner$.

(1)	$A_1, A_2, \ldots, A_n \vdash B$	Assumption
(2)	$A_1, A_2, \ldots, A_n \vdash {\sim} B$	Assumption
(3)	$A_1, A_2, \ldots, A_n \vdash {\sim} B \supset [B \supset {\sim}[p \supset p]]$	From T1
(4)	$A_1, A_2, \ldots, A_n \vdash B \supset {\sim}[p \supset p]$	From (3) and (2)
(5)	$A_1, A_2, \ldots, A_n \vdash {\sim}[p \supset p]$	From (4) and (1)
(6)	$A_1, A_2, \ldots, A_{n-1} \vdash A_n \supset {\sim}[p \supset p]$	Ded. th. on (5)
(7)	$A_1, A_2, \ldots, A_{n-1} \vdash [A_n \supset {\sim}[p \supset p]] \supset$ $[{\sim}{\sim}[p \supset p] \supset {\sim}A_n]$	From T4
(8)	$A_1, A_2, \ldots, A_{n-1} \vdash {\sim}{\sim}[p \supset p] \supset {\sim}A_n$	From (7) and (6)
(9)	$A_1, A_2, \ldots, A_{n-1} \vdash [p \supset p] \supset {\sim}{\sim}[p \supset p]$	From T3
(10)	$A_1, A_2, \ldots, A_{n-1} \vdash p \supset p$	Because $\vdash p \supset p$
(11)	$A_1, A_2, \ldots, A_{n-1} \vdash {\sim}{\sim}[p \supset p]$	From (9) and (10)
(12)	$A_1, A_2, \ldots, A_{n-1} \vdash {\sim}A_n$	From (8) and (11)

30.3.   Completeness Theorem

A *class* Γ (possibly infinite) of wffs is said to be *satisfiable* if there is an interpretation Σ of Γ such that each member of Γ comes out true under Σ.[2] The completeness theorem M3

---

[2] Trivially, the empty set of wffs is satisfiable.

M3.   Every valid wff is a theorem of system P (that is, system P is complete with respect to validity).

is an easy consequence or corollary of the following lemma:

L5.   Every consistent class of wffs of system P is satisfiable.

To see that M3 is a corollary of L5, let A be any valid wff of system P. $\ulcorner \sim A \urcorner$ is contradictory, so clearly the class $\{\ulcorner \sim A \urcorner\}$ is not satisfiable. It follows from L5 that the class $\{\ulcorner \sim A \urcorner\}$ is inconsistent. By definition of inconsistency, we then have both $\ulcorner \sim A \urcorner \vdash B$ and $\ulcorner \sim A \urcorner \vdash \ulcorner \sim B \urcorner$ for some wff B. Therefore, we get $\vdash \ulcorner \sim \sim A \urcorner$ by L4. But also $\vdash \ulcorner \sim \sim A \supset A \urcorner$ by T2. So we have $\vdash A$, whence $\vDash A$. That is, the supposition that A is valid entails that A is a theorem of system P, which is the substance of M3. Thus we will have the completeness theorem once we have proved the very powerful lemma L5.

To prove L5, we let Γ be an arbitrary consistent class of wffs of system P. Let $\bar{\Gamma}$ be some maximal consistent extension of Γ; we know by L3 that such an extension exists. We will show that $\bar{\Gamma}$ exhibits five special properties (A and B are arbitrary wffs):

(a)   If $B \in \bar{\Gamma}$, then $\ulcorner \sim B \urcorner \notin \bar{\Gamma}$.
(b)   If $B \notin \bar{\Gamma}$, then $\ulcorner \sim B \urcorner \in \bar{\Gamma}$.
(c)   If $A \notin \bar{\Gamma}$, then $\ulcorner [A \supset B] \urcorner \in \bar{\Gamma}$.
(d)   If $B \in \bar{\Gamma}$, then $\ulcorner [A \supset B] \urcorner \in \bar{\Gamma}$.
(e)   If $A \in \bar{\Gamma}$ and $B \notin \bar{\Gamma}$, then $\ulcorner [A \supset B] \urcorner \notin \bar{\Gamma}$.

That $\bar{\Gamma}$ exhibits property (a) is obvious from the definition of a maximal consistent class. To prove (b), suppose that $B \notin \bar{\Gamma}$. By the definition of a maximal consistent class, it follows that $\Gamma \cup \{B\}$ is inconsistent, that is, that $A_1, A_2, \ldots, A_n, B \vdash C$ and $A_1, A_2, \ldots, A_n, B \vdash \ulcorner \sim C \urcorner$, where $A_1, A_2, \ldots, A_n$ are members of $\bar{\Gamma}$. So $A_1, A_2, \ldots, A_n \vdash \ulcorner \sim B \urcorner$ by L4. So $\ulcorner \sim B \urcorner \in \bar{\Gamma}$ by L2. To prove (c), suppose $A \notin \bar{\Gamma}$. From (b) we have that $\ulcorner \sim A \urcorner \in \bar{\Gamma}$. From T1, we have $\ulcorner \sim A \urcorner \vdash \ulcorner \sim A \supset [A \supset B] \urcorner$. Whence $\ulcorner \sim A \urcorner \vdash \ulcorner A \supset B \urcorner$. Whence $\ulcorner [A \supset B] \urcorner \in \bar{\Gamma}$ by L2. To prove (d), suppose $B \in \bar{\Gamma}$. From axiom 1, we have $B \vdash \ulcorner B \supset [A \supset B] \urcorner$, whence $B \vdash \ulcorner [A \supset B] \urcorner$. By L2, then, we have $\ulcorner [A \supset B] \urcorner \in \bar{\Gamma}$. Finally, to prove (e), suppose that $A \in \bar{\Gamma}$, that $B \notin \bar{\Gamma}$, but that $\ulcorner [A \supset B] \urcorner \in \bar{\Gamma}$. We will show that this supposition leads to contradiction, from which (e) follows by indirect proof. $A \in \bar{\Gamma}$ and $\ulcorner [A \supset B] \urcorner \in \bar{\Gamma}$ and $A, \ulcorner A \supset B \urcorner \vdash B$, so it follows from L2 that $B \in \bar{\Gamma}$, which contradicts our supposition that $B \notin \bar{\Gamma}$.

Appealing to the five special properties of $\bar{\Gamma}$, we will now show that $\bar{\Gamma}$ is satisfiable. Let Σ be the following interpretation of all the wffs of system P. If a sentential variable is a member of $\bar{\Gamma}$, Σ assigns truth to it; otherwise, Σ assigns it falsehood. Where D is an arbitrary wff of system P, we claim that Σ gives D the value truth or falsehood according as $D \in \bar{\Gamma}$ or $D \notin \bar{\Gamma}$. We substantiate this claim by strong mathematical induction on the number of occurrences of connectives in D. If D contains zero occurrences of connectives, D is a sentential variable. In this case it is obvious that D comes out true or false under Σ according as D is or is not a member of $\bar{\Gamma}$. As hypothesis of induction, we assume that any wff with n or fewer occurrences of connectives comes out true or false under Σ according as it belongs or does not belong to $\bar{\Gamma}$. Let D be an arbitrary wff with $n + 1$ occurrences of connectives. Now D will have either the form $\ulcorner{\sim}D_1\urcorner$ or $\ulcorner D_1 \supset D_2\urcorner$. Suppose D is $\ulcorner{\sim}D_1\urcorner$. Then, because it has n occurrences of connectives, D_1 falls under the hypothesis of induction. If Σ makes D false, then Σ makes D_1 true. Whence $D_1 \in \bar{\Gamma}$ by the hypothesis of induction. By property (a), then, $\ulcorner{\sim}D_1\urcorner \notin \bar{\Gamma}$. So if D comes out false under Σ, it does not belong to $\bar{\Gamma}$. But if Σ makes D true, then it makes D_1 false. Whence $D_1 \notin \bar{\Gamma}$. Whence, by property (b), $\ulcorner{\sim}D_1\urcorner \in \bar{\Gamma}$. So if D comes out true under Σ, it belongs to $\bar{\Gamma}$. Thus, in the event that D is $\ulcorner{\sim}D_1\urcorner$, we see that D comes out true or false under Σ according as it does or does not belong to $\bar{\Gamma}$. But suppose D has the form $\ulcorner D_1 \supset D_2\urcorner$. Clearly, both D_1 and D_2 fall under the hypothesis of induction. If D comes out false under Σ, then obviously D_1 and D_2 come out true and false, respectively, under Σ. So, by the hypothesis of induction, $D_1 \in \bar{\Gamma}$ and $D_2 \notin \bar{\Gamma}$. By property (e), therefore, $D \notin \bar{\Gamma}$. So if D comes out false under Σ, then $D \notin \bar{\Gamma}$. If D comes out true under Σ, there are two subcases to consider. It may be that D comes out true under Σ because D_1 comes out false under Σ. In this event, we have $D_1 \notin \bar{\Gamma}$ by the hypothesis of induction. So $\ulcorner[D_1 \supset D_2]\urcorner \in \bar{\Gamma}$ by property (c); that is, $D \in \bar{\Gamma}$. Or it may be that D comes out true under Σ because D_2 comes out true under Σ. Then $D_2 \in \bar{\Gamma}$ by the hypothesis of induction. So $\ulcorner[D_1 \supset D_2]\urcorner \in \bar{\Gamma}$ by property (d); that is, $D \in \bar{\Gamma}$. Thus we see that, in either subcase, if D comes out true under Σ, then $D \in \bar{\Gamma}$. We have established, therefore, that where D is $\ulcorner D_1 \supset D_2\urcorner$, D comes out true or false under Σ according as $D \in \bar{\Gamma}$ or $D \notin \bar{\Gamma}$. By mathematical induction we conclude that an arbitrary wff of system P comes out true or false under Σ according as it does or does not belong to $\bar{\Gamma}$. It follows that Σ gives the value truth to every member of $\bar{\Gamma}$. And, as Γ is a subclass of $\bar{\Gamma}$, clearly Σ gives the value truth to every member of Γ. By definition of a satisfiable class, therefore, Γ is satisfiable. We assumed about Γ only that it was consistent, so we conclude that L5 is true.

30.4.   Compactness Theorem and Concluding Remarks

To illustrate the power of L5, we derive from it as a corollary another important metatheorem, the compactness theorem.

> M4.   A set of wffs of system P is satisfiable if and only if every finite subset thereof is satisfiable (compactness theorem).

Let Γ be an arbitrary set of wffs of system P. Clearly, if Γ is satisfiable, so are all its finite subsets. The challenge is to show that Γ is satisfiable if all its finite subsets are satisfiable. So, suppose that all its finite subsets are satisfiable but that Γ is not satisfiable. By L5, therefore, Γ is inconsistent. So there are members A_1, A_2, ..., A_n of Γ such that $A_1, A_2, \ldots, A_n \vdash B$ and $A_1, A_2, \ldots, A_n \vdash \ulcorner \sim B \urcorner$ for some wff B. Now $\{A_1, A_2, \ldots, A_n\}$ is a finite subset of Γ, and we shall show that $\{A_1, A_2, \ldots, A_n\}$ is not satisfiable. Clearly, by n applications of the deduction theorem and M1, we have that $\ulcorner A_1 \supset [A_2 \supset [A_3 \supset \ldots [A_n \supset B] \ldots]] \urcorner$ is valid. And since this wff is equivalent to $\ulcorner A_1 \cdot A_2 \cdot \ldots \cdot A_n \supset B \urcorner$, it follows that A_1, A_2, ..., A_n jointly imply B. Similar reasoning shows that

$$\ulcorner A_1 \cdot A_2 \cdot \ldots \cdot A_n \supset \sim B \urcorner$$

is also valid; hence A_1, A_2, ..., A_n jointly imply $\ulcorner \sim B \urcorner$. From the definition of implication and the semantics of the dot, it follows that $\ulcorner A_1 \cdot A_2 \cdot \ldots \cdot A_n \urcorner$ implies $\ulcorner B \cdot \sim B \urcorner$. Only a contradiction implies a contradiction, so $\ulcorner A_1 \cdot A_2 \cdot \ldots \cdot A_n \urcorner$ is a contradiction. Thus $\{A_1, A_2, \ldots, A_n\}$ is not satisfiable. This terminates the proof of the compactness theorem as a corollary of L5.

At the beginning of Section 26.0 we declared that system P specifies or isolates the valid wffs of LSP. The binary connectives of LSP do not belong to system P and vice versa, so our declaration needs amplification. The specification or isolation we have in mind is a vicarious specification through representation. The sense of representation is given by the following inductive definition:

(i)   A sentential variable of LSP is represented by that same variable in system P.

(ii) If a wff A of LSP is represented by a wff B of system P, then the wff $\ulcorner\sim A\urcorner$ of LSP is represented by the wff $\ulcorner\sim B\urcorner$ of system P.

(iii) If wffs A and B of LSP are, respectively, represented by wffs C and D of system P, then the wff $\ulcorner[A \vee B]\urcorner$ of LSP is represented by the wff $\ulcorner[\sim C \supset D]\urcorner$ of system P, and the wff $\ulcorner[A \cdot B]\urcorner$ of LSP is represented by the wff $\ulcorner\sim[C \supset \sim D]\urcorner$ of system P.

The reader should verify that each wff of LSP has a unique representative in system P, although some wffs of system P represent several wffs of LSP while other wffs of system P do not represent any wffs of LSP. It is also left to the reader to establish that a wff of LSP is equivalent to its representative in system P. As there is an effective procedure or algorithm for finding the representative in system P of a given wff of LSP, it is evident that the foregoing results about representation give substance to our claim that system P specifies the valid wffs of LSP vicariously.

The reader who looks for profundity or self-evidence or the like in the axioms and rules of inference of logistic systems will be somewhat disappointed. An axiom is only a wff labeled 'axiom' by the designer of the logistic system. Similarly, a rule of inference is merely a rule that authorizes one to set down certain wffs provided certain other wffs have already been set down, which has been labeled 'rule of inference' by the system's designer. Of course, the formal axiomatic method is sometimes used to formalize a developed part of mathematics. When the formal axiomatic method is so applied, the wffs selected as axioms usually are (under the intended interpretation) fundamental truths of the area of mathematics that is being formalized, and the rules of inference usually have the character of valid deductive principles of reasoning. But what is thus true of the axioms and rules of some logistic systems obviously does not apply to all logistic systems, as the reader may demonstrate by designing as curious or as fatuous systems as he may desire. What has been said of axioms and rules of inference holds also for hypotheses. Relative to a proof from hypotheses, no significance should be attached to a wff being an hypothesis beyond the bare fact that someone has so designated it.

The so-called *decision problem for* a logistic system L is the problem of finding an effective method or algorithm for recognizing theoremhood in L, if indeed such an effective method exists. In virtue of the consistency and completeness of system P with respect to validity, truth tables constitute a solution to the decision problem for system P. Indeed, the possession of a decision procedure may seem to make axiomatization superfluous. That historically axiomatization of a property (that is, creation of a logistic system whose theorems are all and only the wffs having the given property) has almost always preceded the solution of the decision problem for that property is no justification for axiomatization once the solution has been found. If the sole purpose of axiomatization were the isolation or specification of a class of wffs, that purpose would be as well or better served by a decision procedure (if one exists). But the axiomatic method is also used to *systematize* the wffs of a system, that is, to organize them economically and to interrelate them in various interesting ways. By suppressing certain axioms or rules, the logician can study the force of that axiom or rule. By varying his axioms and rules, the logician can unpack, so to speak, the full meaning of the concepts being formalized and discover which results depend on which aspects of their meaning. It is also true that certain properties of importance in logic and mathematics admit of axiomatization but not of decision procedures. For these properties, axiomatization offers the only method of specification. There are, however, properties that do not even fully admit of axiomatization; notable among these is the property of being an arithmetical truth. With respect to such properties, one must rest content with only partial formalization.

31. EXERCISES

(1) Explain why the detour through the variables b_1, b_2, b_3 was necessary in the proof in Section 30.0 that there is a proof of any variant axiom in system P.

(2) Referring to the annotated proof of '$p \supset q$' from the hypothesis '$\sim p$' to be found in Section 30.0, convert the following sequence into a proof of '$\sim p \supset [p \supset q]$' from no hypotheses by making the insertions prescribed in the proof of the deduction theorem:

$\sim p \supset [r \supset (q \supset r)]$
$\sim p \supset [\sim p \supset (q \supset \sim p)]$
$\sim p \supset [\sim p \supset (\sim q \supset \sim p)]$
$\sim p \supset \sim p$
$\sim p \supset [(\sim q \supset \sim p) \supset (p \supset q)]$
$\sim p \supset [\sim q \supset \sim p]$
$\sim p \supset [p \supset q]$

(3) By inserting before each variant axiom a proof thereof, convert the proof from no hypotheses constructed in Exercise (2) into a proof of '$\sim p \supset [p \supset q]$'.

(4) Prove that what can be proved from a set of hypotheses is not diminished by adding new hypotheses to the set. That is, prove that if A_1, A_2, ..., $A_n \vdash B$, then A_1, A_2, ..., A_n, B_1, B_2, ..., $B_k \vdash B$ for all wffs A_1, A_2, ..., A_n, B, B_1, B_2, ..., B_k.

[5] Prove that the wffs of system P can be enumerated without repetition (despite the fact that system P boasts an infinite vocabulary). That is, prove that they can be drawn up in a list (1), (2), (3), ... that omits none of them. (*Hint:* First prove that all the finite tuples of positive integers can be enumerated. Then, from an enumeration of the finite tuples of positive integers, determine an enumeration of the formulas of system P by "identifying" each symbol of system P with a distinct positive integer. Then, from this enumeration of formulas simply drop those that are not wffs.)

[6]   Prove that the proofs in system P can be enumerated. (*Hint:* Take your cue from Exercise [5].)

[7]   Prove that every satisfiable class of wffs of system P is consistent.

[8]   With reference to the five special properties of a maximal consistent class mentioned in Section 30.3, explain what it might mean to say that a maximal consistent class of wffs displays the characteristics of truth itself.

[9]   Find proofs in system P of the following wffs:

$$[p \supset q] \supset [[q \supset r] \supset [p \supset r]]$$
$$[p \supset [p \supset q]] \supset [p \supset q]$$

(10)   To illustrate the value of the deduction theorem for establishing theoremhood, use it to prove that the two wffs exhibited in Exercise [9] are theorems of system P.

⟨11⟩   Prove that neither system P_1 nor system P_2 of Section 28.1 is absolutely complete. (See Exercise ⟨10⟩ in Chapter 29.)

(12)   Is there such a thing as an expression provable in no logistic system?

(13)   By the *computation problem of* a logistic system is meant the problem of finding an effective method or algorithm for generating a proof of a wff given only that it is a theorem of the system. Solve the computation problem for system P. (*Hint:* Make use of the enumeration solicited by Exercise [6].)

(14)   Prove that the deduction theorem would not hold if the restriction on substitution were omitted in the definition of proof from hypotheses. (*Hint:* Show that any wff could be proved from the hypothesis 'p' if the restriction were dropped.)

(15)   Prove that if $A_1, A_2, \ldots, A_n \vdash B$, then $A_1, A_2, \ldots, A_n$ jointly imply B.

(16)   Exhibit two distinct wffs of LSP that have the same representative in system P. Exhibit a wff of system P that represents no wff of LSP.

(17)   Prove that *being a variant of* is an equivalence relation among the wffs of system P.

(18)   Let B be a wff of system P and let Δ be a set of wffs of system P. Let '$\Delta \to B$' mean 'B is a consequence of Δ', and let '$\Delta \vdash B$' mean 'there is a proof of B from a finite number of

members of Δ as hypotheses. Derive the so-called *strong completeness theorem*, namely $\Delta \rightarrow B$ if and only if $\Delta \vdash B$, as a corollary of L5. (*Hint:* Show that the class $\Delta \cup \{\ulcorner \sim B \urcorner\}$ is inconsistent if $\Delta \rightarrow B$.)

(19)   Derive, as a corollary of the compactness theorem, that if $\Delta \rightarrow B$, then B is a consequence of some finite subset of Δ.

(20)   Derive the compactness theorem as a corollary of the statement that, if $\Delta \rightarrow B$, then B is a consequence of some finite subset of Δ.

⟨21⟩   Show that, for any natural number k, there is a consistent class of wffs of system P of which there are exactly 2^k maximal consistent extensions. How many maximal consistent extensions are there of the class $\{'p'\}$? (*Hint:* Show that the membership of a maximal consistent class is completely determined by which sentential variables belong to it.)

PART THREE

Sentential Modal Logic

32. TRUTH TABLES AND MODAL LOGIC

32.0. Motivation

The concepts of necessity and possibility often figure prominently in expositions of symbolic logic. For example, one often finds an analytic truth explained as a sentence true in all possible worlds or as a necessary truth. Similarly, a correct argument is commonly explained as an argument whose conclusion necessarily is true if its premises are all true, that is, as an argument such that it is not possible that its premises all be true but its conclusion false. In our own exposition we have occasionally used these two concepts, relying on the reader's informal and presystematic grasp of their meaning. In the present part of this book we shall clarify and systematize the logic of these two concepts by applying the methods of symbolic logic to their study. There are several reasons for undertaking such an investigation. First, the material is inherently interesting. Second, for those who prefer to explain analyticity and correctness in terms of necessity and possibility an investigation of the latter pair of concepts may shed additional light on the former pair. Third, as modal logic (the logic of the concepts of necessity and possibility) is currently the subject of considerable philosophical reflection, some acquaintance with it is practically indispensable for understanding current trends in analytical philosophy. And finally, the investigation will make manifest the scope and fertility of truth-tabular procedures the potentialities of which are far from exhausted by truth-functional logic.

32.1. Actual and Possible Truth-Value Outcomes

In Section 2.0 an n-ary truth-functional connective was explained as an n-ary connective such that, whenever it joins together n sentences to form a compound, the truth value of the resulting compound sentence depends solely on the truth values of its n components. By the truth value of a sentence was meant, of course, its *actual truth value* or, as we shall now say, its *actual truth-value*

163

outcome. We will say that a sequence of truth values $\langle \alpha_1, \alpha_2, \ldots, \alpha_n \rangle$ is a *possible truth-value outcome of* an n-tuple $\langle A_1, A_2, \ldots, A_n \rangle$ of sentences if it is possible that $A_1, A_2, \ldots, A_n$ have, respectively, the truth values $\alpha_1, \alpha_2, \ldots, \alpha_n$, that is, if the world could have been so constituted that $A_1, A_2, \ldots, A_n$ would, respectively, have had the truth values $\alpha_1, \alpha_2, \ldots, \alpha_n$. For example, both $\langle t,t \rangle$ and $\langle t,f \rangle$ are possible truth-value outcomes of the sentence pair $\langle$'4 = 4', 'Washington is the capital of the United States'$\rangle$, whereas $\langle f,t \rangle$ and $\langle f,f \rangle$ are not, because falsehood is not a possible truth-value outcome of the sentence '4 = 4'. The actual truth-value outcome of the aforementioned pair is $\langle t,t \rangle$, because it is true that 4 = 4 and that Washington is the capital of the United States. As far as the truth value of a truth-functional compound of the sentences $A_1, A_2, \ldots, A_n$ goes, only the actual truth-value outcome of $\langle A_1, A_2, \ldots, A_n \rangle$ is relevant; its possible truth-value outcomes are quite immaterial.

But consider the singulary sentence connective 'it is necessarily true that' or, for short, 'necessarily'. Attaching it to the true sentence '4 = 4' yields the true sentence 'Necessarily 4 = 4', whereas affixing it to the true sentence 'Washington is the capital of the United States' produces the false sentence 'Necessarily Washington is the capital of the United States'. The foregoing is enough to show that the value of such a compound depends on more than the actual truth-value outcome of its component, that is, that 'necessarily' is not a truth-functional sentence connective. But on what more does it depend? Clearly the truth value of a sentence of the form ⌜Necessarily A⌝ depends also on the possible truth-value outcomes of A. The sentence ⌜Necessarily A⌝ is true if truth is the only possible truth-value outcome of A, and is false otherwise. Thus 'Necessarily 4 = 4' is true, because truth is the only possible truth-value outcome of '4 = 4'. But 'Necessarily Washington is the capital of the United States' is false, because the sentence 'Washington is the capital of the United States' has both truth and falsehood as possible truth-value outcomes.

32.2.   Language Schema M

We now enlarge LSP by adding to its vocabulary the singulary sentence connective '□', called the *box*. As the box will answer to the English connective 'necessarily', we will read expressions of the form ⌜□*A*⌝ as ⌜Necessarily *A*⌝. To accommodate this new symbol, we supplement the second formation rule of LSP with the following clause: *If A is a wff, so is* ⌜□*A*⌝. We call the resulting skeletal system "language schema M", or "LSM."

Of course, we have not yet made the meaning of '□' precise. The remark that the box corresponds to the English connective 'necessarily' is inadequate to ensure that the sentences of an M-language, that is, the wffs of a suitably interpreted edition of LSM, satisfy the truth-value assumption discussed in Section 20.4. Furthermore, because '□' is not meant to be a truth-functional connective, a fundamental truth table cannot be used to make definite its meaning. However, as we shall now see, we can formulate its meaning with requisite precision by employing several truth tables simultaneously.

32.3. Full and Partial Truth Tables

Suppose that *A* and *B* are a pair of sentences whose possible truth-value outcomes are ⟨t,t⟩, ⟨f,t⟩, and ⟨f,f⟩. We express this circumstance by the following *partial truth table:*

A	*B*	
t	t	
f	t	
f	f	

The significance of the missing row ⟨t,f⟩ *is that* ⟨t,f⟩ *is not a possible truth-value outcome of the sentence pair* ⟨A,B⟩. When *A* and *B* are so related, what is the truth value of, say, ⌜□[*A* ⊃ *B*]⌝? Truth-functional logic alone enables us to fill in the above table to this point.

A	*B*	□[*A* ⊃ *B*]
t	t	t
f	t	t
f	f	t

The above table signifies that, whichever of the three possible truth-value outcomes of $\langle A,B \rangle$ be actual, the resulting truth-value outcome of $\ulcorner A \supset B \urcorner$ is truth. Or, in other words, when A and B are a pair of sentences whose possible truth-value outcomes are $\langle t,t \rangle$, $\langle f,t \rangle$, and $\langle f,f \rangle$, the only possible truth-value outcome of $\ulcorner A \supset B \urcorner$ is truth. Accordingly, the value of $\ulcorner \Box [A \supset B] \urcorner$ should be truth regardless which of the possible truth-value outcomes of $\langle A,B \rangle$ be actual. So we complete the above table thus:

A	B	$\Box(A \supset B)$	
t	t	t	f̸
f	t	t	f̸
f	f	t	f̸

The second row of the above table, for example, signifies that if the actual truth values of A and B are falsehood and truth, respectively, and if the possible truth-value outcomes of $\langle A,B \rangle$ are $\langle t,t \rangle$, $\langle f,t \rangle$, and $\langle f,f \rangle$, then the actual truth value of $\ulcorner \Box [A \supset B] \urcorner$ is truth.

But suppose that $\langle t,t \rangle$, $\langle t,f \rangle$, $\langle f,t \rangle$, and $\langle f,f \rangle$ are all possible truth-value outcomes of $\langle A,B \rangle$. Then reasoning analogous to that above leads to the following *full truth table* (full in the sense that no rows are missing):

A	B	$\Box[A \supset B]$	
t	t	f	t̸
t	f	f	f̸
f	t	f	t̸
f	f	f	t̸

For, as falsehood is a possible truth-value outcome of $\ulcorner A \supset B \urcorner$ when A and B are sentences of the kind indicated by the above table (namely, so related that $\langle t,t \rangle$, $\langle t,f \rangle$, $\langle f,t \rangle$, and $\langle f,f \rangle$ are possible truth-value outcomes), the sentence $\ulcorner \Box(A \supset B) \urcorner$ should be false, irrespective of the actual truth values of A and B.

But suppose that A and B are so related that just $\langle t,t \rangle$ and $\langle t,f \rangle$ are the possible truth-value outcomes of $\langle A,B \rangle$. Thereupon, to determine the truth value of $\ulcorner B \supset \Box(A \supset B)\urcorner$, one proceeds as above to get

A	B	$B \supset \Box(A \supset B)$		
t	t	t	f	t̸
t	f	f	f	f̸

and finally

A	B	$B \supset \Box(A \supset B)$			
t	t	t̸	f	f̸	t̸
t	f	f̸	t	f̸	f̸

This last table signifies that *if A and B* are so related that $\langle t,t\rangle$ and $\langle t,f\rangle$ are all and only the possible truth-value outcomes of $\langle A,B\rangle$, *then* the actual truth value of $\ulcorner B \supset \Box(A \supset B)\urcorner$ is falsehood if the actual truth values of A and B are both truth (first row) and is truth if the actual truth values of A and B are, respectively, truth and falsehood (second row).

As far as its possible truth-value outcomes go, a sentence A must fall into one of three types: sentences with truth as their only possible truth-value outcome, or with falsehood as the only one, or with both truth and falsehood as possible truth-value outcomes. These three alternatives are represented by the following set of truth tables:

A	
t	

A	
f	

A	
t	
f	

Accordingly, the semantics of the box is fully stipulated by the following *fundamental set of truth tables:*

A	$\Box A$
t	t

A	$\Box A$
f	f

A	$\Box A$
t	f
f	f

The import of the fundamental set of truth tables for the box is this. If in a (partial or full) truth table T there are occurrences only of 't' beneath A, then the value of $\ulcorner \Box A \urcorner$ is truth on every row of T (as stipulated by the first table above). If, however, there are occurrences only of 'f' beneath A in T, then the value of $\ulcorner \Box A \urcorner$ is falsehood on every row of T (as stipulated by the second table). And, finally, if there are occurrences of both 't' and 'f' beneath A in T, then the value of $\ulcorner \Box A \urcorner$ is falsehood on every row of T (as stipulated by the third table). Referring to the tables constructed for $\ulcorner \Box [A \supset B] \urcorner$ and $\ulcorner B \supset \Box [A \supset B] \urcorner$ above, the reader should verify that they were properly constructed in accordance with the semantics of the box as encapsuled in its fundamental set of truth tables. Here are some additional examples:

A	B	$\Box[A \supset B]$
t	f	f f̸

A	B	$\sim\Box[A \equiv B]$
t	f	t f̸ f̸
f	t	t f̸ f̸

A	B	$\Box(A \supset B)\cdot\sim\Box B \supset \sim\Box A$
t	t	f̸ f̸ f̸ f̸ f̸ t f̸ f̸
f	f	f̸ f̸ f̸ f̸ f̸ t f̸ f̸
f	t	f̸ f̸ f̸ f̸ f̸ t f̸ f̸

A	B	$\Box[\Box A \supset \Box(B \supset A)]$
t	f	t f̸ f̸ f̸
t	t	t f̸ f̸ f̸

A	$\sim\Box\sim\Box A \supset A$
t	f t f̸
f	f t f

A	$\sim\Box\sim A \supset A$
t	f̸ t f̸
f	f̸ f f

Thus we see from the sixth table, for example, that if A has both truth and falsehood as possible truth-value outcomes, then the actual truth value of $\ulcorner \sim \square \sim A \supset A \urcorner$ is truth if A is true, and is falsehood if A is false.

Close inspection of the fundamental set of truth tables for the box reveals that its semantic import can be conveniently summarized in the following simple rule: If in a truth table T only 't' occurs beneath A, then the value of $\ulcorner \square A \urcorner$ is truth on every row of T; otherwise, the value of $\ulcorner \square A \urcorner$ is falsehood on every row of T.

32.4. Fundamental Truth Tables Revisited

With respect to filling in a (partial or full) truth table T for a wff of LSM, the third of the fundamental truth tables for the box,

A	$\square A$
t	f
f	f

is relevant to the determination of the truth value of a wff $\ulcorner \square A \urcorner$ on row r of T if and only if both 't' and 'f' occur beneath A in the table. If both 't' and 'f' so occur, and if the value of A on row r is truth, then the table instructs us to enter 'f' as the value of $\ulcorner \square A \urcorner$ on row r. Suppose, however, that only 't' occurs beneath A in T. Then the instructions implicit in the aforementioned table are irrelevant. We look rather to the first of the fundamental tables for the box,

A	$\square A$
t	t

which instructs us to enter 't' as the value of $\ulcorner \square A \urcorner$ on row r of table T.

Unlike the table

A	$\square A$
t	f
f	f

the fundamental table for the tilde

A	$\sim A$
t	f
f	t

was *not* meant to apply *only* to situations where both 't' and 'f' occur beneath A. Had it been so intended, the instructions implicit in it would be irrelevant to filling in the table

p	$\sim(p \supset p)$	
t	f	∤
f	f	∤

because only 't' occurs beneath the component modified by the tilde. Rather, the intended significance of the fundamental truth table for the tilde was this: In any truth table whatsoever, if the value of A is truth (falsehood) on a given row, then the value of $\ulcorner \sim A \urcorner$ is falsehood (truth) on that same row.

Now it is clearly undesirable to attach disparate significance to the truth tables used to express the semantics of the connectives of LSM, as with

A	$\square A$
t	f
f	f

and

A	$\sim A$
t	f
f	t

Accordingly, we supplant the single fundamental truth tables for the various truth-functional connectives by appropriate fundamental *sets* of truth tables. For example, the fundamental table for the tilde exhibited above gives way to the following *fundamental set of truth tables for the tilde.*

A	$\sim A$
t	f

A	$\sim A$
f	t

A	$\sim A$
t	f
f	t

Of these three tables it is the first that instructs us how to fill in

p	$\sim(p \supset p)$
t	t
f	t

so as to get

p	$\sim(p \supset p)$
t	f ~~t~~
f	f ~~t~~

Neither the first nor the second but rather the third table instructs us how to fill in

q	$\sim\sim q$
t	t
f	f

to obtain

q	$\sim\sim q$
t	f ~~t~~
f	t ~~f~~

and

q	$\sim\sim q$
t	t ~~f~~ ~~t~~
f	f ~~t~~ ~~f~~

Similarly, the single fundamental truth table for the wedge

gives way to the following *fundamental set of truth tables for the wedge:*

A B	A ∨ B
t t	t

A B	A ∨ B
t f	t

A B	A ∨ B
f t	t

A B	A ∨ B
f f	f

A B	A ∨ B
t t	t
t f	t

A B	A ∨ B
t t	t
f t	t

A B	A ∨ B
t t	t
f f	f

A B	A ∨ B
t f	t
f t	t

A B	A ∨ B
t f	t
f f	f

A B	A ∨ B
f t	t
f f	f

A B	A ∨ B
t t	t
t f	t
f t	t

A B	A ∨ B
t t	t
t f	t
f f	f

A B	A ∨ B
t t	t
f t	t
f f	f

A B	A ∨ B
t f	t
f t	t
f f	f

A B	A ∨ B
t t	t
t f	t
f t	t
f f	f

Of the fifteen tables here displayed only the eleventh is relevant to filling in

p	q	p ∨ (p ∨ ∼q)
t	f	t t t
t	t	t t f
f	f	f f t

to obtain

p	q	$p \vee (p \vee \sim q)$
t	f	t t̸ t t̸
t	t	t t̸ t f̸
f	f	f f̸ t t̸

Thereupon, the sixth table instructs us how to fill in this latter table so as to get

p	q	$p \vee (p \vee \sim q)$
t	f	t̸ t t̸
t	t	t̸ t t̸
f	f	f̸ t t̸

That is, the sixth table is relevant to the valuation in a table T of a wff $\ulcorner A \vee B \urcorner$ when and only when both $\langle t,t \rangle$ and $\langle f,t \rangle$ accrue to $\langle A,B \rangle$ on rows of T and no other pairs of truth values accrue to $\langle A,B \rangle$ on rows of T. Analogously for the other fourteen tables.

It is left to the reader to exhibit the *fundamental set of truth tables for the dot.*

33. EXERCISES

(1) Mention a pair of English sentences whose possible truth-value outcomes are $\langle t,t \rangle$, $\langle t,f \rangle$, and $\langle f,f \rangle$. Mention a triple of English sentences whose only possible truth-value outcome is $\langle f,f,t \rangle$.

(2) What is the largest number of possible truth-value outcomes that an n-tuple $\langle A_1, A_2, \ldots, A_n \rangle$ of sentences could have?

Explain why an *n*-tuple of sentences must have at least one possible truth-value outcome.

(3)   Exhibit the fundamental sets of truth tables for the horseshoe and triple bar.

(4)   Explain why there are exactly three tables in the fundamental set of truth tables for the box and why there are exactly fifteen tables in the fundamental set of truth tables for the wedge. The fundamental set of truth tables for a ternary connective would contain how many tables?

(5)   As in the case of truth tables in truth-functional logic, the order of the rows and of the value assignment columns of the truth tables developed for LSM is semantically irrelevant. Discuss the sense in which their order is semantically irrelevant.

(6)   By applying the relevant fundamental sets of truth tables, fill in the following:

q	p	r	$\Box[p \equiv r] \cdot \Box[r \supset q] \supset \Box[p \supset q]$
t	t	f	
f	t	f	
t	t	t	

p	q	$\Box[\Box(p \cdot q) \supset \Box p \cdot \Box q]$
t	f	
t	t	

p	q	$\Box[\Box(p \lor q) \supset \Box p \lor \Box q]$
t	f	
f	t	

p	$p \supset \Box \sim \Box \sim p$
t	
f	

p	$p \supset \Box \sim \Box \sim p$
t	

34. VALIDITY IN LSM

34.0. Value Assignments; Plenary Sets of Truth Tables

Recall that in truth-functional logic a value assignment to the variables of a wff consisted simply in assigning a truth value to each variable. For example, the assignment of falsehood to 'p' and truth to 'q' constitutes a value assignment to the variables of '$p \supset q$' under which that wff comes out true, that is, has the value truth. More is required, however, before the semantics of the box determines a truth value for '$\Box[p \supset q]$'. The assignment of $\langle f,t \rangle$ to $\langle 'p','q' \rangle$ suffices to give '$p \supset q$' the value truth because only actual truth-value outcomes are relevant to the semantics of truth-functional connectives. But such an assignment is not enough to confer a truth value on '$\Box[p \supset q]$' because possible truth-value outcomes are also relevant to the semantics of the box. With respect to LSM, therefore, a value assignment to the distinct variables of a wff consists not only in the assignment of an actual truth-value outcome to those variables (as in truth-functional logic) but also in the assignment of their possible truth-value outcomes. For example, besides assigning $\langle f,t \rangle$ as the actual truth-value outcome of $\langle 'p','q' \rangle$, we might also stipulate that $\langle f,t \rangle$, $\langle t,t \rangle$, and $\langle t,f \rangle$ are all the possible truth-value outcomes of $\langle 'p','q' \rangle$. This two-part assignment constitutes the value assignment to the variables of '$\Box[p \supset q]$', which is incorporated into the table below.

p	q	$\Box[p \supset q]$	
f	t	f	t̸
t	t	f	t̸
t	f	f	f̸

The first row of the above table shows that '$\Box[p \supset q]$' comes out false under the aforementioned value assignment. There are, in fact, three distinct value assignments to the variables of '$\Box[p \supset q]$'

compressed into the above table, each corresponding to a distinct row thereof. For example, the second row shows that, if the possible truth-value outcomes of $\langle 'p','q' \rangle$ are $\langle f,t \rangle$, $\langle t,t \rangle$, and $\langle t,f \rangle$ and if $\langle t,t \rangle$ is the actual truth-value outcome of $\langle 'p','q' \rangle$, the value of '$\Box[p \supset q]$' is falsehood. It happens that '$\Box[p \supset q]$' has the same value under the three value assignments incorporated into the above table. The wff '$p \supset \Box q$', however, comes out differently under the two value assignments to its variables incorporated into the table below.

p	q	$p \supset \Box q$
t	t	f
f	f	t

Notice that the first table exhibited in this section incorporates every value assignment to the variables of '$\Box[p \supset q]$' wherein the possible truth-value outcomes of $\langle 'p','q' \rangle$ are $\langle f,t \rangle$, $\langle t,t \rangle$, and $\langle t,f \rangle$. There are exactly three such value assignments; each is obtained by designating one of the three possible truth-value outcomes of $\langle 'p','q' \rangle$ as the actual truth-value outcome of $\langle 'p','q' \rangle$. Similarly, the second table exhibited above incorporates every value assignment to the variables of '$p \supset \Box q$' wherein the possible truth-value outcomes of $\langle 'p','q' \rangle$ are $\langle t,t \rangle$ and $\langle f,f \rangle$. More generally, any truth table, whether partial or full, incorporates every value assignment to the variables of the table wherein the possible truth-value outcomes of those variables are given by the rows of the table.

Let us be quite precise about what we mean by a value assignment. By a *value assignment to* a finite or infinite sequence Γ of distinct variables of LSM we mean an ordered pair $\langle \delta,\Delta \rangle$ such that

(i) δ is a sequence of truth values of the same length as Γ;
(ii) Δ is a set of sequences of truth values of the same length as Γ;
(iii) δ is a member of Δ.

We construe δ to be the actual truth-value outcome of Γ and Δ to be the set of possible truth-value outcomes of Γ. For example, the value assignment to $\langle 'p','q' \rangle$ represented by the second row of the last table above consists of the pair $\langle \delta,\Delta \rangle$, where $\delta = \langle f,f \rangle$ and $\Delta = \{ \langle t,t \rangle, \langle f,f \rangle \}$; the value assignment represented by the first row of the same table consists of the ordered pair ($\langle t,t \rangle$, $\{ \langle t,t \rangle$, $\langle f,f \rangle \}$). By a *value assignment to*, or *interpretation of*, a set Φ of wffs of LSM is meant a value assignment to a sequence Γ of distinct variables, where every variable that occurs in any member of Φ occurs somewhere in the sequence Γ.

By a *plenary set of truth tables for* a wff A we will understand a set Ω of tables such that, given any value assignment Σ to the variables of A, there is a member of Ω that incorporates Σ, that is, in which Σ is represented. In other words, a plenary set of truth tables for A incorporates every value assignment to the variables of A. For example, the following is a plenary set of truth tables for the wff '$\Box[p \cdot q] \supset \Box q$':

p	q	$\Box[p \cdot q] \supset \Box q$
t	t	t

p	q	$\Box[p \cdot q] \supset \Box q$
t	f	t

p	q	$\Box[p \cdot q] \supset \Box q$
f	t	t

p	q	$\Box[p \cdot q] \supset \Box q$
f	f	t

p	q	$\Box[p \cdot q] \supset \Box q$
t	t	t
t	f	t

p	q	$\Box[p \cdot q] \supset \Box q$
t	t	t
f	t	t

p	q	$\Box[p \cdot q] \supset \Box q$
t	t	t
f	f	t

p	q	$\Box[p \cdot q] \supset \Box q$
t	f	t
f	t	t

p	q	$\Box[p \cdot q] \supset \Box q$
t	f	t
f	f	t

p	q	$\Box[p \cdot q] \supset \Box q$
f	t	t
f	f	t

p	q	$\Box[p \cdot q] \supset \Box q$
t	t	t
t	f	t
f	t	t

p	q	$\Box[p \cdot q] \supset \Box q$
t	t	t
t	f	t
f	f	t

p	q	$\Box[p \cdot q] \supset \Box q$
t	t	t
f	t	t
f	f	t

p	q	$\Box[p \cdot q] \supset \Box q$
t	f	t
f	t	t
f	f	t

p	q	$\Box[p \cdot q] \supset \Box q$
t	t	t
t	f	t
f	t	t
f	f	t

And the tables below form a plenary set of tables for the wff '$\sim\Box\sim p \supset p$':

p	$\sim\Box\sim p \supset p$
t	t

p	$\sim\Box\sim p \supset p$
f	t

p	$\sim\Box\sim p \supset p$
t	t
f	f

As the last example, the following is a plenary set of truth tables for '$p \cdot \Box\sim p$':

p	$p \cdot \Box\sim p$
t	f

p	$p \cdot \Box\sim p$
f	f

p	$p \cdot \Box\sim p$
t	f
f	f

There is a simple procedure for constructing a plenary set of truth tables for a wff A that contains occurrences of n distinct sentential variables. First, construct all the different tables for A that contain exactly one row. Then construct all the different tables for A that contain exactly two rows. And so on, until one has produced all the different tables for A that contain exactly 2^n rows (there will be just one such table), whereupon the procedure comes to a halt.

34.1. Validity

In truth-functional logic *valid wffs* were defined as wffs that come out true under all value assignments to their variables. We carry over unchanged into modal logic the foregoing definition. A plenary set of truth tables for a wff incorporates all the value assignments to its variables, so it is evident that a wff of LSM is valid if and only if it has the value truth on every row of every table in a plenary set of truth tables for it. For example, the plenary sets of truth tables displayed in Section 34.0 show that '$\Box [p \cdot q] \supset \Box q$' is valid but that neither '$\sim\Box \sim p \supset p$' nor '$p \cdot \Box \sim p$' is valid. In plenary sets of truth tables, therefore, we possess a decision procedure for validity of wffs of LSM.

Just as in truth-functional logic, by an *invalid* wff of LSM we understand a wff of LSM that comes out false under every value assignment to its variables. Accordingly, a wff is invalid if and only if it comes out false on every row of every table in a plenary set of truth tables for it. For example, as shown by the plenary set of truth tables in Section 34.0, the wff '$p \cdot \Box \sim p$' is invalid. And as in truth-functional logic, a wff of LSM that comes out true under some value assignments and false under others is said to be *contingent*. For example, '$\sim\Box \sim p \supset p$' is a contingent wff.

34.2. Relation of LSP to LSM

There are several senses in which it may be said that the truth-functional LSP forms a subsystem of the modal LSM. First, every wff of LSP is also a wff of LSM. Second, every valid (invalid) wff of LSP is a valid (invalid) wff of LSM. For example, '$p \supset [p \lor q]$' and '$r \lor \sim r$' are both valid wffs of LSM. Third and finally, every wff of LSM that is a substitution instance (that is, the result of a simultaneous substitution) of a valid wff of LSP is itself a valid wff. For example, '$\Box p \supset [\Box p \lor \sim \Box q]$' and '$\Box \Box q \lor \sim \Box \Box q$' are both valid, being substitution instances of the valid wffs '$p \supset [p \lor q]$' and '$r \lor \sim r$', respectively. Of course, not all valid wffs of LSM are valid wffs of LSP (witness: '$\Box \Box q \lor \sim \Box \Box q$') or even substitution instances of valid wffs of LSP (witness: '$\Box p \supset \sim \Box \sim p$').

34.3. Analytic Truth, Logical Truth, Entailment, Implication, and Equivalence

If one turns the variables of LSM into bonafide sentences by endowing them with sense, one obtains what will be called an M-language. In Section 8.1 we argued that a sentence of a P-language that is a valid wff is analytically true. Analogous reasoning establishes that a sentence of an M-language is analytically true if it is a valid wff. In other words, in M-languages as in P-languages validity is a sufficient condition of analytic truth. The reader may show by counterexamples that validity is not a necessary condition of analytic truth in M-languages. Similarly, it is easily shown that in M-languages as in P-languages invalidity [not to be confused with mere nonvalidity) is a sufficient but not a necessary condition of analytic falsehood.

In Section 8.0 it was argued that validity (invalidity) is both a necessary and sufficient condition of the logical truth (falsehood) of sentences of a P-language. Analogous reasoning will show that the same holds for M-languages. That is, in an M-language validity (invalidity) is both necessary and sufficient for logical truth (falsehood).

We also take over unchanged into LSM the definitions of the consequence relation and of the implication relation as given for LSP in Section 14.2. (For example, a wff B of LSM shall be said to be *a consequence of* a set Δ of wffs of LSM if there is no value assignment or interpretation of the set $\Delta \cup \{B\}$ under which each member of Δ comes out true but B comes out false.) Accordingly, the wffs '$\Box(p \supset q)$' and '$\sim \Box \sim p$' jointly imply '$\sim \Box \sim q$', whereas the wffs '$\Box(p \supset q)$' and '$\sim \Box \sim q$' do not jointly imply '$\sim \Box \sim p$'. In Section 14.2 we saw that (joint) implication among wffs of LSP amounts to validity of the conditional. Similarly, it is easily shown that (joint) implication among wffs of LSM also amounts to validity of the conditional, that is, that $A_1, A_2, \ldots, A_n$ jointly imply B if and only if the conditional $\ulcorner A_1 \cdot A_2 \cdot \ldots \cdot A_n \supset B \urcorner$ is valid. We leave it to the reader to establish that (joint) implication is a sufficient but not a necessary condition of (joint) entailment among sentences of an M-language.

Like implication, the concept of equivalence is the same for LSM as for LSP. That is, a wff A of LSM is said to be *equivalent to* a wff B of LSM if there is no interpretation of the set $\{A,B\}$ under which A and B have opposite truth values. For example, '$\Box \sim \Box p$' is equivalent to '$\sim \Box \Box p$', and '$\Box p \supset p$' is equivalent to '$q \vee \sim q$'. Like equivalence in LSP, equivalence in LSM amounts to validity of the biconditional; that is, A is equivalent to B if and only if the biconditional $\ulcorner A \equiv B \urcorner$ is valid. It is easily shown that equivalence is a sufficient but not a necessary condition of mutual entailment in an M-language.

35.   EXERCISES

(1)   Determine how many value assignments can be made to the variables of a wff of LSM which contains occurrences of two distinct variables. (*Hint:* What is the total number of rows in the tables of a plenary set of truth tables for the given wff?)

(2)   Construct a plenary set of truth tables for the wff '$\Box[p \cdot q \supset r] \cdot \Box r \supset \Box p \vee \Box q$'.

(3)   Prove that contingency is not a sufficient condition of the syntheticity of a sentence of an M-language. Is it a necessary condition?

(4)   Devise some short-cut tests for determining whether wffs of LSM are valid.

(5)   By testing the appropriate conditionals for validity by means of plenary sets of truth tables, determine whether
   (a)   '$\sim \Box \sim [p \cdot q]$' implies '$\sim \Box \sim p \cdot \sim \Box \sim q$';
   (b)   '$\sim \Box \sim p$' and '$\sim \Box \sim q$' jointly imply '$\sim \Box \sim [p \cdot q]$';
   (c)   '$\Box p$' and '$\Box q$' jointly imply '$\Box[p \cdot q]$';

    (d) '$\Box[p \cdot q]$' implies '$\Box p \cdot \Box q$';

    (e) '$\Box p \lor \Box q$' implies '$\Box[p \lor q]$';

    (f) '$\Box[p \lor q]$' implies '$\Box p \lor \Box q$';

    (g) '$\sim\Box\sim[p \lor q]$' implies '$\sim\Box\sim p \lor \sim\Box\sim q$';

    (h) '$\sim\Box\sim p \lor \sim\Box\sim q$' implies '$\sim\Box\sim[p \lor q]$'.

(6) Prove that a wff of LSM is contingent if and only if it has the value truth on some row of a table in a plenary set of tables and also has the value falsehood on some row of some table in that same plenary set of truth tables.

(7) Explain why the actual truth-value outcome of an n-tuple of sentences is inevitably found among its possible truth-value outcomes.

(8) Prove that any wff of LSM which is a substitution instance of a valid wff (tautology) of LSP is itself valid. [See Exercise (11).]

(9) Prove that equivalence is an equivalence relation (see Section 10.1) among the wffs of LSM. Prove that implication is reflexive and transitive but not symmetrical among the wffs of LSM.

(10) By testing the appropriate biconditionals for validity, determine whether

    (a) '$\Box[p \cdot q]$' is equivalent to '$\Box p \cdot \Box q$';

    (b) '$\Box[p \lor q]$' is equivalent to '$\Box p \lor \Box q$';

    (c) '$\sim\Box\sim[p \cdot q]$' is equivalent to '$\sim\Box\sim p \cdot \sim\Box\sim q$';

    (d) '$\sim\Box\sim[p \lor q]$' is equivalent to '$\sim\Box\sim p \lor \sim\Box\sim q$';

    (e) '$\Box\Box p$' is equivalent to '$\Box p$';

    (f) '$\Box\sim p$' is equivalent to '$\sim\Box p$'.

(11) A wff of LSM will be called *tautologous* if it is a substitution instance of a valid wff of LSP. (Let $b_1, \ldots, b_k$ be a complete list of the distinct variables of a wff A of LSP. Then a wff B of LSM is said to be a substitution instance of A if there exist wffs $B_1, \ldots, B_k$ of LSM such that B is the result of the simultaneous substitution of the wffs $B_1, \ldots, B_k$ for the variables $b_1, \ldots, b_k$, respectively, in A.) Formulate a decision procedure for recognizing the tautologousness of wffs of LSM.

(12) Supply the grammar of a Polish-notational version of LSM, letting the capital letter 'L' correspond to '$\Box$'.

(13) Translate the premiss and conclusion of the following argument into an M-language in which 'p' means that there will be a sea fight tomorrow.

Necessarily there will be a sea fight tomorrow or not. Therefore, necessarily there will be a sea fight tomorrow or necessarily there won't be a sea fight tomorrow.

Show that the premiss is a logical truth. Show that the premiss does not imply the conclusion. Does the premiss entail the conclusion? Is the argument correct?

(14) Discuss the use of 'necessarily' in the following argument:

If there is a sea fight tomorrow, then the Athenians will be victorious.
But the Athenians will not be victorious.
Necessarily, therefore, there will be no sea fight tomorrow.

(*Hints:* Could the adverb 'necessarily' be dropped without altering the substance of the argument? Is the presence of 'necessarily' merely an additional indicator that the framer of the argument believed it to be correct?) Contrast the use of 'necessarily' in the above argument with its use or uses in the one below:

If God exists necessarily, then some being is the cause of its own existence.
But no being can be the cause of its own existence.
Therefore, it is not true that God exists necessarily.

[15] Formulate an inductive definition of the value of a wff of LSM under a value assignment to its variables.

36. TRUTH-TABULAR CONNECTIVES

36.0. Possibility

Like 'necessarily', the singularly English connective 'it is possible that' or simply 'possibly' can be prefixed to a sentence to form a compound sentence the truth value of which depends on the possible truth-value outcomes of the component sentence. If truth is a possible truth-value outcome of a sentence A, then the compound ⌜Possibly A⌝ is true; otherwise, ⌜Possibly A⌝ is false. Instead of the box, some modal languages contain as a primitive connective the *diamond*, '$\Diamond$', which answers to the use of 'possibly' just discussed. The semantics of the diamond is given, therefore, by the following fundamental set of truth tables:

A	$\Diamond A$
t	t

A	$\Diamond A$
f	f

A	$\Diamond A$
t	t
f	t

(We may read ⌜$\Diamond A$⌝ as ⌜Possibly A⌝.) Notice that ⌜$\sim\Box\sim A$⌝ also satisfies the fundamental set of truth tables for the diamond:

A	$\sim\Box\sim A$
t	t

A	$\sim\Box\sim A$
f	f

A	$\sim\Box\sim A$
t	t
f	t

Since ⌜$\sim\Box\sim A$⌝ is equivalent to ⌜$\Diamond A$⌝, the expressive power of an M-language is in no way impaired by the omission of the diamond from the vocabulary of LSM. By using the tilde and box, one can make any statement that he could have made with the diamond. Still, it is convenient to have the diamond at hand. For example, the import of '$\sim\Box\sim[p \vee q] \supset \sim\Box\sim p \vee \sim\Box\sim q$' is brought out more immediately by the equivalent wff

$$\Diamond[p \vee q] \supset \Diamond p \vee \Diamond q.$$

To realize the advantages of the diamond, we lay down the following definition (abbreviative convention):

Convention 9. $\Diamond A =_{\text{Df}} \sim\Box\sim A$.

Inspection of its fundamental set of truth tables reveals that the semantics of the diamond can be summarized thus: If 't' occurs anywhere beneath A in a truth table T, then the value of ⌜$\Diamond A$⌝ is truth on every row of T; otherwise, the value of ⌜$\Diamond A$⌝ is falsehood on every row of T. For example, the tables below are constructed in accordance with the foregoing rule.

p	q	$\Diamond p \supset \Diamond [p \cdot q]$
t	t	t̸ t t̸
f	f	t̸ t t̸

p	q	$\Diamond p \supset \Diamond [p \cdot q]$
t	f	t̸ f f̸
f	t	t̸ f f̸
f	f	t̸ f f̸

p	q	$\Diamond p \supset \Diamond [p \cdot q]$
t	t	t̸ t t̸

36.1. The Singular Truth-Tabular Connectives

By a *singulary truth-tabular connective* let us understand a singulary sentence connective $\otimes$ such that the truth value of $\ulcorner \otimes A \urcorner$ depends on nothing more than the actual and possible truth-value outcomes of the component A. The tilde, box, and diamond, for example, are all singulary truth-tabular connectives. The semantics of $\otimes$ is completely specified when one has stipulated the value of $\ulcorner \otimes A \urcorner$ for each way in which actual and possible truth-value outcomes can accrue to A. That is, one completely specifies the meaning of $\otimes$ by filling in the following set of tables:

A	$\otimes A$
t	

A	$\otimes A$
f	

A	$\otimes A$
t	
f	

The result is called *the fundamental set of truth tables for* $\otimes$. And since there are 2^4, or 16, ways to fill in the above tables, there are exactly sixteen (semantically) different singulary truth-tabular connectives—those given by the sixteen fundamental sets of truth tables exhibited below.

A	$\otimes_1 A$
t	t

A	$\otimes_2 A$
t	f

A	$\otimes_3 A$
t	t

A	$\otimes_4 A$
t	f

A	$\otimes_1 A$
f	f

A	$\otimes_2 A$
f	t

A	$\otimes_3 A$
f	t

A	$\otimes_4 A$
f	f

A	$\otimes_1 A$
t	f
f	t

A	$\otimes_2 A$
t	t
f	f

A	$\otimes_3 A$
t	t
f	f

A	$\otimes_4 A$
t	f
f	t

A	$\otimes_5 A$
t	t

A	$\otimes_6 A$
t	f

A	$\otimes_7 A$
t	t

A	$\otimes_8 A$
t	f

A	$\otimes_5 A$
f	t

A	$\otimes_6 A$
f	f

A	$\otimes_7 A$
f	t

A	$\otimes_8 A$
f	f

A	$\otimes_5 A$
t	f
f	t

A	$\otimes_6 A$
t	t
f	f

A	$\otimes_7 A$
t	f
f	f

A	$\otimes_8 A$
t	t
f	t

A	$\otimes_9 A$
t	t

A	$\otimes_{10} A$
t	f

A	$\otimes_{11} A$
t	t

A	$\sim A$
t	f

A	$\otimes_9 A$
f	t

A	$\otimes_{10} A$
f	f

A	$\otimes_{11} A$
f	f

A	$\sim A$
f	t

A	$\otimes_9 A$
t	t
f	t

A	$\otimes_{10} A$
t	f
f	f

A	$\otimes_{11} A$
t	t
f	f

A	$\sim A$
t	f
f	t

A	$\Diamond A$
t	t

A	$\lozenge A$
t	f

A	$\Box A$
t	t

A	$\boxminus A$
t	f

A	$\Diamond A$
f	f

A	$\lozenge A$
f	t

A	$\Box A$
f	f

A	$\boxminus A$
f	t

A	$\Diamond A$
t	t
f	t

A	$\lozenge A$
t	f
f	f

A	$\Box A$
t	f
f	f

A	$\boxminus A$
t	t
f	t

Of the sixteen connectives characterized by the above sets of tables, four are truth functional: '$\otimes_9$', '$\otimes_{10}$', '$\otimes_{11}$', and '$\sim$'. The connective '$\otimes_{11}$' corresponds to the inane English connective 'it is the case that', as the reader may verify by inspecting its fundamental set of truth tables. The connective '$\otimes_9$' corresponds to the perfectly noncommital connective 'it is either true or false that', whereas '$\otimes_{10}$' answers to the hopelessly overcommital expression 'it is both true and false that'. It is evident that all four of these connectives can be defined in LSM, because the vocabulary of LSM includes the functionally complete tilde, wedge, and dot.

By a *modal connective* we will understand a truth-tabular connective that is not truth functional. There are twelve singulary modal connectives, therefore, only one of which, the box, is a primitive symbol of LSM. The omission of the other eleven in no way impairs the expressive power of an M-language, however, because each of them can be defined in terms of the connectives of LSM. For example, as we have already noted, the diamond can be defined in terms of the tilde and box. The connective '$\boxminus$', answering to 'it is not necessarily the case that', can also be defined in terms of the tilde and box:

$$\boxplus A \ =_{\mathrm{Df}} \ \sim\!\Box A$$

Similarly, the connective '$\Diamond\!\!\!/$', which corresponds to 'it is impossible that' can be defined thus:

$$\Diamond\!\!\!/ A \ =_{\mathrm{Df}} \ \Box \sim\!A$$

The connectives '$\otimes_8$' (meaning 'it is neither necessarily true nor necessarily false that'), '$\otimes_7$' (meaning 'it is either necessarily true or necessarily false that'), and '$\otimes_1$' (meaning 'it is either necessarily true or else false but not necessarily false that') can be defined as follows:

$$\otimes_8 A \ =_{\mathrm{Df}} \ \Diamond A \cdot \Diamond \sim\!A \qquad \otimes_7 A \ =_{\mathrm{Df}} \ \Box A \ \vee \ \Box \sim\!A$$
$$\otimes_1 A \ =_{\mathrm{Df}} \ \Box A \ \vee \ \Diamond A \cdot \sim\!A$$

Definitions of the other singulary modal connectives in terms of the tilde, wedge, dot, and box are left to the reader.

Although it is noteworthy that the connectives of LSM serve to define all the singulary truth-tabular connectives, it is perhaps more surprising that any of the eleven other singulary modal connectives could have been chosen as primitive in LSM in lieu of the box without any sacrifice of expressive power. This follows from the fact that, together with the tilde, wedge, and dot, each of the eleven serves to define the box. The following definitions prove this for the connectives '$\Diamond$', '$\boxplus$', '$\otimes_8$', and '$\otimes_1$':

$$\Box A \ =_{\mathrm{Df}} \ \sim\!\Diamond \sim\!A \qquad \Box A \ =_{\mathrm{Df}} \ \sim\!\boxplus A$$
$$\Box A \ =_{\mathrm{Df}} \ A \cdot \sim\!\otimes_8 A \qquad \Box A \ =_{\mathrm{Df}} \ A \cdot \otimes_1 A$$

It is left to the reader to prove about each of the seven remaining singulary modal connectives that, together with the tilde, wedge, and dot, it serves to define the box.

36.2.   *N*-ary Truth-Tabular Connectives: Strict Implication

By an *n*-ary *truth-tabular connective* we will understand an *n*-ary sentence connective $\otimes$ such that the truth value of a compound sentence $\ulcorner\otimes(A_1, A_2, \ldots, A_n)\urcorner$ depends on nothing more than the actual and possible truth-value outcomes of $\langle A_1, A_2, \ldots, A_n \rangle$. Just as the semantics of a singulary truth-tabular connective $\otimes$ is given by a plenary set of truth tables for $\ulcorner \otimes A \urcorner$, namely the fundamental set of truth tables for $\otimes$, so, too, the semantics of an n-ary truth-tabular connective $\otimes$ is completely specified by the plenary set of truth tables for $\ulcorner \otimes (A_1, A_2, \ldots, A_n) \urcorner$. For example, the semantics of the binary truth-tabular connective '$\rightarrow3$' is given by the following fundamental set of truth tables:

A B	$A \rightarrow3 B$
t t	t

A B	$A \rightarrow3 B$
t f	f

A B	$A \rightarrow3 B$
f t	t

A B	$A \rightarrow3 B$
f f	t

A B	$A \rightarrow3 B$
t t	f
t f	f

A B	$A \rightarrow3 B$
t t	t
f t	t

A B	$A \rightarrow3 B$
t t	t
f f	t

A B	$A \rightarrow3 B$
t f	f
f t	f

A B	$A \rightarrow3 B$
t f	f
f f	f

A B	$A \rightarrow3 B$
f t	t
f f	t

A B	$A \rightarrow3 B$
t t	f
t f	f
f t	f

A B	$A \rightarrow3 B$
t t	f
t f	f
f f	f

A B	$A \rightarrow3 B$
t t	t
f t	t
f f	t

A B	$A \rightarrow3 B$
t f	f
f t	f
f f	f

A B	$A \rightarrow3 B$
t t	f
t f	f
f t	f
f f	f

The connective '$\dashv$', called the *fishhook*, answers to the binary English connective ⌜that ... entails that ...⌝.[1] Following tradition, we will read ⌜$A \dashv B$⌝ as ⌜A strictly implies B⌝ rather than as ⌜A entails B⌝. Inspection of its fundamental set of truth tables reveals that the semantics of the fishhook may be summarized thus: If $\langle t,f \rangle$ accrues to $\langle A,B \rangle$ on any row of a truth table T, then the value of ⌜$A \dashv B$⌝ is falsehood on every row of T; otherwise, the value of ⌜$A \dashv B$⌝ is truth on every row of T.

To get the fundamental set of truth tables for the fishhook, one had to make 32 entries in the value columns beneath '$A \dashv B$' in the tables of the set. There are two choices for each entry, 't' or 'f', so there are 2^{32}, or 4,294,967,296, ways to fill in a plenary set of tables for a binary connective. There are, therefore, 2^{32} semantically different binary truth-tabular connectives. Of these, 16 are truth functional; the remaining 4,294,967,280 are modal connectives. Now it so happens that the fishhook can be defined in terms of the connectives of LSM:

$$A \dashv B =_{\text{Df}} \Box[A \supset B]$$

The reader should verify the correctness of the above definition by establishing, by means of plenary sets of truth tables, that ⌜$\Box[A \supset B]$⌝ is equivalent to ⌜$A \dashv B$⌝. The question arises whether or not every binary truth-tabular connective can be defined in terms of the tilde, wedge, dot, and box. If so, the fact that the vocabulary of LSM contains only two binary truth-tabular connectives (the wedge and dot) entails nonetheless no loss of expressive power. In Section 36.3 we will prove an even stronger result: Every truth-tabular connective, whatever its degree, is definable in terms of the connectives of LSM.

The following[2] are a few of the noteworthy valid wffs involving the fishhook:

$p \dashv \Diamond p$ (actuality strictly implies possibility)
$\Box p \dashv p$ (necessity strictly implies actuality)

[1] Notice that the blanks in 'that ... entails that ...' are appropriately filled by sentences, *not* by names of sentences. This contrasts markedly with the use of 'entails' in Section 1.0, wherein 'entails' was appropriately flanked not by sentences but by names of sentences. The difference is mainly that between a binary connective and a binary predicate. The two uses of 'entails' are, of course, closely related. Let 'N_1' and 'N_2' be names of the sentences S_1 and S_2, respectively. Then the expression ⌜That S_1 entails that S_2⌝ is true if and only if the expression 'N_1 entails N_2' is true.

[2] We let '$\dashv$' outrank the dot and wedge.

$[p \dashv q] \cdot [q \dashv r] \dashv [p \dashv r]$ (transitivity of strict implication)

$[{\sim}p \dashv q \cdot {\sim}q] \dashv p$ (indirect proof)

$p \dashv p$ (reflexivity of strict implication)

$[p \dashv q] \cdot \Diamond p \dashv \Diamond q$ (the possible strictly implies only the possible)

$[p \dashv q] \cdot \Box p \dashv \Box q$ (the necessary strictly implies only the necessary)

$\Box q \dashv [p \dashv q]$ (any statement strictly implies a necessary statement)

${\sim}\Diamond p \dashv [p \dashv q]$ (an impossible statement strictly implies every statement)

The last two wffs in the above list have been called *the paradoxes of strict implication*. Some logicians[3] deem it paradoxical that a necessary statement, that is, a statement which is analytically true, be entailed or strictly implied by *every* statement. They insist that one statement cannot entail another unless the meaning of the former is somehow relevant to the meaning of the latter. Because the meaning of 'Washingtion is the capital of the United States' seems completely irrelevant to the truth value of the necessary statement 'If $2 = 1$, then $2 = 1$', these logicians reject the claim that Washington is the capital of the United States entails that if $2 = 1$, then $2 = 1$. We have bypassed this objection by stipulating in Section 1.0 that entailment obtains between a pair of statements if it follows from their meanings that if the first should be true, the second would also be true. Given this stipulation, it is incontrovertible that any statement entails an analytic statement, although there is considerable room for disagreement over which statements, if any, are analytically true.[4]

36.3.   Strict Equivalence; Compatibility; the Star

Another important binary modal connective is the quadruple bar '$\equiv$', which corresponds to the English connective ⌜that ... and

---

[3] Among others, Alan Anderson and Nuel Belnap.

[4] Some logicians who read ⌜$A \supset B$⌝ as ⌜A materially implies B⌝ rather than as ⌜If A, then B⌝ speak of the so-called *paradoxes of material implication:* that a false statement materially implies every statement and that a true statement is materially implied by every statement. The former amounts to nothing more than the fact that a conditional sentence is true if its antecedent is false; the latter, to the fact that a conditional sentence with a true consequent is itself true. Neither of these restatements seems paradoxical, so we conclude that the air of paradox stems from the misleading rendering of ⌜$A \supset B$⌝ as ⌜A materially implies B⌝.

that ... are mutually entailing $^\urcorner$. Again following tradition, we will read $\ulcorner A \equiv B \urcorner$ as $\ulcorner A$ is strictly equivalent to $B \urcorner$. Rather than present its fundamental set of truth tables, we summarize the semantics of the quadruple bar in the following rule: If either $\langle t,f \rangle$ or $\langle f,t \rangle$ or both accrue to $\langle A,B \rangle$ on rows of a truth table T, then the value of $\ulcorner A \equiv B \urcorner$ is falsehood on every row of T; otherwise, the value of $\ulcorner A \equiv B \urcorner$ is truth on every row of T. $\ulcorner \Box [A \equiv B] \urcorner$ is equivalent to $\ulcorner A \equiv B \urcorner$, so the quadruple bar can be defined in terms of the connectives of LSM thus:

$$A \equiv B =_{\mathrm{Df}} \Box [A \equiv B]$$

Here are a few noteworthy valid wffs involving the quadruple bar:[5]

$p \equiv p$ (reflexivity of strict equivalence)
$[p \equiv q] \dashv 3 [q \equiv p]$ (symmetry of strict equivalence)
$[p \equiv q] \cdot [q \equiv r] \dashv 3 [p \equiv r]$ (transitivity of strict equivalence)
$[p \equiv q] \cdot \Box p \dashv 3 \Box q$
$[p \equiv q] \cdot \Diamond p \dashv 3 \Diamond q$
$[p \dashv 3 q] \cdot [q \equiv r] \dashv 3 [p \dashv 3 r]$
$[p \dashv 3 q] \cdot [p \equiv r] \dashv 3 [r \dashv 3 q]$
$\Box p \cdot \Box q \dashv 3 [p \equiv q]$
$\sim \Diamond p \cdot \sim \Diamond q \dashv 3 [p \equiv q]$

The penultimate binary modal connective that we single out for special mention corresponds to the English expression $\ulcorner$ that ... is compatible with that ... $\urcorner$ and is traditionally symbolized by a small bold circle '$\circ$'. We will read $\ulcorner A \circ B \urcorner$ as $\ulcorner A$ is compatible with $B \urcorner$. Rather than display its fundamental set of truth tables or even summarize its semantics by a rule, we define '$\circ$' in terms of the connectives of LSM:

$$A \circ B =_{\mathrm{Df}} \Diamond [A \cdot B]$$

We leave it to the reader to reconstruct the fundamental set of truth tables for '$\circ$' on the basis of the foregoing definition. Listed below are some important valid wffs involving '$\circ$'.

$[p \circ q] \dashv 3 [q \circ p]$ (symmetry of compatibility)
$[p \circ p] \equiv \Diamond p$
$[p \dashv 3 q] \equiv \sim [p \circ \sim q]$
$[p \circ q] \equiv \sim [p \dashv 3 \sim q]$
$[p \equiv q] \cdot [q \circ r] \dashv 3 [p \circ r]$

[5] We let '$\equiv$' have the same rank as '$\dashv 3$'.

In Section 36.1 we observed that any singulary modal connective could have supplanted the box in the vocabulary of LSM without curtailing expressive power. Although the analogous claim is not universally true of the binary modal connectives, nevertheless many of them could supplant the box in the vocabulary of LSM to no detriment of expressive power. In particular, as the following definitions show, any one of the three connectives '$\dashv$', '$\equiv$', and '$\mathbf{o}$' could so replace the box:

$$\Box A =_{Df} \sim A \dashv A \cdot \sim A \qquad \Box A =_{Df} A \equiv [A \vee \sim A]$$
$$\Box A =_{Df} \sim [\sim A \mathbf{o} \sim A]$$

The last binary modal connective to be discussed, the star, '$\star$', is a remarkable connective which plays the same role in modal logic that Sheffer's stroke plays in truth-functional logic: It serves to define *all* truth-tabular connectives, both truth functional and modal.[6] (Or, what comes to the same, this connective is functionally complete by itself in truth-tabular logic—see Section 38.0.) The semantics of the star is given by the following fundamental set of truth tables:

A B	$A \star B$
t t	f

A B	$A \star B$
t f	t

A B	$A \star B$
f t	t

A B	$A \star B$
f f	t

A B	$A \star B$
t t	t
t f	f

A B	$A \star B$
t t	f
f t	t

A B	$A \star B$
t t	f
f f	t

A B	$A \star B$
t f	t
f t	t

A B	$A \star B$
t f	t
f f	t

[6] This connective was discovered in 1967 by the author, who in 1966 discovered more complicated connectives with the same property.

A B	A ☆ B
f t	t
f f	t

A B	A ☆ B
t t	t
t f	f
f t	t

A B	A ☆ B
t t	t
t f	f
f f	t

A B	A ☆ B
t t	f
f t	t
f f	t

A B	A ☆ B
t f	t
f t	t
f f	t

A B	A ☆ B
t t	t
t f	f
f t	t
f f	t

Assuming what will be proved in Section 38.0—that any truth-tabular connective can be defined in terms of the tilde, horseshoe, and diamond—we prove by the following definitions that the star serves by itself to define all truth-tabular connectives:

$\sim A =_{Df} A ☆ A \qquad A \supset B =_{Df} A ☆ [A ☆ B]$
$\Diamond A =_{Df} [[(A ☆ A) ☆ A] ☆ A] \supset A$

It is left to the reader to verify, by means of plenary sets of truth tables, that the foregoing definitions are correct, that is, that ⌜$\sim A$⌝ is equivalent to ⌜$A ☆ A$⌝, and so on.

We could have effected maximum economy at no loss of expressive power by adopting the star as the sole primitive connective of LSM. Our reasons for not doing so were the same as those which induced us to forego Sheffer's stroke in favor of a redundant set of connectives for LSP: Measured in loss of perspicuity, the price of maximum economy seems pedagogically exorbitant.

37. EXERCISES

(1) Define each of the singulary truth-tabular connectives in terms of the connectives of LSM. Similarly, define each of them in terms of the tilde, horseshoe, and diamond.

(2) Exhibit the fundamental sets of truth tables for '$\equiv$' and '$\circ$'.

{3} In what sense, if any, are the valid wffs '$\Box p \cdot \Box q \supset [p \equiv q]$' and '$\sim \Diamond p \cdot \sim \Diamond q \ni [p \equiv q]$' paradoxical?

(4) Define the box in terms of the connectives of each of the eleven sets formed by adding a singulary modal connective other than the box to the set that contains the tilde, wedge, and dot.

(5) Prove that omission from the vocabulary of LSM of either the dot or the wedge would not diminish the expressive power of an M-language.

(6) In Section 36.1 *modal* connectives were said to be truth-tabular connectives that are not truth functional. Where $\otimes$ is a singulary modal connective, explain the sense in which the value of a compound $\ulcorner \otimes A \urcorner$ depends on the *mode* or manner in which A possesses its truth value.

(7) Inspection of the fundamental set of truth tables for the wedge reveals that each table is a subtable of the one full table of the set, in the sense that each row of the former occurs unaltered in the latter. Let us call such a set of truth tables *telescopic*, to suggest that all the partial tables are telescoped into the one full table. Prove that the fundamental set of truth tables for a truth-tabular connective is telescopic if and only if the connective is truth functional.

(8) Verify by plenary sets of truth tables or by short-cut procedures the validity of every wff alleged to be valid in Sections 36.2 and 36.3.

{9} We have established by means of indirect proof many metatheorems about the languages that we have studied. That is, we showed that the negation of a metatheorem entails a contradiction, from which we inferred the truth of the metatheorem. Does the validity of the law of indirect proof, '[$\sim p \prec q \cdot \sim q$] $\prec p$', justify this proof procedure? Does the validity of '[$\sim p \supset q \cdot \sim q$] $\supset p$' justify this proof procedure?

[10]   Calculate the number of semantically different ternary truth-tabular connectives. [See Exercise (3) in Chapter 3.] Determine the number of semantically different n-ary truth-tabular connectives.

(11)   Some philosophers seem to defend determinism on the ground that a proposition necessarily follows from itself. Which of the following wffs best represents this ground, '$p \prec p$' or '$p \prec \Box p$'? Which wff is valid? Explain how the determinist thesis 'What is, is necessarily' is ambiguous between '$\Box[p \supset p]$' and '$p \supset \Box p$'.

[12]   Modify and enlarge the dictionary given in Section 18.0 for translating Boolean equations as follows: Translate '=' by the sign '$\equiv$' for strict equivalence, and let truth-functional connectives be their own translations. This new dictionary translates the wffs of TFBE (see Exercise ⟨5⟩ of Chapter 19) into wffs of LSM. Prove that a wff of TFBE is valid if and only if its translation in LSM is valid. Let A^* be the translation in LSM of a wff A of TFBE. If A is not valid, show how to read off a false interpretation of A from the plenary set of truth tables for A^*. Let k be the number of distinct class variables that occur in A. Prove that, if A is not valid, there is a false interpretation of A in which the universal class has 2^k members.

38. FUNCTIONAL COMPLETENESS; REDUCTION OF MODAL WFFS

38.0. Functional Completeness

We shall say that a wff *A satisfies* a set Δ of truth tables if A satisfies each member of Δ. (See Section 12.1 for the concept of a wff satisfying a truth table.) For example, the wff '$\sim q \cdot \Diamond q$' satisfies the plenary set of tables below:

q	
t	f

q	
f	f

q	
t	f
f	t

And the wff '$p \supset \Box q$' satisfies the following plenary set of tables:

p	q	
t	t	t

p	q	
t	f	f

p	q	
f	t	t

p	q	
f	f	t

p	q	
t	t	f
t	f	f

p	q	
t	t	t
f	t	t

p	q	
t	t	f
f	f	t

p	q	
t	f	f
f	t	t

p	q	
t	f	f
f	f	t

p	q	
f	t	t
f	f	t

p	q	
t	t	f
t	f	f
f	t	t

p	q	
t	t	f
t	f	f
f	f	t

p	q	
t	t	f
f	t	t
f	f	t

p	q	
t	f	f
f	t	t
f	f	t

p	q	
t	t	f
t	f	f
f	t	t
f	f	t

Is it purely coincidental that there are wffs of LSM which satisfy the plenary sets of truth tables displayed above? (Both '$\sim q \cdot \Diamond q$' and '$p \supset \Box q$' abbreviate wffs of LSM.) Put otherwise, are there plenary sets of truth tables that are not satisfied by any wffs of LSM? The correct answer, we will prove, is negative.

Let us call a set Γ of truth-tabular connectives *functionally complete* if, for every plenary set Δ of truth tables, there is a grammatical formula A which satisfies Δ, where A contains no symbols besides connectives of Γ, grouping indicators, and variables of the tables of Δ. We now prove that the tilde, wedge, dot, and diamond form a functionally complete set of connectives. Let Σ be in arbitrary order a complete list of all the distinct n-tuples of truth values; that is, Σ is $\langle \alpha_1^1, \alpha_2^1, \ldots, \alpha_n^1 \rangle$, $\langle \alpha_1^2, \alpha_2^2, \ldots, \alpha_n^2 \rangle$, $\ldots$, $\langle \alpha_1^{2^n}, \alpha_2^{2^n}, \ldots, \alpha_n^{2^n} \rangle$. Consider the following partial or full truth table T ($1 \leq k \leq 2^n$):

a_1	a_2	$\ldots$	a_n	
α_1^1	α_2^1	$\ldots$	α_n^1	β_1
α_1^2	α_2^2	$\ldots$	α_n^2	β_2
$\cdot$				$\cdot$
$\cdot$				$\cdot$
$\cdot$				$\cdot$
α_1^k	α_2^k	$\ldots$	α_n^k	β_k

As in Section 12.1, we associate with each member $\langle \alpha_1^i, \alpha_2^i, \ldots, \alpha_n^i \rangle$ of Σ a certain continued conjunction C_i called *the associated conjunction of* $\langle \alpha_1^i, \alpha_2^i, \ldots, \alpha_n^i \rangle$, letting $C_i = \ulcorner B_1 \cdot B_2 \cdot \ldots \cdot B_n \urcorner$, where B_j is a_j or $\ulcorner \sim a_j \urcorner$ according as α_j^i is truth or falsehood. Thus $C_1, C_2, \ldots, C_{2^n}$ are the associated conjunctions of all the members of Σ. Of these 2^n wffs only $C_1, C_2, \ldots, C_k$ are associated with actual rows of T; the rest (if any), namely $C_{k+1}, C_{k+2}, \ldots, C_{2^n}$, are associated with *missing* rows of T. Let $D_1, D_2, \ldots, D_m$ be a complete list of those wffs among $C_1, C_2, \ldots, C_k$ wherein 't' occurs in the value column of the associated row of T. (If only 'f' occurs in the value column of T, there will be no wffs $D_1, D_2, \ldots, D_m$.) First we notice that the continued disjunction $\ulcorner D_1 \vee D_2 \vee \ldots \vee D_m \urcorner$ satisfies T. Let T' be a truth table with the same column headings as T. Observe that, whereas the wff $\ulcorner \Diamond C_1 \cdot \Diamond C_2 \cdot \ldots \cdot \Diamond C_k \urcorner$ comes out true on every row of T, it comes out false on every row of T′ if any of the rows of T [namely $\langle \alpha_1^1, \alpha_2^1, \ldots, \alpha_n^1 \rangle$, $\langle \alpha_1^2, \alpha_2^2, \ldots, \alpha_n^2 \rangle$, ..., $\langle \alpha_1^k, \alpha_2^k, \ldots, \alpha_n^k \rangle$] are missing in T′. Similarly, the conjunction $\ulcorner \sim\!\Diamond C_{k+1} \cdot \sim\!\Diamond C_{k+2} \cdot \ldots \cdot \sim\!\Diamond C_{2^n} \urcorner$ comes out true on every row of T but false on every row of T′ if any row of T′ is one of the missing rows of T. Let Δ be any plenary set of truth tables to which T belongs. If 't' occurs in the value column of T, let

$$A = [D_1 \vee D_2 \vee \ldots \vee D_m] \cdot [\Diamond C_1 \cdot \Diamond C_2 \cdot \ldots \cdot \Diamond C_k] \cdot$$
$$[\sim\!\Diamond C_{k+1} \cdot \sim\!\Diamond C_{k+2} \cdot \ldots \cdot \sim\!\Diamond C_{2^n}]$$

and otherwise let $A = \ulcorner a_1 \cdot \sim\! a_1 \urcorner$. It follows from the foregoing considerations that A not only satisfies T but that A comes out false on every row of every other table in Δ. So we call A *the characteristic wff of* T. Let $T_1, T_2, \ldots, T_r$ be a complete list of the truth tables in Δ, and let $A_1, A_2, \ldots, A_r$ be their respective characteristic wffs. Obviously, the disjunction $\ulcorner A_1 \vee A_2 \vee \ldots \vee A_r \urcorner$ satisfies Δ. We call $\ulcorner A_1 \vee A_2 \vee \ldots \vee A_r \urcorner$ *the characteristic wff of* Δ. Since $\ulcorner A_1 \vee A_2 \vee \ldots \vee A_r \urcorner$ contains no connectives other than the tilde, dot, wedge, and diamond, it follows that those four connectives form a functionally complete set of truth-tabular connectives. As corollaries, we have the functional completeness of the following sets of truth-tabular connectives: {'$\sim$', '$\vee$', '$\cdot$', '$\Box$'}, {'$\sim$', '$\vee$', '$\Box$'}, {'$\sim$', '$\cdot$', '$\Box$'}, {'$\sim$', '$\supset$', '$\Box$'}, {'$\sim$', '$\supset$', '$\Diamond$'}, {'$\sim$', '$\supset$', '$\dashv$'}, {'$\sim$', '$\supset$', '$\equiv$'}, {'$\sim$', '$\supset$', '$\mathbf{o}$'}, {'$|$', '$\Box$'}, and {'$\maltese$'}.

To lend some concreteness to the foregoing proof of the functional completeness of {'$\sim$','$\vee$','$\cdot$','$\Diamond$'}, we supply the characteristic wffs of several of the tables in the second set of plenary tables exhibited in this section. The following is the characteristic wff of the first table:

$$[p \cdot q] \cdot \Diamond(p \cdot q) \cdot [\sim\!\Diamond(p \cdot \sim\! q) \cdot \sim\!\Diamond(\sim\! p \cdot q) \cdot \sim\!\Diamond(\sim\! p \cdot \sim\! q)]$$

The characteristic wff of the fifth table is '$p \cdot \sim\! p$', and the next-to-last table has the following characteristic wff:

$$[\sim\! p \cdot q \vee \sim\! p \cdot \sim\! q] \cdot [\Diamond(p \cdot \sim\! q) \cdot \Diamond(\sim\! p \cdot q) \cdot \Diamond(\sim\! p \cdot \sim\! q)] \cdot$$
$$\sim\!\Diamond(p \cdot q)$$

The last table possesses the following characteristic wff:

$$[\sim\! p \cdot q \vee \sim\! p \cdot \sim\! q] \cdot$$
$$[\Diamond(p \cdot q) \cdot \Diamond(p \cdot \sim\! q) \cdot \Diamond(\sim\! p \cdot q) \cdot \Diamond(\sim\! p \cdot \sim\! q)]$$

By writing the disjunction of the characteristic wffs of all the tables in the aforementioned set, the reader will obtain the characteristic wff of the set.

Because the semantics of a truth-tabular connective is characterized by a plenary set of truth tables, any truth-tabular connective can be defined in terms of the members of a functionally complete set of truth-tabular connectives. For example, by following the procedure used above to obtain the characteristic wff for a set of truth tables, we can define the connective '$\otimes_4$' on the basis of its fundamental set of truth tables (see Section 36.1) thus:

$$\otimes_4 A =_{\text{Df}} [A \cdot \sim A] \vee [A \cdot \sim A] \vee [\sim A \cdot \Diamond A \cdot \Diamond \sim A]$$

Though correct, definitions so obtained are often outrageously inelegant. For example, the connective '$\otimes_4$' could be defined much more elegantly thus:

$$\otimes_4 A =_{\text{Df}} \sim A \cdot \Diamond A$$

The moral is that elegance and effectiveness are unlikely bedfellows.

38.1.   Reduction of Modal Wffs

We define the *modal degree of* a wff of LSM inductively as follows:

(i)   If A is a sentential variable, then the modal degree of A is zero.

(ii)   If the modal degree of A is k, then
  (a)   the modal degree of $\ulcorner \sim A \urcorner$ is also k;
  (b)   the modal degree of $\ulcorner \Box A \urcorner$ is $k + 1$.

(iii)   If the modal degree of A is k and the modal degree of B is m, then the modal degree of both $\ulcorner A \cdot B \urcorner$ and $\ulcorner A \vee B \urcorner$ is n, where n is the greater of k and m. (If $k = m$, then $n = k = m$.)

For example, the modal degree of each wff below is indicated immediately to its right:

$\Box[p \vee q]$	(1)	$\Box \sim \Box \Box \sim [(p \vee \Box q) \vee \Box \Box \Box r]$	(6)
$\Box[p \vee \Box q]$	(2)	$\sim \Box \sim \Box \sim \Box \sim [p \vee \sim p]$	(3)
$\sim[p \cdot \sim q]$	(0)	$\sim \sim \sim \sim [\Box \sim \sim p \vee \sim \Box \sim q]$	(1)

By the *scope of an occurrence of* a sentence connective in a wff is meant the components actually joined or combined by that occurrence of the connective. For example, the scope of the first box (that is, the first occurrence of the box) in '$\square\square[q \vee \square q]$' is the component '$\square[q \vee \square q]$', that is, the occurrence of '$\square[q \vee \square q]$' which immediately follows the first box. The scope of the second box in '$\square\square[q \vee \square q]$' is the component '$[q \vee \square q]$'. The scope of the third box in '$\square\square[q \vee \square q]$' is the component '$q$' immediately following it. Note carefully that the first occurrence of 'q' in '$\square\square[q \vee \square q]$' is not the scope of the third box; only the second occurrence of 'q' is. An occurrence of '$\square$' in a wff A is said to be *nested in A* if it is part of the scope of another occurrence of '$\square$' in A. For example, the first box in '$\square\square[q \vee \square q]$' is not nested in that wff, whereas the second and third boxes are both nested in that wff. We leave it to the reader to prove that a wff of LSM contains nested boxes if and only if its modal degree is two or greater.

A wff A is said to be *reducible to* a wff B if B is equivalent to A. For example, the wff '$\square\square[p \vee q]$' of modal degree two is reducible to the wff '$\square[p \vee q]$' of modal degree one, because the two are equivalent. Of some moment in modal logic is the fact that any wff of LSM is reducible to a wff of modal degree zero or one. The foregoing is an easy corollary of our proof of the functional completeness of $\{'\sim', '\vee', '\cdot', '\diamondsuit'\}$. To see this, let Δ be the plenary set of truth tables for a wff A of LSM, and let $\ulcorner A_1 \vee A_2 \vee \ldots \vee A_r \urcorner$ be the characteristic wff of Δ. Construing $\ulcorner \diamondsuit B \urcorner$ to abbreviate $\ulcorner \sim\square\sim B \urcorner$, the reader will find $\ulcorner A_1 \vee A_2 \vee \ldots \vee A_r \urcorner$ to be of modal degree one. $\ulcorner A_1 \vee A_2 \vee \ldots \vee A_r \urcorner$ is equivalent to A, so it follows that any wff of LSM is reducible to a wff of degree one. Some wffs, for example, '$p \vee q$' and '$\square[p \vee \sim p]$', are further reducible to wffs of degree zero. (The wff '$\square[p \vee \sim p]$' is reducible to '$p \vee \sim p$'.) So any wff of LSM is reducible to a wff of degree zero or one. The significance of this reduction result is that nesting of modal connectives adds nothing to the expressive power of an M-language.

38.2. The Six Modalities

By a *modality* some authors understand any singulary connective definable in terms of the tilde and box. For example, the following definitions show that '$\sim$' (negation), '$\otimes_{11}$' (affirmation), '$\square$' (necessity), '$\boxdot$' (nonnecessity), '$\diamondsuit$' (possibility), and '$\lozenge$' (impossibility) are all modalities.

$$\sim A \ =_{\mathrm{Df}} \ \sim A \qquad\qquad \square A \ =_{\mathrm{Df}} \ \square A \qquad\qquad \otimes_{11} A \ =_{\mathrm{Df}} \ A$$
$$\Diamond A \ =_{\mathrm{Df}} \ \sim\square\sim A \qquad \varardown A \ =_{\mathrm{Df}} \ \square\sim A \qquad \boxplus A \ =_{\mathrm{Df}} \ \sim\square A$$

A survey of the fundamental sets of truth tables of these six modalities will show that they are semantically different from one another. We will now prove that there are no other (semantically different) modalities.

Our proof that there are no modalities besides '$\sim$', '$\otimes_{11}$', '$\square$', '$\boxplus$', '$\Diamond$', and '$\varardown$' will proceed by weak mathematical induction on the number of occurrences of '$\sim$' and '$\square$' in the *definiens* (the right-hand side of a definition) of a definition of an arbitrary modality $\otimes$. If the *definiens* of $\otimes$ contains zero occurrences of '$\sim$' and '$\square$', then we have $\otimes A \ =_{\mathrm{Df}} \ A$. Clearly, then, $\otimes$ has the same fundamental set of truth tables as '$\otimes_{11}$'. As hypothesis of induction, let us assume that any modality in the *definiens* of a definition of which there occur exactly n occurrences of '$\square$' and '$\sim$' has the same fundamental set of truth tables as one of the six aforementioned modalities. Let $\otimes$ be an arbitrary modality definable by means of $n + 1$ occurrences of '$\square$' and '$\sim$', and let B be the *definiens* of $\otimes$. So we have $\otimes A \ =_{\mathrm{Df}} \ B$, where B consists of $n + 1$ occurrences of '$\sim$' and '$\square$' prefixed to A. So B is either $\ulcorner \square B_1 \urcorner$ or $\ulcorner \sim B_1 \urcorner$, where B_1 consists of n occurrences of '$\sim$' and '$\square$' prefixed to A. Suppose B is $\ulcorner \square B_1 \urcorner$. By the hypothesis of induction, the plenary set of truth tables for B_1 is given by one of the fundamental sets of truth tables for the six aforementioned modalities. So we have six subcases:

(1)   Suppose the plenary set of tables for B_1 is the fundamental set for the modality '$\sim$'. Then we have

A	$\square B_1$		A	$\square B_1$		A	$\square B_1$
t	f *f*		f	t *t̸*		t	f *f*
						f	f *t̸*

So the plenary set of tables for $\ulcorner \square B_1 \urcorner$ is the same as the fundamental set for '$\varardown$'. So $\otimes$ is semantically the same as '$\varardown$'.

(2)   Suppose the plenary set of tables for B_1 is the fundamental set for the modality '$\boxplus$'. Then we have

A	$\Box B_1$
t	f ~~f~~

A	$\Box B_1$
f	t ~~t~~

A	$\Box B_1$
t	t ~~t~~
f	t ~~t~~

So the plenary set of tables for $\ulcorner \Box B_1 \urcorner$ is the same as the fundamental set for '$\boxplus$'. That is, $\otimes$ is semantically the same as '$\boxplus$'.

(3)–(6) These four subcases are left to the reader.

But suppose B is $\ulcorner {\sim} B_1 \urcorner$. Again we have six subcases:

(1) Suppose the plenary set of tables for B_1 is the fundamental set for the modality '$\sim$'. Then we have

A	$\sim B_1$
t	t ~~f~~

A	$\sim B_1$
f	f ~~f~~

A	$\sim B_1$
t	t ~~f~~
f	f ~~f~~

So the plenary set of tables for $\otimes$ is the same as the fundamental set for '$\otimes_{11}$'. So $\otimes$ is semantically the same as '$\otimes_{11}$'.

(2) Suppose the plenary set of tables for B_1 is the fundamental set for the modality '$\boxplus$'. Then we have

A	$\sim B_1$
t	t ~~f~~

A	$\sim B_1$
f	f ~~f~~

A	$\sim B_1$
t	f ~~f~~
f	f ~~f~~

So the plenary set of tables for $\ulcorner {\sim} B_1 \urcorner$ is the same as the fundamental set for '$\Box$'. So $\otimes$ is semantically the same as '$\Box$'.

(3)–(6) These subcases are left to the reader.

By mathematical induction, therefore, we conclude that any connective definable in terms of the tilde and box is semantically the same as one of the six modalities '$\sim$', '$\otimes_{11}$', '$\Box$', '$\boxplus$', '$\Diamond$', and '$\lozenge\!\!\!\lozenge$'.

Modalities must not be confused with singulary modal connectives. On the one hand, there are sixteen singulary truth-tabular connectives, of which twelve are modal; all sixteen are definable in terms of $\{`\sim`,`v`,`\cdot`,`\square`\}$. On the other hand, there are six modalities, of which only four are modal connectives; they are the only six singulary truth-tabular connectives definable in terms of $\{`\sim`,`\square`\}$.

39.   EXERCISES

(1)   Prove that no set of truth-functional truth-tabular connectives is functionally complete.

(2)   Define the star '$\stackrel{\leftrightarrow}{\varnothing}$' in terms of $\{`\sim`,`v`,`\cdot`,`\square`\}$.

(3)   Find a ternary truth-tabular connective that is functionally complete by itself.

(4)   Let $\otimes$ be the binary connective characterized by the fundamental set of truth tables that results on simultaneously interchanging 't' and 'f' throughout the fundamental set of truth tables for the star. Prove that $\otimes$ is functionally complete by itself.

(5)   Though we have spoken of *the* characteristic wff of a plenary set of tables, there are, in fact, many characteristic wffs for such a set of truth tables. Explain why our mode of speaking was nonetheless harmless.

(6)   Reduce each of the following wffs of LSM to wffs of modal degree zero or one:

$$[\Diamond p \dashv 3\ p] \dashv 3\ \square p \qquad \Diamond \square [p \dashv 3\ q] \dashv 3\ [\Diamond q \dashv 3\ \Diamond p]$$

(7)   Can singulary connectives define only singulary connectives? Can binary connectives define only binary connectives?

(8)   Determine the modal degree of the wffs exhibited in Exercise (6). (*Hint:* Eliminate abbreviations.)

{9}   Verify that the Anselmian formula '$[\Diamond p \dashv 3\ p] \dashv 3\ [\Diamond p \supset \square p]$' is valid. Some philosophers credit St. Anselm with the discovery that the possibility of God logically implies His actuality, whence they infer that God is necessary if He is possible. Does the Anselmian formula justify their reasoning? (*Hint:* Consider an M-language wherein '*p*' means 'God exists'.) Is '$[\Diamond p \dashv 3\, p] \supset [\Diamond p \dashv 3\, \Box p]$' also valid?

(10) Explain why the variables of LSM may not be classified with respect to their values as truth-value variables. What, if anything, are the values of these variables?

(11) Prove that a set of truth-tabular connectives is functionally complete if and only if every truth-tabular connective is definable in terms of its members.

(12) Prove that a wff of LSM contains nested boxes if and only if it is of modal degree greater than one.

(13) Indicate the scope of each occurrence of a connective in the following wffs:

$$\sim p \dashv 3\, \Box \sim p \qquad [p \vee q] \vee \Diamond [p \vee q] \qquad \Box \Diamond \Box [p \otimes\!\!\!\!\times p]$$

{14} Would 'truth-tabular logic' be a more descriptive rubric than 'modal logic' for the material treated in Chapters 32–38?

(15) Prove that $\{`\sim\textrm',`\Box\textrm'\}$ and $\{`\sim\textrm',`\Diamond\textrm'\}$ serve to define exactly the same connectives. Does $\{`\sim\textrm',`\otimes_8\textrm'\}$ serve to define the same connectives as $\{`\sim\textrm',`\Box\textrm'\}$?

40. AXIOMATIC MODAL LOGIC

40.0. Primitive Basis of the System S5

Logistic systematizations of LSM are commonly known as S5 systems.[1] The particular systematization which we will study will

---

[1] The label 'S5' comes from the philosopher and logician C. I. Lewis, who used the labels ⌜S*n*⌝, where *n* is a numeral, to designate various modal calculi which he invented and studied. Roughly speaking, the larger the numeral, the stronger the modal calculus. For example, S5 is stronger than S4 in that every theorem of S4 is also a theorem of S5, but not conversely.

be referred to as S5 and is characterized by the following primitive basis:

Vocabulary of S5

  (i)   An infinite stock of sentential variables 'p', 'q', 'r', 's', 'p_1', ...

 (ii)   Grouping indicators: '[' and ']'.

(iii)   Two singulary sentence connectives: '$\sim$' and '$\Box$'.

(iv)   One binary sentence connective: '$\supset$'.

Formation Rules of S5

  (i)   A sentential variable is a wff.

 (ii)   If A is a wff, then $\ulcorner \sim A \urcorner$ and $\ulcorner \Box A \urcorner$ are also wffs.

(iii)   If A and B are wffs, then $\ulcorner [A \supset B] \urcorner$ is a wff.

(iv)   A formula is a wff if and only if it can be constructed by a finite number of applications of the preceding rules.

Axioms of S5

      Axiom 1. $p \supset [q \supset p]$.

      Axiom 2. $[p \supset (q \supset r)] \supset [(p \supset q) \supset (p \supset r)]$.

      Axiom 3. $[\sim p \supset \sim q] \supset [q \supset p]$.

      Axiom 4. $\Box p \supset p$.

      Axiom 5. $\Box [p \supset q] \supset [\Box p \supset \Box q]$.

      Axiom 6. $\sim \Box p \supset \Box \sim \Box p$.

The remaining axioms of S5 are given by the following stipulation: If A is an axiom of S5, so is $\ulcorner \Box A \urcorner$.

The last statement stipulates to be an axiom of S5 the result of prefixing any finite string of boxes to any of the first six axioms. For example, not only is '$p \supset [q \supset p]$' an axiom, but '$\Box [p \supset (q \supset p)]$' and '$\Box \Box \Box [p \supset (q \supset p)]$' are also axioms of S5. The system S5, therefore, contains infinitely many axioms. It is important to notice that the axioms of S5 remain effectively recognizable, notwithstanding their infinite multiplicity. That is, there is a simple mechanical test to determine whether or not a given wff is an axiom of S5.

Rules of Inference of S5

      Rule 1.   *Modus ponens.* (See Section 26.0.)

      Rule 2.   Substitution. (See Section 26.0.)

The concepts of *proof, theorem, proof from hypotheses, consistency,* and *completeness* are all defined for S5 as for system P (see Sections

26.1ff.) except that references to system P are, of course, changed to references to S5. For example, a *proof* is defined as a finite sequence of wffs (of S5), each of which is either an axiom (of S5) or inferable by substitution from an earlier member of the sequence or inferable by *modus ponens* from two earlier members of the sequence.

40.1. Relationship to System P; Consistency of S5

A comparison of their respective primitive bases reveals that system P is a subsystem of S5. That is, because every wff of system P is also a wff of S5, and each axiom and rule of inference of system P is an axiom or rule of inference of S5, it is evident that

M1. Every theorem of system P is a theorem of S5.

Together with our decision procedure for deciding theoremhood in system P, the metatheorem M1 enables us to recognize as theorems of S5 valid wffs of system P such as '$p \supset p$', '$\sim\sim p \supset p$', and '$[p \supset q] \supset [\sim q \supset \sim p]$'. It does not, however, certify that '$\Box p \supset \Box p$' is a theorem of S5, even though '$\Box p \supset \Box p$' is tautologous, that is, a substitution instance of the valid wff '$p \supset p$'. [See Exercise (11) of Chapter 35.] But, the primitive basis of S5 contains the rule of substitution, so it is evident that any substitution instance of a theorem of S5 is itself a theorem of S5. So we have the following lemma:

L1. Every wff of S5 that is a substitution instance of a theorem of S5 is itself a theorem of S5.

As a corollary of L1 and M1, we get the following metatheorem:

M2. Every tautologous wff of S5 is a theorem of S5.

Metatheorem M2 certifies as theorems of S5 such wffs as '$\Box p \supset \Box p$' and '$[\Diamond p \supset \Diamond q] \supset [\Box \sim q \supset \Box \sim p]$'. (It is understood, of course, that $\ulcorner \Diamond A \urcorner$ abbreviates $\ulcorner \sim\Box \sim A \urcorner$.) The metatheorems M1 and M2 make precise the sense in which S5 comprehends system P as a subsystem.

Until the semantics of its well-formed expressions is formulated, a logistic system must be regarded as an *uninterpreted calculus*, that is, as a meaningless axiomatic system. The *principal* interpretation of S5 is given by the fundamental sets of truth tables for the tilde, horseshoe, and box. Under this interpretation, S5 becomes the skeleton of a family of languages, namely of the languages that result when the variables of S5 are endowed with sense.

Under the principal interpretation of S5, some of its wffs, such as '$\sim \Box p \supset \Box \sim \Box p$', are valid, while others, such as '$\Diamond p \supset p$', are not. From the fundamental set of truth tables for the box, it is clear that

L2.   If A is valid, so is $\ulcorner \Box A \urcorner$.

Furthermore, by employing appropriate plenary sets of truth tables, the reader can verify that axioms 1–6 of S5 are all valid. From this result together with L2, we may infer that every axiom of S5 is valid. And by reasoning similar to that of Section 28.0, we can establish that both *modus ponens* and substitution preserve validity. It follows that

M3.   Every theorem of S5 is valid (consistency theorem).

That is, S5 is consistent with respect to validity.

40.2.   Deduction Theorem; Key Theorem Schemata

As mentioned above, the notion of *proof from hypotheses* in S5 is the same as in system P except for specific references to the two systems. Hence a finite sequence $B_1, B_2, \ldots, B_k$ of wffs (of S5) is a *proof of B_k from the hypotheses $A_1, A_2, \ldots, A_n$* if each B_i is either an axiom (of S5), a variant of an axiom (of S5), one of the n hypotheses, inferable by *modus ponens* from two earlier members of the sequence, or inferable by substitution from one earlier member where the variable for which substitution is made occurs in none of the n hypotheses. And we write '$A_1, A_2, \ldots, A_n \vdash B$' to mean 'there is in S5 a proof of B from the hypotheses $A_1, A_2, \ldots, A_n$'. It is left to the reader to prove that

M4.   If $A_1, A_2, \ldots, A_n \vdash B$, then $A_1, A_2, \ldots, A_{n-1} \vdash \ulcorner A_n \supset B \urcorner$ (deduction theorem).

(A proof of M4 can be given which parallels exactly the proof of the deduction theorem for system P presented in Section 30.0.) It is also left to the reader to prove [see Exercise (4) of Chapter 31] as a corollary of M4 that the class of wffs which can be proved from a set of hypotheses is not diminished by enlarging the set of hypotheses. That is, proof of M5 is left to the reader.

> M5. If $A_1, A_2, \ldots, A_n \vdash B$, then $A_1, A_2, \ldots, A_n, B_1, B_2, \ldots, B_k \vdash B$.

From the definition of proof from hypotheses, it is obvious that the order and repetition of hypotheses is irrelevant to what can be proved from them. So, from M5, we have this metatheorem:

> M6. If every wff that occurs in the list $A_1, A_2, \ldots, A_n$ also occurs in the list $B_1, B_2, \ldots, B_k$ and if $A_1, A_2, \ldots, A_n \vdash B$, then $B_1, B_2, \ldots, B_k \vdash B$.

Where '$\vDash A$' is understood to mean 'A is a theorem of S5', we have

> L3. $\vDash A$ if and only if $\vdash A$.

(To prove L3, see proof of L1 in Section 30.0.)

The following lemma will prove useful for establishing one of the key theorem schemata needed in our proof that S5 is complete with respect to validity:

> L4. If $\vdash A$, then $\vDash \ulcorner \Box A \urcorner$.

Proof of L4. Let $B_1, B_2, \ldots, B_k$ be a proof of $A (A = B_k)$. We will show how, by appropriate insertions, to convert the sequence $\ulcorner \Box B_1 \urcorner, \ulcorner \Box B_2 \urcorner, \ldots, \ulcorner \Box B_k \urcorner$ into a proof of $\ulcorner \Box B_k \urcorner$, that is, into a proof of $\ulcorner \Box A \urcorner$. If B_i is an axiom of S5, so is $\ulcorner \Box B_i \urcorner$. In this event no insertion is made immediately before $\ulcorner \Box B_i \urcorner$ in the new sequence. If B_i comes from B_j by substitution ($i > j$), then $\ulcorner \Box B_i \urcorner$ comes from $\ulcorner \Box B_j \urcorner$ by the same substitution, and again we insert nothing immediately before $\ulcorner \Box B_i \urcorner$ in the new sequence. But suppose B_i comes from two earlier lines $\ulcorner B_j \supset B_i \urcorner$ and B_j by *modus ponens*. Then, where b_1 and b_2 are distinct variables that occur in none of $B_1, B_2, \ldots, B_k$, we insert in the new sequence immediately before $\ulcorner \Box B_i \urcorner$ the following six-membered sequence:

(1)	$\Box[p \supset q] \supset [\Box p \supset \Box q]$	Axiom
(2)	$\Box[b_1 \supset q] \supset [\Box b_1 \supset \Box q]$	Sub. in (1)
(3)	$\Box[b_1 \supset b_2] \supset [\Box b_1 \supset \Box b_2]$	Sub. in (2)
(4)	$\Box[B_j \supset b_2] \supset [\Box B_j \supset \Box b_2]$	Sub. in (3)
(5)	$\Box[B_j \supset B_i] \supset [\Box B_j \supset \Box B_i]$	Sub. in (4)
(6)	$\underline{\Box B_j \supset \Box B_i}$	*Modus ponens*
	$\Box B_i$	*Modus ponens*

Because $\ulcorner \Box[B_j \supset B_i]\urcorner$ already occurs in the new sequence, (6) comes from it and (5) by *modus ponens*. Similarly, $\ulcorner \Box B_i\urcorner$ comes by *modus ponens* from (6) and the wff $\ulcorner \Box B_j\urcorner$, which also occurs somewhere earlier in the new sequence. All insertions in the new sequence having been made, it is clear that the resulting sequence is a proof of $\ulcorner \Box A\urcorner$.

We will now establish some key theorem schemata for S5:

> T1. $\vDash \Box A \supset A$.   From axiom 4 and the rule of substitution.
> T2. $\vDash \sim\Box A \supset \Box \sim\Box A$.   Axiom 6 and substitution.
> T3. $\vDash A \supset \Diamond A$.

(1)	$\vDash \Box \sim A \supset \sim A$	By T1
(2)	$\vDash A \supset \sim\Box \sim A$	From (1) via M2

The sense in which (2) comes from (1) *via* M2 needs explanation. Because it is tautologous, the wff $\ulcorner[\Box \sim A \supset \sim A] \supset [A \supset \sim\Box \sim A]\urcorner$ is certified by M2 to be a theorem of S5. Line (2) comes from this wff and line (1) by *modus ponens*. And T3, of course, merely abbreviates (2). Hereafter when such use is made of M2, we will simply remark "via M2", leaving it to the reader to fill in the missing steps.

> T4. $\vDash A \supset \Box \Diamond A$.

(1)	$\vDash \sim\Box \sim A \supset \Box \sim\Box \sim A$	By T2
(2)	$\vDash A \supset \sim\Box \sim A$	T3
(3)	$\vDash A \supset \Box \Diamond A$	From (1) and (2) via M2

> T5. $\vDash \Diamond \Box A \supset \Box A$.

(1)	$\vDash \sim\Box A \supset \Box \sim\Box A$	T2
(2)	$\vDash \sim\Box \sim\Box A \supset \Box A$	From (1) via M2

> T6. $\vDash \Box A \supset \Box \Box A$.

(1)	$\vDash \Box A \supset \Box \Diamond \Box A$	By T4
(2)	$\vDash \Box[\Diamond \Box A \supset \Box A] \supset [\Box \Diamond \Box A \supset \Box \Box A]$	From axiom 5 by sub
(3)	$\vDash \Diamond \Box A \supset \Box A$	T5
(4)	$\vDash \Box[\Diamond \Box A \supset \Box A]$	From (3) by L4
(5)	$\vDash \Box A \supset \Box \Box A$	From (1), (2), and (4) via M2

We terminate this section by proving a metatheorem essential to our proof of the completeness theorem for S5 presented in Section 40.3.

M7.   If A_1, A_2, ..., $A_n \vdash B$, then $\ulcorner \Box A_1 \urcorner$, $\ulcorner \Box A_2 \urcorner$, ..., $\ulcorner \Box A_n \urcorner \vdash \ulcorner \Box B \urcorner$.

We prove M7 by weak mathematical induction on the number of hypotheses. If there are zero hypotheses, then $\vdash B$. So by L3 and L4 we have $\vdash \ulcorner \Box B \urcorner$. Thus M7 holds for zero hypotheses. Assume that M7 holds for n hypotheses and let there be a proof of B from the $n + 1$ hypotheses A_1, A_2, ..., A_n, C. Since A_1, A_2, ..., A_n, $C \vdash B$, we have A_1, A_2, ..., $A_n \vdash \ulcorner C \supset B \urcorner$ by the deduction theorem. By the hypothesis of induction, therefore, $\ulcorner \Box A_1 \urcorner$, $\ulcorner \Box A_2 \urcorner$, ..., $\ulcorner \Box A_n \urcorner \vdash \ulcorner \Box [C \supset B] \urcorner$. But $\vdash \ulcorner \Box [C \supset B] \supset [\Box C \supset \Box B] \urcorner$ by axiom 5 and the rule of substitution. So $\ulcorner \Box A_1 \urcorner$, $\ulcorner \Box A_2 \urcorner$, ..., $\ulcorner \Box A_n \urcorner \vdash \ulcorner \Box C \supset \Box B \urcorner$. So $\ulcorner \Box A_1 \urcorner$, $\ulcorner \Box A_2 \urcorner$, ..., $\ulcorner \Box A_n \urcorner$, $\ulcorner \Box C \urcorner \vdash \ulcorner \Box B \urcorner$. Thus M7 holds for $n + 1$ hypotheses if it holds for n hypotheses. By weak mathematical induction, we infer that M7 is true.

40.3.   Completeness Theorem for S5

Except for specific reference to the particular systems, we take over unchanged from system P (see Section 30.2) the concepts of a *consistent class* of wffs (now of S5) and of a *maximal class* of wffs (of S5). It is left to the reader to prove the following lemmas by presenting proofs analogous to those given in Section 30.2 for the corresponding lemmas about system P.

L5.   Any consistent class of wffs of S5 can be extended to a maximal consistent class. (See Section 30.2 for a careful explanation of the meaning of this lemma.)

L6.   If $\bar{\Gamma}$ is a maximal consistent class of wffs (of S5), and A_1, A_2, ..., A_n all belong to $\bar{\Gamma}$, and A_1, A_2, ..., $A_n \vdash B$, then B also belongs to $\bar{\Gamma}$.

L7.   If $\bar{\Gamma}$ is a maximal consistent class of wffs (of S5) and A and B are any wffs of S5, then
  (a)   If $B \in \bar{\Gamma}$, then $\ulcorner \sim B \urcorner \notin \bar{\Gamma}$;
  (b)   If $B \notin \bar{\Gamma}$, then $\ulcorner \sim B \urcorner \in \bar{\Gamma}$;
  (c)   If $A \notin \bar{\Gamma}$, then $\ulcorner A \supset B \urcorner \in \bar{\Gamma}$;

(d)   If $B \in \bar{\Gamma}$, then $\ulcorner A \supset B \urcorner \in \bar{\Gamma}$;

(e)   If $A \in \bar{\Gamma}$ and $B \notin \bar{\Gamma}$, then $\ulcorner A \supset B \urcorner \notin \bar{\Gamma}$.

L8.   If $A_1, A_2, \ldots, A_n \vdash B$ and $A_1, A_2, \ldots, A_n \vdash \ulcorner \sim B \urcorner$, then $A_1, A_2, \ldots, A_{n-1} \vdash \ulcorner \sim A_n \urcorner$.

We are now equipped to prove the following principal meta-theorem:

M8.   If A is valid, then $\vdash A$ (completeness theorem).

The gist of M8 is that S5 is complete with respect to validity. We begin our proof of M8 by letting D be an arbitrary nontheorem of S5. (S5 is consistent with respect to validity, so some wffs of S5 are clearly not theorems, for example, '$p \supset \square p$'.) We notice first that the set $\{\ulcorner \sim D \urcorner\}$, that is, the set whose sole member is $\ulcorner \sim D \urcorner$, is a consistent class of wffs of S5. To see this, suppose $\{\ulcorner \sim D \urcorner\}$ is an inconsistent class. By the definition of an inconsistent class, then, we know that there is a wff B such that $\ulcorner \sim D \urcorner \vdash B$ and $\ulcorner \sim D \urcorner \vdash \ulcorner \sim B \urcorner$. By L8, we infer $\vdash \ulcorner \sim \sim D \urcorner$, from which $\vdash D$ follows via M2 and L3. But this contradicts the supposition that D is a nontheorem. By indirect proof, therefore, we conclude that $\{\ulcorner \sim D \urcorner\}$ is consistent. Furthermore, we know from L5 that there is at least one maximal consistent extension of $\{\ulcorner \sim D \urcorner\}$; that is, there is at least one maximal consistent class to which $\ulcorner \sim D \urcorner$ belongs. We let $\bar{\Gamma}_d$ be such a class; that is, $\bar{\Gamma}_d$ is a maximal consistent class of wffs of S5 such that $\ulcorner \sim D \urcorner \in \bar{\Gamma}_d$.

Let us say that a class Γ_1 of wffs (of S5) *necessitates* a class Γ_2 of wffs if, for every wff of the form $\ulcorner \square A \urcorner$ which belongs to Γ_1, the wff A belongs to Γ_2. We observe first that any maximal consistent class necessitates itself. To show this, let $\ulcorner \square A \urcorner$ belong to some maximal consistent class $\bar{\Gamma}$. From T1 we have $\ulcorner \square A \urcorner \vdash A$. So, by L6, we conclude that A also belongs to $\bar{\Gamma}$. Thus $\bar{\Gamma}$ necessitates itself, which is what was to be shown. We let Ω be the set of all maximal consistent classes (of wffs of S5) which are necessitated by $\bar{\Gamma}_d$. Because it necessitates itself, $\bar{\Gamma}_d$ is obviously a member of Ω. Moreover, every member of Ω is a maximal consistent class, so every member of Ω necessitates itself. The relation of necessitation, therefore, is reflexive among the members of Ω. To show that necessitation is also transitive among the members of Ω, let $\bar{\Gamma}_1, \bar{\Gamma}_2,$ and $\bar{\Gamma}_3$ be members of Ω so related that $\bar{\Gamma}_1$ necessitates $\bar{\Gamma}_2$ and $\bar{\Gamma}_2$ necessitates $\bar{\Gamma}_3$. Let $\ulcorner \square A \urcorner$ be a member of $\bar{\Gamma}_1$. If we can show that $A \in \bar{\Gamma}_3$, we will have shown that $\bar{\Gamma}_1$ necessitates $\bar{\Gamma}_3$, thus establishing the transitivity of necessitation among the members of Ω. By T6, we have $\ulcorner\Box A\urcorner \vdash \ulcorner\Box\Box A\urcorner$. By L6, then, $\ulcorner\Box\Box A\urcorner \in \bar{\Gamma}_1$. $\bar{\Gamma}_1$ necessitates $\bar{\Gamma}_2$, so we have $\ulcorner\Box A\urcorner \in \bar{\Gamma}_2$. And similarly, $\bar{\Gamma}_2$ necessitates $\bar{\Gamma}_3$, so we have $A \in \bar{\Gamma}_3$. So much, then, for transitivity. To prove that necessitation is symmetrical among the members of Ω, we assume that $\bar{\Gamma}_1$ necessitates $\bar{\Gamma}_2$ but that $\bar{\Gamma}_2$ does not necessitate $\bar{\Gamma}_1$. There is, then, some wff A such that $\ulcorner\Box A\urcorner \in \bar{\Gamma}_2$ while $A \notin \bar{\Gamma}_1$. By clause (b) of L7, therefore, $\ulcorner\sim A\urcorner \in \bar{\Gamma}_1$. Clearly, in view of T1 and L6, if $\ulcorner\Box A\urcorner \in \bar{\Gamma}_1$, then A would be a member of $\bar{\Gamma}_1$, thus rendering $\bar{\Gamma}_1$ inconsistent. So $\ulcorner\Box A\urcorner \notin \bar{\Gamma}_1$. By L7, then, $\ulcorner\sim\Box A\urcorner \in \bar{\Gamma}_1$. And since $\ulcorner\sim\Box A\urcorner \vdash \ulcorner\Box\sim\Box A\urcorner$ by T2, we have $\ulcorner\Box\sim\Box A\urcorner \in \bar{\Gamma}_1$ from L6. But since $\bar{\Gamma}_1$ necessitates $\bar{\Gamma}_2$, it follows that $\ulcorner\sim\Box A\urcorner \in \bar{\Gamma}_2$. Both $\ulcorner\Box A\urcorner$ and $\ulcorner\sim\Box A\urcorner$ belong to $\bar{\Gamma}_2$, so $\bar{\Gamma}_2$ is inconsistent, contrary to our assumption that it is maximal consistent. By indirect proof we conclude that $\bar{\Gamma}_2$ necessitates $\bar{\Gamma}_1$ if $\bar{\Gamma}_1$ necessitates $\bar{\Gamma}_2$. Thus necessitation is symmetrical among the members of Ω. We have shown, therefore, that necessitation is an equivalence relation on the members of Ω.

Let $d_1, d_2, \ldots, d_n$ be a complete list of the distinct variables that occur in the given nontheorem D. With each member $\bar{\Gamma}$ of Ω we correlate an n-tuple $\langle\alpha_1, \alpha_2, \ldots, \alpha_n\rangle$ of truth values in the following manner. We let α_1 be truth or falsehood according as $d_i \in \bar{\Gamma}$ or $d_i \notin \bar{\Gamma}$. (It is quite possible that the same n-tuple of truth values is thus correlated with many members of Ω.) Let $\langle\alpha_1^1, \alpha_2^1, \ldots, \alpha_n^1\rangle$, $\langle\alpha_1^2, \alpha_2^2, \ldots, \alpha_n^2\rangle$, $\ldots$, $\langle\alpha_1^k, \alpha_2^k, \ldots, \alpha_n^k\rangle$ be a complete list of the distinct n-tuples of truth values thus correlated with members of Ω. (Obviously, $1 \leq k \leq 2^n$.) Using these n-tuples, we construct the following truth table T:

d_1	d_2	$\ldots$	d_n	B
α_1^1	α_2^1	$\ldots$	α_n^1	
α_1^2	$\ldots$			
$\cdot$				
$\cdot$				
$\cdot$				
α_1^k	α_2^k	$\ldots$	α_n^k	

Let B be any wff of S5 in which there occur no variables besides $d_1, d_2, \ldots, d_n$. We will now show that B has the following property, which we shall call ϕ: The value of B on row j of T is truth if and only if B belongs to every class $\bar{\Gamma}$ of Ω correlated with row j, that is, correlated with $\langle \alpha_1^j, \alpha_2^j, \ldots, \alpha_n^j \rangle$, and the value of B is falsehood on row j of T if and only if B belongs to none of the classes $\bar{\Gamma}$ of Ω correlated with row j. Our proof will proceed by strong mathematical induction on the number of occurrences of connectives in B. If there are zero occurrences of connectives in B, then B is one of the variables $d_1, d_2, \ldots, d_n$. It then is evident from the way the n-tuples of truth values were correlated with members of Ω that B has ϕ; that is, B is true on row j if and only if B belongs to every class $\bar{\Gamma}$ correlated with row j, and B is false on row j if and only if B belongs to no class $\bar{\Gamma}$ correlated with row j. As the hypothesis of induction, we suppose that any wff which contains no variables besides $d_1, d_2, \ldots, d_n$ and which contains r or fewer occurrences of connectives has the property ϕ. Assume, then, that B contains $r + 1$ occurrences of connectives. B must have one of the three forms $\ulcorner \sim B_1 \urcorner$, $\ulcorner B_1 \supset B_2 \urcorner$, or $\ulcorner \Box B_1 \urcorner$. Suppose, first, that $B = \ulcorner \sim B_1 \urcorner$. B_1 falls under the hypothesis of induction, so we know that B_1 has ϕ. If B_1 is true on row j of T, then B_1 belongs to every class $\bar{\Gamma}$ correlated with row j. By clause (a) of L7, therefore, $\ulcorner \sim B_1 \urcorner$ belongs to none of the classes $\bar{\Gamma}$ correlated with row j. Moreover, in virtue of the semantics of the tilde, $\ulcorner \sim B_1 \urcorner$ is false on row j of T. So if B_1 is true on row j, then B has ϕ. If B_1 is false on row j, the hypothesis of induction entails that B_1 belongs to none of the classes $\bar{\Gamma}$ correlated with row j. By clause (b) of L7, then, $\ulcorner \sim B_1 \urcorner$ belongs to every such $\bar{\Gamma}$, and $\ulcorner \sim B_1 \urcorner$ clearly comes out true on row j of T. So if B_1 is false on row j, B also has ϕ. It follows from what we have proved that B has ϕ if B has the form $\ulcorner \sim B_1 \urcorner$. It is left to the reader to show that B has ϕ when $B = \ulcorner B_1 \supset B_2 \urcorner$. We now treat the last and most difficult case, when $B = \ulcorner \Box B_1 \urcorner$. Let us begin by supposing that $\ulcorner \Box B_1 \urcorner$ comes out false on row j of T, but that $\ulcorner \Box B_1 \urcorner$ belongs to at least one class $\bar{\Gamma}$ correlated with row j, say $\bar{\Gamma}_j$. From the semantics of the box, then, we know that B_1 comes out false on some row of T, say row m. Since B_1 comes under the hypothesis of induction, B_1 has ϕ. So B_1 belongs to none of the classes $\bar{\Gamma}$ correlated with row m. Each member of Ω necessitates every member thereof, so B_1 belongs to every member of Ω because $\ulcorner \Box B_1 \urcorner \in \bar{\Gamma}_j$. In particular, B_1 belongs to every class $\bar{\Gamma}$ correlated with row m of T, which contradicts our result that B_1 belongs to none of those classes. By indirect proof, therefore, if $\ulcorner \Box B_1 \urcorner$ comes out false on row j of T, then $\ulcorner \Box B_1 \urcorner$ belongs to none of the classes $\bar{\Gamma}$ correlated with row j.

Suppose, however, that $\ulcorner \Box B_1 \urcorner$ comes out true on row j of T, but that $\ulcorner \Box B_1 \urcorner$ does not belong to some class $\bar{\Gamma}$ correlated with row j, say $\bar{\Gamma}_j$. By the semantics of the box, then, B_1 comes out true on every row of T. By the hypothesis of induction, therefore, B_1 belongs to any class $\bar{\Gamma}$ correlated with any row of T. Or, in other words, B_1 belongs to every member of Ω. Let Γ be the set of all wffs C such that $\ulcorner \Box C \urcorner$ is a member of $\bar{\Gamma}_j$. Clearly Γ is a subclass of any class necessitated by $\bar{\Gamma}_j$. It follows, then, that Γ is a subclass of every member of Ω, because each member of Ω is necessitated by $\bar{\Gamma}_j$. Clearly, too, $\bar{\Gamma}_j$ necessitates Γ. We now show that the class $\Gamma \cup \{\ulcorner \sim B_1 \urcorner\}$ is inconsistent. To prove this, we suppose that $\Gamma \cup \{\ulcorner \sim B_1 \urcorner\}$ is consistent. By L5, this class can be extended to a maximal consistent class $\bar{\Delta}$. $\Gamma \cup \{\ulcorner \sim B_1 \urcorner\}$ is a subclass of $\bar{\Delta}$, so obviously Γ_j necessitates $\bar{\Delta}$. It follows readily that $\bar{\Gamma}_d$ also necessitates $\bar{\Delta}$. So $\bar{\Delta}$ is a member of Ω. But we proved above that B_1 belongs to every member of Ω, hence to $\bar{\Delta}$. $\ulcorner \sim B_1 \urcorner$ also belongs to $\bar{\Delta}$, so $\bar{\Delta}$ is inconsistent, contrary to our assumption that $\bar{\Delta}$ is a maximal consistent extension of $\Gamma \cup \{\ulcorner \sim B_1 \urcorner\}$. By indirect proof, therefore, we conclude that the class $\Gamma \cup \{\ulcorner \sim B_1 \urcorner\}$ is inconsistent. By the definition of an inconsistent class, then, there are finitely many members $C_1, C_2, \ldots, C_s$ of $\bar{\Gamma} \cup \{\ulcorner \sim B_1 \urcorner\}$ such that $C_1, C_2, \ldots, C_s$, $\ulcorner \sim B_1 \urcorner \vdash C$ and $C_1, C_2, \ldots, C_s, \ulcorner \sim B_1 \urcorner \vdash \ulcorner \sim C \urcorner$ for some wff C. By L8 and M2, then, $C_1, C_2, \ldots, C_s \vdash B_1$. So by M7, $\ulcorner \Box C_1 \urcorner, \ulcorner \Box C_2 \urcorner$, $\ldots, \ulcorner \Box C_s \urcorner \vdash \ulcorner \Box B_1 \urcorner$. $C_1, C_2, \ldots, C_s$ all belong to Γ, so it follows from the definition of Γ that $\ulcorner \Box C_1 \urcorner, \ulcorner \Box C_2 \urcorner, \ldots, \ulcorner \Box C_s \urcorner$ all belong to $\bar{\Gamma}_j$. By L6, therefore, $\ulcorner \Box B_1 \urcorner$ also belongs to $\bar{\Gamma}_j$. This, however, contradicts our initial supposition that $\ulcorner \Box B_1 \urcorner$ does not belong to $\bar{\Gamma}_j$. So we conclude by indirect proof that if $\ulcorner \Box B_1 \urcorner$ comes out true on a row of T, then it is a member of every class $\bar{\Gamma}$ correlated with that row. We have just shown that, whether $\ulcorner \Box B_1 \urcorner$ comes out true or false on a row of T, $\ulcorner \Box B_1 \urcorner$ has the property ϕ. Taking the three subcases together, we have seen that where B contains $r + 1$ occurrences of connectives, B has ϕ if all wffs have ϕ that contain r or fewer occurrences of connectives and no variables except d_1, $d_2, \ldots, d_n$. By strong mathematical induction, we infer that every wff B that contains no variables other than $d_1, d_2, \ldots, d_n$ possesses ϕ. Since the given nontheorem D is such a wff, D has the property ϕ. Since $\ulcorner \sim D \urcorner$ belongs to $\bar{\Gamma}_d$, we know that D does not belong to

$\bar{\Gamma}_d$. By the definition of ϕ, therefore, D does not come out true on the row of T correlated with $\bar{\Gamma}_d$. So D comes out false on that row of T. (Clearly the semantics of the connectives of D determines a truth value for D on every row of T.) So D, an arbitrary non-theorem of S5, is not valid. From this it follows that if a wff of S5 is valid, then it is a theorem of S5. This terminates our proof of M8.

40.4.   The System S5′ (Completeness)

A systematization of LSM quite different from S5 is the strikingly elegant logistic system[2] which we will call S5′. The vocabulary and formation rules of S5′ are the same as those of S5. Unlike S5, the system S5′ contains only a finite number of axioms, the three axioms of System P:

Axiom 1. $p \supset [q \supset p]$.
Axiom 2. $[p \supset (q \supset r)] \supset [(p \supset q) \supset (p \supset r)]$.
Axiom 3. $[{\sim}p \supset {\sim}q] \supset [q \supset p]$.

Before formulating the rules of inference for S5′, we introduce some special terminology. We will say that an occurrence of a sentential variable b in a wff B is *modalized in B* if that occurrence of b is part of the scope of an occurrence of '$\square$' in B. For example, all occurrences of 'p' except the third are modalized in

$$\square[\square p \supset p] \supset [{\sim}p \supset \square(q \supset p)].$$

A wff A will be said to be *fully modalized* if all occurrences of sentential variables in A are modalized in A. For example, neither '$\square p \supset [\square q \supset p]$' nor '$\square p \supset [q \supset \square p]$' is fully modalized; however, both '$\square\square[p \supset q]$' and '$\square p \supset \square[q \supset {\sim}r]$' are fully modalized. We now state the rules of inference of S5′.

Rule 1.   *Modus ponens.*
Rule 2.   Substitution.
Rule 3.   From $\ulcorner A \supset B \urcorner$, one may infer $\ulcorner \square A \supset B \urcorner$.
Rule 4.   If A is fully modalized, then one may infer $\ulcorner A \supset \square B \urcorner$ from $\ulcorner A \supset B \urcorner$.

Rule 3, for example, licenses the inference from '$p \supset [q \supset \square r]$' to '$\square p \supset [q \supset \square r]$'; rule 4 licenses no inference from '$p \supset [q \supset \square r]$'

---

[2] Due to A. N. Prior.

because the antecedent of that wff is not fully modalized. But rule 4 does authorize the inference from '$[\Box p \supset \Box \sim q] \supset q$' to '$[\Box p \supset \Box \sim q] \supset \Box q$'.

Because every axiom and rule of inference of system P is also an axiom or rule of inference of S5′, and one of those rules is substitution, it is evident that S5′ comprehends system P as a subsystem in the sense of the following metatheorem:

M1.   Every tautologous wff of S5′ is a theorem of S5′.

And it so happens that S5 is also a subsystem of S5′ in the sense that

M2.   Every theorem of S5 is also a theorem of S5′.

To prove M2, it clearly suffices to show that every axiom of S5 is a theorem of S5′ and, what is obvious, that every rule of inference of S5 is also a rule of inference of S5′. (In the context of discussion about S5′, the expression '$\vDash A$' means 'A is a theorem of S5″.) First we have

T1. $\vDash \Box p \supset p$.

(1)	$\vDash p \supset p$	By M1
(2)	$\vDash \Box p \supset p$	From (1) by R3

T2. $\vDash \sim \Box p \supset \Box \sim \Box p$.

(1)	$\vDash \sim \Box p \supset \sim \Box p$	By M1
(2)	$\vDash \sim \Box p \supset \Box \sim \Box p$	From (1) by R4

T3. $\vDash \Box[p \supset q] \supset [\Box p \supset \Box q]$

(1)	$\vDash p \supset [(p \supset q) \supset q]$	By M1
(2)	$\vDash \Box p \supset [(p \supset q) \supset q]$	From (1) by R3
(3)	$\vDash [p \supset q] \supset [\Box p \supset q]$	From (2) via M1
(4)	$\vDash \Box[p \supset q] \supset [\Box p \supset q]$	From (3) by R3
(5)	$\vDash \Box[p \supset q] \cdot \Box p \supset q$	From (4) via M1 and abbreviation
(6)	$\vDash \Box[p \supset q] \cdot \Box p \supset \Box q$	From (5) by R4
(7)	$\vDash \Box[p \supset q] \supset [\Box p \supset \Box q]$	From (6) via M1

So far we know only that the first six axioms of S5 are theorems of S5′. Because the other axioms of S5 are obtained by prefixing strings of boxes to the first six axioms, we will have shown that every axiom of S5 is a theorem of S5′ when we have proved the following lemma:

L1.   If A is a theorem of S5′, so is $\ulcorner \Box A \urcorner$.

Where A is an arbitrary theorem of S5′, we have

(1)	$\vDash A \supset [(\Box p \supset \Box p) \supset A]$	By M1
(2)	$\vDash A$	Assumption
(3)	$\vDash [\Box p \supset \Box p] \supset A$	From (1) and (2) by *modus ponens*
(4)	$\vDash [\Box p \supset \Box p] \supset \Box A$	From (3) by R4
(5)	$\vDash \Box p \supset \Box p$	By M1
(6)	$\vDash \Box A$	From (4) and (5) by *modus ponens*

This terminates our proof of M2. From M2 and the completeness theorem for S5, we draw the following metatheorem:

M3.   Every valid wff of S5′ is a theorem of S5′ (completeness theorem).

40.5.   The System S5′ (Consistency)

Metatheorem M3 tells us that whatever can be proved in S5 can also be proved in S5′. We now set for ourselves the task of showing that nothing else can be proved in S5′, that is, that S5 and S5′ have exactly the same theorems. Essentially what we must show is that S5′ is consistent with respect to validity. This consistency result, together with the consistency theorem for S5 and the completeness theorems for S5 and S5′, entails that S5 and S5′ have the same theorems. First, we establish a useful lemma:

L2.   If A is fully modalized and T is a truth table for A, then the value of A is either truth on every row of T or falsehood on every row of T.

The table T may, of course, be either partial or full. To say that T is a truth table for A is merely to say that each variable of A heads one of the value assignment columns of T. We prove L2 by strong mathematical induction on the number of occurrences of connectives in A. Let A be a fully modalized wff with just one occurrence of a connective. Then A has the form $\ulcorner \Box b \urcorner$, where b is a sentential variable. And it is evident from the semantics of the box that L2 is true when $A = \ulcorner \Box b \urcorner$. For the hypothesis of induction, we assume that L2 is true when A is any wff with n or fewer occurrences of connectives. Let A be a fully modalized wff with $n + 1$ occurrences of connectives. Then A has one of the three forms $\ulcorner \Box A_1 \urcorner$, $\ulcorner \sim A_1 \urcorner$, or $\ulcorner A_1 \supset A_2 \urcorner$. Suppose $A = \ulcorner \Box A_1 \urcorner$. Then L2 is obviously true of $\ulcorner \Box A_1 \urcorner$ in virtue of the semantics of the box. But suppose $A = \ulcorner \sim A_1 \urcorner$. A_1 falls under the hypothesis of induction, so L2 is true of A_1. By the semantics of the tilde, therefore, L2 is true of $\ulcorner \sim A_1 \urcorner$. Suppose, however, that $A = \ulcorner A_1 \supset A_2 \urcorner$. Both A_1 and A_2 fall under the hypothesis of induction, so L2 is true of both of them. So the truth value α accrues to A_1 on every row of T; similarly, the truth value β accrues to A_2 on every row of T. So $\ulcorner A_1 \supset A_2 \urcorner$ is true on every row of T unless α is truth and β is falsehood; in the latter event, the value of $\ulcorner A_1 \supset A_2 \urcorner$ is falsehood on every row of T. In either event, then, L2 is true of $\ulcorner A_1 \supset A_2 \urcorner$. By strong mathematical induction, therefore, we conclude that L2 is universally true.

For its own interest, we draw as a corollary of L2 the following metatheorem:

M4. If A is fully modalized, then A is equivalent to $\ulcorner \Box A \urcorner$.

Suppose that A is fully modalized and that T is a truth table for A. By L2, the value of A is truth on every row of T or falsehood on every row of T. If A is true on every row of T, then the value of $\ulcorner \Box A \urcorner$ is also truth on every row of T in virtue of the semantics of the box. And, if A is false on every row of T, clearly the value of $\ulcorner \Box A \urcorner$ is also falsehood on every row of T. In sum, whatever be the values of A on rows of T, A and $\ulcorner \Box A \urcorner$ agree in truth value on each row of T. T was an arbitrary truth table, so it follows that A and $\ulcorner \Box A \urcorner$ agree in truth value on every row of every table in a plenary set of truth tables for A and $\ulcorner \Box A \urcorner$. Or, in other words, A is equivalent to $\ulcorner \Box A \urcorner$.

M5. Every theorem of S5′ is valid (consistency theorem).

To prove M5 it suffices to show that each axiom of S5′ is valid and that each rule of inference of S5′ preserves validity. In proving the consistency of S5 in Section 40.1, we observed that the three axioms of S5′ are valid and that the first two rules of S5′, *modus ponens* and substitution, preserve validity. Rule 3 is easily dispatched by verifying, by means of a plenary set of truth tables, that $\ulcorner [A \supset B] \supset [\Box A \supset B] \urcorner$ is valid. Clearly, therefore, if $\ulcorner A \supset B \urcorner$ is valid, so is $\ulcorner \Box A \supset B \urcorner$. Therefore, R3 preserves validity. To see that R4 preserves validity, suppose that A is fully modalized and that $\ulcorner A \supset B \urcorner$ is valid. It is to be shown that $\ulcorner A \supset \Box B \urcorner$ is also valid. Suppose that $\ulcorner A \supset \Box B \urcorner$ is not valid. Then there is a row of some truth table T on which the value of A is truth and the value of $\ulcorner \Box B \urcorner$ is falsehood. By the semantics of the box, then, the value of B is falsehood on some row or other of T, say row r. A is fully modalized, so we know from L2 that the value of A is truth on every row of T, in particular on row r of T. By the semantics of the horseshoe, therefore, the value of $\ulcorner A \supset B \urcorner$ is falsehood on row r of T. So $\ulcorner A \supset B \urcorner$ is not valid, which contradicts our initial supposition. By indirect proof we conclude that $\ulcorner A \supset \Box B \urcorner$ is valid if A is fully modalized and $\ulcorner A \supset B \urcorner$ is valid. In other words, R4 preserves validity. This terminates our proof of the consistency theorem for S5′.

41.   EXERCISES

(1)   Prove that the addition of the following rule of inference to the primitive basis of S5 would yield no new theorems: From A, infer $\ulcorner \Box A \urcorner$.

(2)   Prove that *modus ponens* and substitution are independent rules in S5. (*Hint:* To prove the independence of substitution, show that without it no theorem would contain any variables besides 'p', 'q', and 'r'.) Notice that there is no upper bound on the length of axioms in S5.

(3)   Prove that the theorems of S5″ are the same as those of S5, where S5″ has this primitive basis:

Vocabulary of S5″: same as vocabulary of S5.

Formation rules of S5″: same as S5.

Axioms of S5″: the first six axioms of S5.

Rules of inference of S5″:

  (i)   *Modus ponens.*

  (ii)   Substitution.

  (iii)   From A, infer $\ulcorner \Box A \urcorner$ (rule of necessitation).

(4) Why was the detour through b_1 and b_2 necessary in the proof of L4 in Section 40.2? Or, put otherwise, why would it be sometimes unsatisfactory to put the following four-line sequence in front of $\ulcorner \square B_i \urcorner$ instead of the six-line sequence prescribed in our proof?

(1)	$\square[p \supset q] \supset [\square p \supset \square q]$	Axiom
(2)	$\square[B_j \supset q] \supset [\square B_j \supset \square q]$	Sub. in (1)
(3)	$\square[B_j \supset B_i] \supset [\square B_j \supset \square B_i]$	Sub in (2)
(4)	$\underline{\square B_j \supset \square B_i}$	*Modus ponens*
	$\square B_i$	*Modus ponens*

[5] Prove that S5 is not absolutely complete. (*Hint:* Show that the addition of '$p \supset \square p$' as an axiom yields an absolutely consistent system. "Interpreting" $\ulcorner \square A \urcorner$ as $\ulcorner \otimes_{11} A \urcorner$, show that all the theorems of the new system are "valid".) Similarly, prove that neither S5′ nor S5″ is absolutely complete.

(6) State the primitive basis of a Polish-notation version of S5.

(7) Prove that if rule 4 of S5′ were replaced by the following rule, the resulting system would be inconsistent with respect to validity: From $\ulcorner A \supset B \urcorner$, infer $\ulcorner A \supset \square B \urcorner$.

(8) Where A is a fully modalized wff of S5, prove that A, $\ulcorner \diamondsuit A \urcorner$, and $\ulcorner \square A \urcorner$ are all equivalent to one another.

(9) Show that the following logistic system has the same theorems as S5:

Vocabulary: same as S5.

Formation rules: same as S5.

Axioms:

(i) Six axiom schemata (each schema yields an infinity of axioms):

$A \supset [B \supset A]$

$[A \supset (B \supset C)] \supset [(A \supset B) \supset (A \supset C)]$

$[\sim A \supset \sim B] \supset [B \supset A]$

$\square A \supset A$

$\square[A \supset B] \supset [\square A \supset \square B]$

$\sim \square A \supset \square \sim \square A$

(ii) If A is an axiom, so is $\ulcorner \square A \urcorner$.

Rule of inference: *modus ponens*.

(10) Carefully explain the sense in which S5 systematizes LSM. (See Section 30.4 for the sense in which system P systematizes LSP.)

[11] The system that results when axiom 6 is replaced by
'$\Box p \supset \Box\Box p$' in the primitive basis of S5 is called "S4".
(Notice that none of the axioms of S5 which are formed by
putting boxes in front of axiom 6 will be axioms of S4.)
Prove that '$\sim\Box p \supset \Box\sim\Box p$' is not a theorem of S4. (*Hint:*
Show that all the axioms of S4 have the value 1 under every
assignment of the values 1, 2, 3, and 4 to their variables,
and that *modus ponens* and substitution preserve validity,
when 1 and 2 are taken as the designated truth values, and
the connectives of S4 are given the following truth tables:

$\supset$	1	2	3	4	$\sim$	$\Box$
1	1	2	3	4	4	1
2	1	1	3	3	3	4
3	1	2	1	2	2	3
4	1	1	1	1	1	4

To help the reader decipher the tables above, we rewrite the
familiar tables for '$\supset$' and '$\sim$' in the same space-saving
format:

$\supset$	t	f	$\sim$
t	t	f	f
f	t	t	t

[12] Prove that there is no finite characteristic matrix for S5.
See Exercise $\langle 14 \rangle$ of Chapter 29 for an explanation of the
relevant notions. (*Hint:* Assume that there is such a matrix.
Let $\{\alpha_1, \ldots, \alpha_n\}$ be the set of truth values. Show that
'$(p_1 \equiv p_2) \vee (p_1 \equiv p_3) \vee \ldots \vee (p_1 \equiv p_{n+1}) \vee (p_2 \equiv p_3) \vee$
$(p_2 \equiv p_4) \vee \ldots \vee (p_2 \equiv p_{n+1}) \vee \ldots \vee (p_n \equiv p_{n+1})$' is not a
theorem of S5, by finding a false interpretation of it with
respect to the principal semantics of S5. Then show that the
aforementioned wff is valid with respect to the alleged finite
characteristic matrix. Make use of the fact that '$p \equiv p$' is
valid with respect to the matrix, because '$p \equiv p$' is a theorem
of S5, and the fact that, if the value of A_j is one of the values
that '$p \equiv p$' takes on under interpretation, then $\ulcorner A_1 \vee \ldots \vee A_j \vee \ldots \vee A_r \urcorner$ has a designated value.)

PART FOUR
Quantification Theory

42. ATOMIC ANALYSIS

42.0. Molecular Analysis versus Atomic Analysis

Thus far sentences have been our ultimate units of logical analysis. The only sentences we were able to resolve into more basic components were compound sentences. Compound sentences were resolved into component sentences joined by (truth-functional or modal) sentence connectives. Analysis of sentence structure which terminates thus at sentences will be called *molecular analysis* to suggest that it lays bare only gross structure. Truth-functional analysis, for example, is a species of molecular analysis.

Atomic analysis lays bare internal structure of noncompound sentences. There are many arguments, some of them quite simple, whose correctness turns on atomic structure alone or on atomic structure and molecular structure together. Such, for example, are the following correct arguments:

(1)   The Eiffel Tower is 1056 feet high.
      Therefore, something is 1056 feet high.
(2)   Triangles are plane figures.
      Euclid constructed a triangle.
      Euclid, therefore, constructed a plane figure.

At the molecular level of P-languages the best we can do with argument (1) is to let '*p*' mean that the Eiffel Tower is 1056 feet high, and to let '*q*' mean that something is 1056 feet high. This analysis does not substantiate the correctness of (1) because it fails to render the relevant atomic structure explicit. Molecular analysis is similarly powerless to substantiate the correctness of (2). In the pages immediately following we shall develop a combined theory of atomic analysis and molecular analysis which is adequate to the logical investigation not only of simple arguments such as those above but of practically all arguments whatsoever. This theory is variously known as *quantification theory*, *first-order logic*, or *lower predicate logic*.

42.1. Singular Terms

By a *singular term* we shall understand an expression that purports to denote or refer to exactly one thing. The following expressions, for example, are all singular terms: 'Abraham Lincoln', 'Santa

Claus', 'the tallest building in New York City in 1969', 'the brother of John F. Kennedy', and 'the largest prime number'. Singular terms that, in fact, do denote or refer to exactly one thing shall be called *referring* singular terms. Of the five singular terms exhibited above, only the first and third are referring. The others are *non-referring* singular terms, either because there is nothing they denote (as with 'Santa Claus' and 'the largest prime number') or because there is more than one thing which they denote (as with 'the brother of John F. Kennedy').

Whether a singular term is referring or nonreferring is ordinarily a matter that calls for empirical investigation. No amount of reflection on the meaning of 'the brother of John F. Kennedy' will disclose whether that singular term uniquely refers; one must also look into John F. Kennedy's family history. There are exceptions, however. Analysis of the meaning of the expression 'the singulary truth-functional connective functionally complete by itself' can establish that that singular term is nonreferring.

42.2. Predicates and Circled Numerals

The sentence 'The Eiffel Tower is 1056 feet high' is formed by attaching the expression 'is 1056 feet high' to the singular term 'the Eiffel Tower'. Similarly, by attaching 'fell on' to the singular terms 'the oak tree' and 'the garage' one gets the sentence 'The oak tree fell on the garage'. And the expression 'slapped ... on the face' attaches to 'Dorothy' and 'Clarence' to yield the sentence 'Dorothy slapped Clarence on the face'. Expressions that yield sentences when thus attached to singular terms are called *predicates*. For example, 'is 1056 feet high', 'fell on', and 'slapped ... on the face' are all predicates.

Notice how very irregularly predicates attach to singular terms to form sentences. With 'fell on', the singular terms are put at either end. With 'slapped ... on the face', one singular term goes out in front and one goes in the middle. Furthermore, the number of singular terms to which a predicate attaches is sometimes ambiguous. To how many singular terms, for example, does 'attacked' attach to generate a sentence? By the *degree of* a predicate let us provisionally understand the number of singular terms to which it attaches to form a sentence, a predicate of degree n being called an *n-ary* predicate. We can now rephrase our question about 'attacked' as a question of what its degree is, singulary or binary.

Dots could be used to put order into the above-described chaos, but it is more convenient to adopt Quine's device of circled numerals for this purpose. Rather than write '... slapped ... on the face' to indicate where the singular terms go, we shall write '① slapped ② on the face' instead. One attaches an n-ary predicate ϕ to a sequence $\langle t_1, t_2, \ldots, t_n \rangle$ of singular terms by replacing each occurrence of the circled numeral $\ulcorner \textcircled{i} \urcorner$ in ϕ by an occurrence of t_i, $1 \le i \le n$. For example, the binary predicate '① loves ②' attaches to the sequence $\langle$'John','Mary'$\rangle$ of singular terms to generate the sentence 'John loves Mary', while '② loves ①' attaches to that same sequence to yield 'Mary loves John'. And the ternary predicate '① lives next to ③ who secretly admires ② who is a cousin of ①' attaches to the sequence of singular terms $\langle$'Floyd','Dorothy','Clarence'$\rangle$ to form the sentence 'Floyd lives next to Clarence who secretly admires Dorothy who is a cousin of Floyd'. Corresponding to 'attacked' are the singulary predicate '① attacked' and the binary predicate '① attacked ②'. The binary predicate attaches to $\langle$'the Israelis', 'the Arabs'$\rangle$ to yield the sentence 'The Israelis attacked the Arabs'. The singulary predicate attaches to 'the Arabs' to form 'The Arabs attacked'.

An n-ary predicate may now be described as a predicate that contains at least one occurrence of $\ulcorner \textcircled{n} \urcorner$ and of every smaller circled numeral but no occurrences of any larger circled numerals. Notice that the degree of a predicate is independent of the number of occurrences of circled numerals it contains. For example, although it contains two occurrences of circled numerals, the predicate '① is identical with ①' is singulary. Thus it attaches to 'Santa Claus' to generate the sentence 'Santa Claus is identical with Santa Claus'.

We have seen that substitution of singular terms for the circled numerals of a predicate generates a sentence. This suggests that the reverse process of replacing singular terms with circled numerals generates predicates. For example, by replacing in every possible way the singular terms of the sentence 'Oedipus married Jocasta' with circled numerals, we generate the five predicates exhibited below:

Singulary $\begin{cases} \text{① married Jocasta} \\ \text{Oedipus married ①} \\ \text{① married ①} \end{cases}$

Binary $\begin{cases} \text{① married ②} \\ \text{② married ①} \end{cases}$

The two binary predicates displayed above must be kept quite distinct. The first attaches to ⟨'Oedipus','Jocasta'⟩ to give 'Oedipus married Jocasta', but the second attaches to that same sequence of singular terms to form 'Jocasta married Oedipus'. Note that the generation of predicates through replacement of singular terms by circled numerals does not require that every occurrence of a singular term be supplanted by an occurrence of the same circled numeral. Indeed, as the above example shows, some singular terms may not be supplanted at all.

42.3.   Transparent versus Opaque Predicates

The predicate '① is white' may be regarded as *true of* every white thing and as *false of* everything else. For example, it is true of the Taj Mahal but false of the Caribbean Sea. Similarly, the predicate '① > ②' may be regarded as true of every ordered pair ⟨α,β⟩ such that α is a larger number than β, and as false of every other ordered pair. For example, it is true of the pair ⟨the number nine, the number seven⟩ but false of the pair ⟨the number three, the number twelve⟩. Predicates such as the foregoing manifest a remarkable indifference as to which referring singular terms they attach to form a sentence with a given truth value. For example, the predicate '① is white' not only attaches to 'the Taj Mahal' to form a true sentence, but it attaches to *any* singular term that refers to the Taj Mahal to form a true sentence. And '① is white' attaches to any singular term that refers to the Caribbean Sea to form a false sentence. Similarly, '① > ②' attaches to any ordered pair of singular terms, which refer, respectively, to nine and seven, to form a true sentence. For example, it attaches to ⟨'9','7'⟩ and to ⟨'the number of planets', '7'⟩ to form a true sentence. And '① > ②' attaches to any ordered pair of singular terms, which refer, respectively, to three and twelve, to form a false sentence. Predicates that manifest such indifference to referring singular terms will be said to be *transparent*.

Not all predicates are transparent. Although '9' and 'the number of planets' refer to the same thing, the predicate 'Necessarily ① > ②' attaches to ⟨'9','7'⟩ to form a true sentence whereas it attaches to ⟨'the number of planets', '7'⟩ to yield a false one. Predicates such as this are said to be *opaque*. The truth value of a sentence formed by attaching an opaque predicate to a sequence of referring singular terms depends on more than the referents of those singular terms. In the case of transparent predicates, however, the truth value of the resulting sentence depends only on the referents of the singular terms.

The aforesaid truth-value indifference of transparent predicates to singular terms has led logicians to introduce the notion of the *extension* of a transparent predicate, a concept that looks beyond referring singular terms to the referents behind them. By the *extension of* an n-ary transparent predicate ϕ is meant the set of all n-tuples $\langle \alpha_1, \ldots, \alpha_n \rangle$ such that ϕ is true of $\langle \alpha_1, \ldots, \alpha_n \rangle$. For example, the set of all wedded couples is the extension of the transparent predicate '① is married to ②', the empty set is the extension of '① is a unicorn', and the set of primes is the extension of the transparent predicate '① is a positive integer divisible only by itself and 1'. (More precisely, the extension of the last predicate is the set of ordered 1-tuples of primes. However, we will find it convenient in the case of a *singulary* transparent predicate ϕ to say that the extension of ϕ is the set of objects α such that ϕ is true of $\langle \alpha \rangle$.) It follows readily that a transparent predicate ϕ is true of (false of) an n-tuple $\langle \alpha_1, \ldots, \alpha_n \rangle$ of objects if and only if $\langle \alpha_1, \ldots, \alpha_n \rangle$ belongs to (does not belong to) the extension of ϕ. For example, the transparent predicate '① + ② = ③' is true of $\langle 5,8,13 \rangle$ because $\langle 5,8,13 \rangle$ is a member of its extension, but it is false of $\langle 3,7,9 \rangle$, which does not belong to its extension.

It makes no sense to say of opaque predicates that they are true of (false of) objects. One might be tempted to say that the opaque predicate 'Necessarily ① > ②' is true of $\langle 9,7 \rangle$ because it attaches to '9' and '7' to form a true sentence. But with equal warrant one could say that it is false of $\langle 9,7 \rangle$ because it attaches to 'the number of planets' and 'seven' to form a false sentence. The notion of *being true of* is inapplicable to opaque predicates, so there is for such predicates no concept of an extension.

Strictly speaking, it is not predicates but their *uses* that are transparent or opaque in natural languages. Ordinarily, for example, the predicate 'George IV wanted to know whether ① was ②' is used opaquely, attaching to 'Scott' and 'the author of *Waverly*' to form a true sentence but attaching to 'Scott' and 'Scott' to form a false one. Still, there is an infrequent transparent use of that same predicate under which the sentence 'George IV wanted to know whether Scott was Scott' is true. As already remarked, expressions that have several uses are said to be *ambiguous*. Rather than make provision for ambiguous predicates used both transparently and opaquely, we shall construe a predicate to be a predicate expression together with a particular use of it. Thus, when we speak of the opaque predicate 'George IV wanted to know whether ① was ②', there is an implicit restriction to the opaque use of that predicate, which happens to be its normal use.

42.4.   Individual Variables and Predicate Variables

In the language schema about to be developed, the symbols 'w', 'x', 'y', 'z', 'w_1', and so on, will, in one of their capacities, be made synonymous with referring singular terms. The referents of these referring singular terms will be called *individuals*. In consequence, the symbols 'w', 'x', 'y', 'z', 'w_1', and so on, shall be called *individual variables*. This language schema, which shall be called "language schema Q" or simply "LSQ," will also contain variables that are to be rendered synonymous with transparent predicates and which will be called *predicate variables*. For each positive integer n, the symbols $\ulcorner F^n \urcorner$, $\ulcorner G^n \urcorner$, $\ulcorner H^n \urcorner$, $\ulcorner F_1^n \urcorner$, and so on, will be the n-ary predicate variables. For example, 'G^2' is a binary and 'F_3^4' a quaternary predicate variable.

If ϕ is an n-ary predicate variable and $a_1, \ldots, a_n$ are all individual variables, then the expression $\ulcorner \phi a_1 \ldots a_n \urcorner$ is an (atomic) wff. The following, for example, are all atomic wffs of LSQ: 'F^2xy', 'H^1z', and 'H_2^3yxx'. Note that in an atomic wff of LSQ the superscript on the predicate variable matches the number of occurrences of individual variables that immediately follow it. This happenstance enables us to dispense with these superscripts through the following abbreviative convention.

> Convention 10.   The superscripts on predicate variables may be deleted.

By virtue of convention 10 the wff 'F^2xy' may be written 'Fxy'. Whoever desires to restore these superscripts need only count the number of individual variable occurrences immediately following a predicate variable.

Besides individual and predicate variables, LSQ also contains the familiar sentential variables 'p', 'q', 'r', 's', 'p_1', and so on. Accordingly, LSQ boasts two kinds of atomic wffs: those composed of predicate variables applied to individual variables, and those consisting of sentential variables standing alone. Of these two kinds of atomic wffs, only the former make explicit the internal or atomic structure of sentences.

43. EXERCISES

(1)   Mention ten referring singular terms and an equal number of nonreferring singular terms.

(2)   Show by counterexample that not every expression that yields a sentence when it is put in the blank in 'Something is identical with ...' is a singular term.

(3)   Which of the following expressions are predicates?

(a)   ① gave ② to ③   (d)   ① gave ③ to ①
(b)   ① gave ① to ②   (e)   ③ gave ② to ④
(c)   ① gave ① to ①   (f)   ③ gave ① to ②

(4)   Attach each of the predicates below to the indicated sequence of singular terms.

(a)   ② believed ① was unfaithful: ⟨'Desdemona', 'Othello'⟩
(b)   ① believed ② was unfaithful: ⟨'Desdemona', 'Othello'⟩
(c)   ① + ③ = ② + ④: ⟨'5', '3', '2', '10'⟩
(d)   ① ≤ ①: ⟨'+ $\sqrt{2}$'⟩
(e)   ① = ② or ① > ②; ⟨'7', '+ $\sqrt{25}$'⟩

(5)   Exhibit all the predicates that can be generated from the sentence 'George IV wanted to know whether Scott was the author of *Waverly*'. Which are (in normal use) transparent?

{6}   Discuss the claim that opaque predicates typically contain modal expressions or expressions relating to mental states or attitudes. Is the transparency or opacity of predicates a matter of meaning analysis or empirical inquiry?

44. SEMANTICS OF ATOMIC WFFS

44.0. Semantics of Individual Variables

Language schemata become languages when their wffs have been invested with meaning. We have already remarked that there are two aspects to meaning: sense and reference. And we observed that, while sense determines reference, reference underdetermines (leaves partially open) sense.

The term 'referent' was stretched somewhat to include truth values as the referents of sentences. The *referent of* a (referring) singular term, however, is quite naturally understood to be the thing the singular term refers to. Scott, for example, is the referent of 'the author of *Waverly*' and Canada is the referent of 'Canada'. Now an individual variable is properly endowed with reference when some *eligible* thing is appointed to be its referent or value. The things so eligible are the things that belong to the so-called *universe of discourse* or *domain of discourse* and are called *individuals*. Any nonempty set, no matter how bizarre, may be taken as the universe of discourse or, as it is sometimes also called, the *domain of individuals*. For example, the set whose members are the prime numbers and the big toe on Charles De Gaulle's left foot would make a perfectly good universe of discourse. Eligibility as a referent or value of an individual variable depends on the composition of the universe of discourse, so the choice of some nonempty set as the universe of discourse must be made before one can assign referents or values to individual variables. Accordingly, the first semantical step toward endowing the wffs of LSQ with meaning consists in the designation of some nonempty set as the universe of discourse (hereafter UD for short).

There are two ways to assign a value or referent to an individual variable. One way is to invest the individual variable with sense by declaring it synonymous with a referring singular term that denotes a member of the UD. For example, if the UD were the set of human beings, we could make Scott the value or referent of 'y' by stipulating that 'y' is to be synonymous with 'the author of *Waverly*'. Care must be taken to assure that a referring singular term declared synonymous with an individual variable actually denotes a member of the UD. Given the UD just mentioned, for example, it would be illicit to declare 'x' synonymous with 'the capital of France', because Paris is not a member of that UD.

The other way to assign a value or referent to an individual variable consists in merely assigning some member of the UD to be its value or referent. For example, with the set of human beings as the UD, one might declare that Scott is to be the value of 'x' and that De Gaulle is to be the value of 'y'. This latter way leaves the senses of 'x' and 'y' rather open, because these variables could subsequently be invested with any senses compatible with their referring to Scott and De Gaulle, respectively. Thus with individual variables as with sentential variables, sense determines reference but reference underdetermines sense.

44.1.   Semantics of Predicate Variables

Once again we stretch the meaning of the term 'referent', this time to embrace extensions as the referents of transparent predicates. Heretofore we have spoken of extensions as things that transparent predicates have absolutely or unqualifiedly. We stated without qualification, for example, that the set of primes is the extension of the transparent predicate '① is a positive integer divisible only by itself and 1'. It is time for qualifications. Henceforth we shall understand the *extension of* an n-ary transparent predicate ϕ *with respect to a universe of discourse* $\mathfrak{D}$ to be the set of all n-tuples $\langle \alpha_1, \ldots, \alpha_n \rangle$ of members of $\mathfrak{D}$ such that ϕ is true of $\langle \alpha_1, \ldots, \alpha_n \rangle$. Thus we relativize the notion of the extension of a predicate to the UD of a language. The last-mentioned predicate, for example, has the set of primes as its extension with respect to the integers as UD. But with respect to the first ten positive integers as UD, it has the set $\{1,2,3,5,7\}$ as its extension. The extension of a transparent predicate ϕ with respect to a universe of discourse $\mathfrak{D}$, therefore, depends not only on the sense of ϕ but also on the composition of $\mathfrak{D}$. Hence, with regard to transparent predicates, sense determines reference only relative to a UD.

A UD having been chosen, there are two ways to assign a value or referent to an n-ary predicate variable. One way is to declare it synonymous with some n-ary transparent predicate. This confers on the predicate variable as its value whatever set is the extension of the transparent predicate with respect to the given UD. The other way consists in stipulating that some set of n-tuples of individuals is to be the value or extension of the n-ary predicate variable. (Remember that the individuals are merely the members of the UD.)

When investing predicate variables with sense, one must take care to assure that the predicates with which they are declared synonymous are transparent. No value assignment to 'F^2' is made by the stipulation that 'F^2' is to be synonymous with 'Necessarily ① > ②', for the latter is an opaque predicate that has no extension.

44.2.   Semantics of Atomic Wffs

The semantics of one of the two kinds of atomic wffs of LSQ, the sentential variables, has already been treated thoroughly in Part One. We turn now to the semantics of atomic wffs of the form $\ulcorner \phi a_1 \ldots a_n \urcorner$, where ϕ is an n-ary predicate variable and $a_1, \ldots, a_n$ are individual variables. Let A be such a wff; that is, let A be $\ulcorner \phi a_1 \ldots a_n \urcorner$. An *interpretation* Σ of A consists of a universe of discourse $\mathfrak{D}$ together with a value assignment to each variable in A. Let Σ assign the set Δ of n-tuples of individuals (members of $\mathfrak{D}$) to the predicate variable ϕ as its value, and, for each i, the individual α_i to the individual variable a_i as its value. Then the *value of A under* Σ is truth if the n-tuple $\langle \alpha_1, \ldots, \alpha_n \rangle$ is a member of Δ; otherwise the value of A under Σ is falsehood. The table below shows the value of the wff 'Gxy' under several interpretations.

Interpretation	*UD*	'G'	'x'	'y'	*Value*
Σ_1	Positive integers	'① > ②'	'6'	'3'	t
Σ_2	Positive integers	'① > ②'	'3'	'6'	f
Σ_3	Human beings	'① taught ②'	Socrates	Plato	t

As another example, the table below indicates the value of '*Fyxx*' under several value assignments.

Value Assignment	UD	'F'	'x'	'y'	Value
Σ_4	Positive integers	'① + ② = ③'	'6'	'3'	f
Σ_5	Positive integers	'① = ② + ③'	'6'	'3'	f
Σ_6	Positive integers	'① = ② + ③'	'3'	'6'	t

Reflection on the semantical clause that stipulates the value of an atomic wff $\ulcorner \phi a_1 \ldots a_n \urcorner$ under an interpretation Σ will reveal that the value of the wff under Σ is completely determined by the *values* that Σ assigns to the variables of the wff. We will soon discover that the foregoing is a general feature of all the wffs of Q-languages, the languages that result when the variables of LSQ are endowed with meaning.

Besides the symbols already mentioned, LSQ contains the left and right brackets and five truth-functional sentence connectives: '$\sim$', '$\vee$', '$\cdot$', '$\supset$', and '$\equiv$'. The semantics of these connectives is already familiar. By utilizing the fundamental truth tables for these connectives, the reader can easily determine the value of any truth-functional compound of atomic wffs of LSQ under a given interpretation. Some examples are incorporated into the table below.

wff	Interpretation	Value
$Fxyy \supset Fxxx$	Σ_5	f
$\sim Gxy \vee Fxyy$	$\Sigma_1 + \Sigma_5$	t
$\sim Gxy \equiv Fxyy$	$\Sigma_1 + \Sigma_5$	f

(By "$\Sigma_1 + \Sigma_5$" we mean the interpretation whose UD is the same as the UD of Σ_1 and Σ_5 and which makes all the value assignments made by either Σ_1 or Σ_5. Σ_1 and Σ_3 cannot be so combined because they have different UDs. Σ_2 and Σ_5 cannot be so combined because they make incompatible value assignments.)

45. EXERCISES

(1)   If the UD is the set of positive integers, may one assign a value to 'y' by stipulating that 'y' is to be synonymous with 'the positive square root of 2'? May the set of square circles be taken as the UD of a Q-language?

(2)   State carefully as much of the grammar and semantics of LSQ as has been thus far introduced.

(3)   In what way does the extension or value of a predicate variable in a Q-language depend on more than its sense?

(4)   Determine the extensions of the following predicates in the indicated UDs: '① = ①', '① > ①', '① ≥ ②', '① + ② = ③', '① + ① = ②'.

> UD 1:   positive integers
> UD 2:   positive rational numbers
> UD 3:   real numbers
> UD 4:   rational numbers

(5)   Determine the values of the following wffs of LSQ under the interpretations Σ_i indicated in the table below: 'Fy', 'Fxx', 'Fzx', 'Gxy', 'Gyx', '$Fy \supset \sim Gxy$', '$\sim(Gxy \equiv \sim Gzx)$', '$Fx \cdot Fy \supset (Gxy \equiv Fyx)$'.

Value Assignment	UD	'F^1'	'F^2'	'G'	'x'	'y'	'z'
Σ_1	Positive integers	'① is prime'	'① = ②'	'① > ②'	'3'	'47'	'1'
Σ_2	Positive integers	'① is odd'	'① ≠ ②'	'① < ②'	'3'	'2'	'2'
Σ_3	Positive integers	'① is even'	'① < ②'	'① = ②'	'3'	'4'	'3'

46. QUANTIFIERS

46.0. Existential and Universal Quantifiers

One way to transform a transparent predicate such a '① is prime' into a sentence is to attach it to a referring singular term such as '7'. This transformation is the natural-language counterpart of interpreting 'Fx' by stipulating that 'F' means '① is prime' and that 'x' means '7'. Here 'F' plays the role of a transparent predicate while 'x' functions as a referring singular term. But there are other ways to turn '① is prime' into a sentence. For example, one can substitute the pronoun 'it' for the circled numeral and prefix the expression 'there is something such that' to the result. This operation yields the true sentence 'There is something such that it is prime'. Note that this operation generates a true sentence if and only if the extension of the transparent predicate to which it is applied is nonempty. The foregoing operation is the natural-language counterpart of prefixing a so-called *existential quantifier* '$(\exists x)$' to the wff 'Fx' to get '$(\exists x)Fx$', with 'F' interpreted as '① is prime'. The expression '$(\exists x)Fx$' is a wff that may be read as 'There is something such that it is F' or as 'For some x, Fx'. The value of '$(\exists x)Fx$' is truth if and only if the extension of 'F' is nonempty.

As the informal reading of '$(\exists x)Fx$' brings out, the second occurrence of 'x' does not function as a referring singular term but rather as a pronoun referring back to the occurrence of 'x' in the existential quantifier '$(\exists x)$'. *Individual variables*, therefore, *may function in either of two quite disparate ways*. They may play the role of referring singular terms or they may function as pronouns, that is, as devices for cross-reference. Some authors regard as *variables* only symbols that are functioning as pronouns. They prefer to speak of symbols that play the role of a certain type of linguistic expression as a *dummy* expression of that type. For example, they would not call the 'p' in '$p \vee Fx$' a variable but a *dummy sentence*. Similarly, the 'F' would be a *dummy predicate* and the 'x' a *dummy referring singular term*. We have followed, however, an old and nearly universal mathematical tradition which counts as *variables* symbols that perform either function. Still, we must not let our terminology obscure the fact that individual variables can perform two quite different functions, whereas sentential variables and predicate variables are limited to the one function of playing the role of certain linguistic expressions. (In some systems not treated in this book, both sentential variables and predicate variables may also function as pronouns.)

Yet another way to convert '① is prime' into a sentence consists in substituting the pronoun 'it' for the circled numeral and prefixing the expression 'everything is such that' to the result. This operation yields the false sentence 'Everything is such that it is prime'. Clearly, the operation yields a true sentence if and only if the extension of the predicate to which it is applied contains everything there is (in the universe of discourse). The foregoing operation is the natural-language counterpart of prefixing a so-called universal quantifier '(y)' to 'Fy' to give '$(y)Fy$', where 'F' is interpreted as '① is prime'. The expression '$(y)Fy$' is a wff that may be read as 'Everything is such that it is F' or as 'For every y, Fy'. As its informal rendering suggests, the wff '$(y)Fy$' is true if and only if the extension of 'F' is universal, that is, if and only if everything in the UD is a member of the extension of 'F'. The occurrences of 'y' in '$(y)Fy$' function as pronouns, not as dummy referring singular terms.

46.1.   Grammar of LSQ

Preparatory to supplying a full account of its semantics, let us consolidate what we have already learned about the grammar of LSQ.

Vocabulary of LSQ

Sentential variables: 'p', 'q', 'r', 's', 'p_1', ...

Individual variables: 'w', 'x', 'y', 'z', 'w_1', ...

For each positive integer n, the n-ary predicate variables: $\ulcorner F^n \urcorner$, $\ulcorner G^n \urcorner$, $\ulcorner H^n \urcorner$, $\ulcorner F_1^n \urcorner$, ...

Sentence connectives: '$\sim$', '$\vee$', '$\cdot$', '$\supset$', '$\equiv$'.

Grouping indicators: '[' and ']'.

Quantifier symbol: '∃'.

The exaggerated redundancy of sentence connectives manifests only one of several willful prodigalities of LSQ. Presently we will systematize the logic of LSQ by means of a so-called *natural deduction system* in which proofs or derivations are constructed in a manner that closely reproduces informal mathematical reasoning. Too much austerity of vocabulary would reduce the naturalness of such a system. The reader may have wondered, too, what became of the parentheses that appeared in the quantifiers '($\exists x$)' and '(y)'. We remind the reader of our unofficial convention to regard parentheses as poorly printed brackets. In this devious way we respect the universal custom among logicians of writing quantifiers with parentheses.

Formation Rules of LSQ

(i)   A sentential variable is a wff.

(ii) If ϕ is an *n*-ary predicate variable and $a_1, \ldots, a_n$ are all individual variables, then $\ulcorner \phi a_1 \ldots a_n \urcorner$ is a wff.

(iii) If A and B are wffs, then $\ulcorner \sim A \urcorner$, $\ulcorner [A \cdot B] \urcorner$, $\ulcorner [A \vee B] \urcorner$, $\ulcorner [A \supset B] \urcorner$, and $\ulcorner [A \equiv B] \urcorner$ are all wffs.

(iv) If A is a wff and b is an individual variable, then $\ulcorner (\exists b)A \urcorner$ and $\ulcorner (b)A \urcorner$ are wffs.

(v)   A formula is a wff if and only if it can be constructed through a finite number of applications of the above rules.

46.2.   Free and Bound Variables

Any individual variable may occur in a quantifier, and a quantifier may be prefixed to any wff to produce another wff. The following, for example, are all wffs of LSQ: '$(x)Gyz$', '$(\exists y)Fy$', '$(x)(\exists y)Gxy$', '$\sim(x)[Fx \supset (z)(\exists y)Hy]$', and '$q \vee (\exists x)p$'. In one respect both universal quantifiers $\ulcorner (b) \urcorner$ and existential quantifiers $\ulcorner (\exists b) \urcorner$ behave like singulary sentence connectives. Namely, prefixing an occurrence of a quantifier to a wff yields a wff. The wff occurrence to which an occurrence of a quantifier is prefixed to form a wff is called the *scope of* that occurrence of the quantifier. For example, the scope of the second occurrence of '($\exists y$)' in '$(\exists y)[Gy \supset (\exists y)Fy]$' is the occurrence of '$Fy$' which immediately follows it, and the scope of the first occurrence of '($\exists y$)' is the occurrence of '$[Gy \supset (\exists y)Fy]$'. Quantifiers may, of course, lie within the scope of other quantifiers. A quantifier that lies within the scope of another quantifier is said to be *nested within* the latter. In the example above, the second occurrence of '($\exists y$)' is nested within the first.

An occurrence of a (sentential, individual, or predicate) variable V in a wff A is said to be *bound in A* if that occurrence of V is part of a quantifier, or lies within the scope of a quantifier of A which contains an occurrence of V. For example, both occurrences of 'y' are bound in the wff '$(\exists y)[p \supset Gxy]$', but the occurrences of 'p', 'G', and 'x' are not bound therein. (The formation rules of LSQ permit only individual variables to occur as parts of quantifiers, so clearly no sentential or predicate variables are ever bound in wffs of LSQ.) In '$(y)[Fx \supset (\exists x)Gyx]$', of the three occurrences of 'x' only the second and third are bound. An occurrence of a variable V in a wff A is said to be *free in A* if that occurrence of V is not bound in A. In the wff last exhibited, for example, the first occurrence of 'x' and the occurrences of 'F' and 'G' are free. The notions of freedom and bondage enable us to indicate precisely when a variable is functioning as a pronoun and when as a dummy linguistic expression. *Bound occurrences of variables in a wff function as pronouns in that wff; free occurrences of variables in a wff function as dummy linguistic expressions in that wff.* Therefore, if an occurrence of an individual variable is free in a wff A, it functions as a dummy referring singular term in A. If it is bound in A, it behaves as a pronoun in A.

A variable V is said to be a *bound variable of* a wff A if at least one occurrence of V is bound in A. For example, 'y' is a bound variable of '$Fy \equiv (y)Hy$' because there are bound occurrences of 'y' in that wff. A variable V is said to be a *free variable of* a wff A if at least one occurrence of V is free in A. For example, 'y' is a free variable of '$Fy \equiv (y)Hy$' as are also 'F' and 'H'. Notice that the same variable may be both a free and a bound variable of the same wff. A particular occurrence of a variable, however, is either bound in a wff or free in it but never both.

46.3. Interpretations; Minimal Interpretations

Our informal rendering of quantifiers into English has already furnished a glimpse of their semantics. For simple wffs such as '$(\exists x)Fx$' and '$(x)Fx$', and truth-functional compounds of these simple wffs, that glimpse is perhaps sufficient. But as soon as we are faced with more complicated wffs such as

$(x)(\exists y)[Fx \supset (z)(Hzy \equiv Hxy)]$

our informal rendering avails little. Suppose that we wish to know the value of the foregoing wff under that interpretation whose UD is the set of positive integers and which takes 'F' and 'H' to mean 'ⓘ is prime' and 'ⓘ divides ② without remainder', respectively. The informal rendering 'For every x, for some y, x is prime only if for every z, z divides y without remainder if and only if x divides y without remainder' is too involuted to be grasped on a mere reading. If we try diligently to unravel its meaning, we will find ourselves reducing the value of the whole wff to values of less complicated parts, and the values of these latter parts to the values of less complicated parts of themselves, and so on, until we have arrived at simple parts whose values under the relevant value assignments we can readily grasp. In other words, we will naturally follow the path of an inductive definition. In Part One we faced a similar problem with complicated truth-functional wffs which we solved by formulating, in the form of truth tables, an inductive definition of the value of a wff under a value assignment. In a moment we will provide an analogous solution of the present problem, but first a few preliminaries.

By an *interpretation of* a wff A, we shall understand a nonempty UD together with value assignments to at least all the free variables of A. (Bound occurrences of individual variables function as pronouns rather than as dummy singular terms, so there is no need to assign values to the bound individual variables of a wff unless, of course, they are also free variables of the wff.) An interpretation of A that assigns values to only the free variables of A will be said to be a *minimal interpretation of* A. Let Σ^* be the minimal interpretation of A that results from an interpretation Σ of A by the omission of any value assignments to variables not free in A. We shall speak of Σ^* as the minimal interpretation of A *determined by* the interpretation Σ of A. Obviously an interpretation of A determines exactly one minimal interpretation of A. If Σ is already a minimal interpretation of A, then the minimal interpretation of A determined by Σ is Σ itself. Where Σ is an interpretation of a wff A of LSQ, we define the *value of A under* Σ to be the same as the value of A under the minimal interpretation of A determined by Σ. Accordingly, to define inductively the value of a wff under an interpretation, it suffices to explain inductively the value of a wff under a minimal interpretation.

46.4.   Inductive Definition of the Value of a Wff Under a Minimal Interpretation

Let Σ be a minimal interpretation of a wff A of LSQ. Then

(i)   If A is a sentential variable, the value of A under Σ is the truth value which Σ assigns to A;

(ii)   If A is an atomic wff $\ulcorner \phi a_1 \ldots a_n \urcorner$, the value of A under Σ is truth if $\langle \alpha_1, \ldots, \alpha_n \rangle$ is a member of Δ, where Δ is the extension that Σ assigns to the predicate variable ϕ and $\alpha_1, \ldots, \alpha_n$ are the individuals that Σ assigns to the individual variables $a_1, \ldots, a_n$, respectively; otherwise the value of A under Σ is falsehood;

(iii)   If A is $\ulcorner {\sim} B \urcorner$, the value of A under Σ is opposite to the value of B under Σ (note that Σ will also be a minimal interpretation of B);

(iv)   If A is $\ulcorner [B \cdot C] \urcorner$, the value of A under Σ is truth if B and C come out true under Σ_1 and Σ_2, respectively, where Σ_1 is the minimal interpretation of B determined by Σ and where Σ_2 is the minimal interpretation of C determined by Σ; otherwise the value of A under Σ is falsehood;

(v)–(vii)   The clauses for '$\vee$', '$\supset$', and '$\equiv$' are analogous to clause (iv) and are left to the reader;

(viii)   If A is $\ulcorner (\exists b) B \urcorner$, the value of A under Σ is truth if B comes out true under at least one minimal interpretation of B that determines Σ; otherwise the value of A under Σ is falsehood;

(ix)   If A is $\ulcorner (b) B \urcorner$, the value of A under Σ is truth if B comes out true under every minimal interpretation of B that determines Σ; otherwise the value of A under Σ is falsehood.

Suppose that Σ is a minimal interpretation of a wff $\ulcorner (\exists b) B \urcorner$ that has the nonempty set $\mathfrak{D}$ as its UD. How many minimal interpretations of B determine Σ? If b is not free in B, then the only minimal interpretation of B that determines Σ is Σ itself. In this special case, then, clause (viii) reduces the value of $\ulcorner (\exists b) B \urcorner$ under Σ to the value of B under Σ. But if b is free in B, then any minimal interpretation of B that determines Σ will differ from Σ solely in making the additional assignment of some individual (member of $\mathfrak{D}$) to b.

There are as many possible values for b as there are individuals, so the number of minimal interpretations of B that determine Σ is the same as the number of individuals. If b is free in B, therefore, clause (viii) reduces the value of $\ulcorner(\exists b)B\urcorner$ under Σ to the values of B under the minimal interpretations in a set Γ of minimal interpretations, where Γ and $\mathfrak{D}$ have the same number of members. In particular, if $\mathfrak{D}$ is a finite set, the value of $\ulcorner(\exists b)B\urcorner$ under Σ is reduced by clause (viii) to the values that B has under a finite number of minimal interpretations. What has just been said about the value of an existentially quantified wff $\ulcorner(\exists b)B\urcorner$ under a minimal interpretation applies, *mutatis mutandis*, to the value of a universally quantified wff $\ulcorner(b)B\urcorner$ under a minimal interpretation.[1]

46.5. Applying the Inductive Definition

Let us apply the inductive definition of Section 46.4 to some examples. First, let us determine the value of '$\sim(\exists x)(y)Gxy$' under the minimal interpretation Σ whose UD is the set of positive integers and which takes 'G' to mean '① $>$ ②'. By clause (iii), the wff comes out oppositely to the value of '$(\exists x)(y)Gxy$' under Σ. By clause (viii), this latter wff comes out true under Σ if and only if '$(y)Gxy$' comes out true under at least one minimal interpretation that determines Σ. Let Σ_1 be any minimal interpretation of '$(y)Gxy$' that determines Σ. Then Σ_1 is like Σ except that Σ_1 assigns some positive integer k to 'x'. By clause (ix), the value of '$(y)Gxy$' under Σ_1 is truth if and only if 'Gxy' comes out true under every minimal interpretation of it that determines Σ_1. Let Σ_2 be the minimal interpretation of 'Gxy' which is just like Σ_1 except that Σ_2 also assigns k to 'y'. Clearly Σ_2 determines Σ_1. Moreover 'Gxy' comes out false under Σ_2, because $\langle k,k \rangle$ does not belong to the extension of '① $>$ ②', which is the value that Σ_2 assigns to 'G'. Hence '$(y)Gxy$' comes out false under Σ_1. But Σ_1 was an *arbitrary* minimal interpretation of '$(y)Gxy$' that determines Σ. Hence '$(y)Gxy$' comes out false under every minimal interpretation that determines Σ. Therefore, '$(\exists x)(y)Gxy$' comes out false under Σ, and thus '$\sim(\exists x)(y)Gxy$' comes out true under Σ.

As our second example, let us determine the value of '$(\exists y)[Fy \supset (z)\sim Hzz]$' under the interpretation Σ whose UD is the set of people and which makes 'F' synonymous with '① is a

---

[1] See Appendix G for alternative approaches to the semantics of quantifiers.

dictator' and 'H' synonymous with '① is fond of ②'. Let Σ_1 be like Σ except that Σ_1 makes the additional assignment of the comedian Bob Hope to 'y'. Clearly 'Fy' comes out false under the minimal interpretation of it determined by Σ_1. By the semantical clause for the horseshoe, then, '$Fy \supset (z) \sim Hzz$' comes out true under Σ_1. But Σ_1 determines Σ. By clause (viii), therefore, '$(\exists y)[Fy \supset (z) \sim Hzz]$' comes out true under Σ. Notice that this determination did not even require us to ascertain the value of '$(z) \sim Hzz$' under Σ_1.

The inductive definition of Section 46.4 explains the value of a wff A under a minimal interpretation Σ as a function of the values of the atomic subformulas of A under certain minimal interpretations related to Σ. It sometimes happens that, for each atomic subformula and minimal interpretation thereof, we can effectively determine the value of the subformula under the interpretation but nonetheless do not know what value the whole wff has under the given minimal interpretation. For example, consider the minimal interpretation of the wff '$(\exists x)Fx$' which has the set of positive integers as UD and which takes 'F' to mean '① is even but is not the sum of two primes'. By clause (viii) of the inductive definition, the wff comes out true under the given interpretation if 'Fx' comes out true under at least one minimal interpretation that determines the given interpretation. Given any one of these minimal interpretations, it is a trivial matter to ascertain the value of 'Fx' under it. The value has been found to be falsehood for all minimal interpretations which anyone has ever worked through. Still it is an unsolved problem of mathematics whether 'Fx' comes out true under a minimal interpretation that determines the given minimal interpretation of '$(\exists x)Fx$'. Hence, whether '$(\exists x)Fx$' is true under the given interpretation is itself an unsolved problem of mathematics. This state of affairs contrasts markedly with that of Part One. If we know which truth values have been assigned to the sentential variables of a wff of LSP, it is a trivial, though occasionally tedious, task to find the value of the wff under the given interpretation.

47. EXERCISES

(1) In the following wffs determine which occurrences of variables are free therein and which bound therein. Also, indicate for each wff which are the free variables thereof and which are the bound variables thereof. Finally, determine the scope of each occurrence of a quantifier.

$(x)[Fy \cdot Gxz \supset (y)(z)Hxyz]$ $\quad (x)[p \supset Fx]$

$(\exists x)(\exists x)Fx \supset (y)Gyx$ $\quad (x)(y)(\exists z)q$

$(\exists x)[(\exists x)Fx \supset (y)Gyx]$ $\quad (\exists w)(\exists y)[Gy \equiv Gw]$

$(\exists w)Gy \equiv (\exists y)Gw$ $\quad (\exists w)[Gy \equiv (\exists y)Gw]$

(2) Use the inductive definition of Section 46.4 to determine the values of the following wffs under the indicated interpretations:

'$\sim(y)(\exists x)Gxy$': UD is the set of positive integers; 'G' means '①　>　②'.

'$(\exists x)(\exists y)Gxy$': same interpretation as above.

'$(x)(y)Gxy$': same interpretation as above.

'$(w)[Fw \supset \sim Gw]$': UD is the set of positive integers; 'F' means '① is even' and 'G' means '① is prime'.

'$(\exists y)[Fy \cdot Gy]$': same interpretation as above.

'$(x)[(\exists y)(Fy \cdot Hxy) \supset (\exists y)(Gy \cdot Hxy)]$': UD is the set of living things; 'F' means '① is a horse', 'G' means '① is an animal', and 'H' means '① is the head of ②'.

'$(y)[(z)Fyz \supset Fyy]$': UD is the set of human beings; 'F' means '① loves ②'.

'$(\exists x)(y)Fxy \supset (\exists w)Fww$': same interpretation as above.

'$(\exists x)Fx \equiv \sim(x)\sim Fx$': UD is the set of human beings; 'F' means '① is pretty'.

(3) An occurrence of a quantifier in a wff A is said to be *vacuous* if its scope in A contains no free occurrences of the variable that occurs as part of the quantifier. For example, the first and third occurrences of quantifiers in '$(\exists x)(x)Gx \equiv (y)(w)Gxw$'

are vacuous but the second and fourth are not. Let Σ be any interpretation of a wff A which does not contain free occurrences of the individual variable b. Prove that A, $\ulcorner(\exists b)A\urcorner$, and $\ulcorner(b)A\urcorner$ all come out with the same truth value under Σ. That is, prove that vacuous quantifiers are immaterial to the value of a wff under an interpretation and hence may be deleted without affecting the value of the wff under a given interpretation.

(4)   Let Σ be an interpretation of $\ulcorner(a)A_a\urcorner$ and let b be an individual variable that does not occur in A_a. Prove that $\ulcorner(a)A_a\urcorner$ and $\ulcorner(b)A_b\urcorner$ come out with the same value under Σ, where A_b results from A_a on replacing each occurrence of a in A_a by an occurrence of b.

(5)   Let $S_b^a A|$ be the result of replacing each *free* occurrence of the variable a in A by an occurrence of the variable b. Let $\ulcorner(a)A\urcorner$ be a wff which contains none of the variables 'w_1', 'w_2', and so on. Let Σ be any interpretation of $\ulcorner(a)A\urcorner$ in a finite UD $\{\alpha_1, \ldots, \alpha_n\}$ such that Σ assigns α_i to $\ulcorner w_i\urcorner$, $1 \leq i \leq n$. Prove that $\ulcorner(a)A\urcorner$ and the conjunction $\ulcorner S_{w_1}^a A| \cdot S_{w_2}^a A| \cdot \ldots \cdot S_{w_n}^a A|\urcorner$ come out with the same value under Σ. Show that $\ulcorner(\exists a)A\urcorner$ and the continued disjunction of all the wffs $\ulcorner S_{w_i}^a A|\urcorner$, where $1 \leq i \leq n$, also come out with the same value under Σ.

(6)   Exercise (5) suggests a way of eliminating quantifiers when only interpretations in a finite domain of known cardinality are pertinent. The method consists in replacing universally quantified subformulas of a wff by certain continued conjunctions, and replacing existentially quantified subformulas by certain continued disjunctions. For example, it turns '$(\exists x)(y)Fxy$' into

$$[Fw_1w_1 \cdot Fw_1w_2 \cdot Fw_1w_3] \lor [Fw_2w_1 \cdot Fw_2w_2 \cdot Fw_2w_3] \lor$$
$$[Fw_3w_1 \cdot Fw_3w_2 \cdot Fw_3w_3]$$

when the relevant domain has three members. State in detail how this eliminative method proceeds. Use it to eliminate quantifiers from the following wffs, assuming that only interpretations in a domain of three members are pertinent:

$(y)(\exists x)Fxy$ $\qquad\qquad$ $(\exists x)(\exists y)Fxy$

$(x)(y)Fxy$ $\qquad\qquad$ $(y)(x)Fxy$

$$(\exists y)(\exists x)Fxy \qquad\qquad (x)(\exists y)Fxy$$
$$(x)Fx \supset (\exists x)Fx \qquad\qquad (x)Fx \equiv\, \sim(\exists x)\!\sim\!Fx$$
$$(\exists x)Fx \equiv\, \sim(x)\!\sim\!Fx \qquad (x)Fx \supset Fy$$
$$Fy \supset (\exists x)Fx \qquad\qquad (\exists y)[Fy \supset (x)Fx]$$
$$(\exists x)[(\exists y)Fy \supset Fx] \qquad (\exists x)(Fx \vee Gx) \equiv [(\exists x)Fx \vee (\exists x)Gx]$$
$$(x)(Fx \cdot Gx) \equiv (x)Fx \cdot (x)Gx$$

(7) When interpretations in an infinite domain of known cardinality are pertinent, the method of eliminating quantifiers developed in Exercise (6) breaks down. Why? Show that even when only interpretations in a finite domain of known cardinality are pertinent, a wff containing quantifiers does not have the same sense as its eliminative surrogate.

(8) By a *sentential wff* of LSQ we shall understand a wff that contains no symbols besides sentential variables, truth-functional sentence connectives, and grouping indicators. Let A be a sentential wff that is a tautology and let $b_1, \ldots, b_n$ be a complete list of the distinct variables in A. Let $B_1, \ldots, B_n$ be any wffs of LSQ and let B result from A by simultaneously replacing each occurrence of b_i by B_i for all $i, 1 \leq i \leq n$. Prove that B comes out true under any interpretation of it.

(9) A wff B of LSQ is said to be *tautologous* if it comes from a sentential wff A, where A is a tautology, by the simultaneous substitution of $B_1, \ldots, B_n$ for $b_1, \ldots, b_n$, respectively, where $b_1, \ldots, b_n$ is a complete list of the distinct variables of A, and $B_1, \ldots, B_n$ are any wffs of LSQ (not necessarily distinct). It was proved in Exercise (8) that a tautologous wff is valid, that is, that it comes out true under every interpretation thereof. Develop an effective method for recognizing tautologous wffs. Use the method to determine which of the following are tautologous:

$$(x)[Fx \vee \sim\!Fx] \qquad\qquad (x)Fx \vee \sim(x)Fx$$
$$(x)Fx \vee \sim(y)Fy \qquad\qquad (\exists x)Hxy \supset [Fy \vee (\exists x)Hxy]$$
$$(\exists x)(\exists y)[Gyx \supset Gyx] \qquad (\exists y)Gy \supset (\exists w)Gw$$

(10) A wff of LSQ that is related to a contradictory sentential wff in the way that a tautologous wff is related to a valid sentential wff is said to be *truth-functionally contradictory*. For example, '$(\exists y)Hy \cdot \sim(\exists y)Hy$' is truth-functionally con-

tradictory. Formulate a precise definition of a truth-functionally contradictory wff. Develop an effective test for recognizing such wffs. Prove that truth-functionally contradictory wffs are invalid.

48.   MODEL THEORY

48.0.   Models: Satisfiability and Validity

By a *model of* a wff A of LSQ we shall understand any true interpretation of A, that is, any value assignment under which A has the value truth. For example, the interpretation of ' $\sim(\exists x)(y)Gxy$ ' discussed in the first paragraph of Section 46.5 is a model of that wff. A wff is said to be *satisfiable* if there is a model of it, that is, if it comes out true under at least one interpretation. The wff ' $\sim(\exists x)(y)Gxy$ ' is satisfiable, for example, but the wff ' $(x)Fx \cdot (\exists x)\sim Fx$ ' is not satisfiable. Again, by a *valid* wff we understand a wff which comes out true under every interpretation. By an *invalid* wff is meant a wff that comes out false under every interpretation. For example, the wff ' $(x)Fx \equiv \sim(\exists x)\sim Fx$ ' is valid, ' $(x)Fx \cdot (\exists x)\sim Fx$ ' is invalid, and the nonvalid wff ' $(\exists x)Fx$ ' is neither valid nor invalid. Obviously a wff is invalid if and only if it is not satisfiable. Below is a list of a few other obvious consequences of the preceding definitions.

(1)   A wff A is valid if and only if $\ulcorner \sim A \urcorner$ is not satisfiable.

(2)   A wff A is valid if and only if $\ulcorner (b_1)\ldots(b_n)A \urcorner$ is valid, where $b_1, \ldots, b_n$ are any individual variables.

(3)   A wff A is satisfiable if and only if $\ulcorner (\exists b_1)\ldots(\exists b_n)A \urcorner$ is satisfiable, where $b_1, \ldots, b_n$ are any individual variables.

(4)   A disjunction $\ulcorner A \lor B \urcorner$ is satisfiable if and only if A or B (or both) is satisfiable.

(5)   A conjunction $\ulcorner A \cdot B \urcorner$ is valid if and only if both A and B are valid.

A wff A is said to be *satisfiable in a domain* $\mathfrak{D}$ if there is a true interpretation of A wherein $\mathfrak{D}$ is the UD, that is, if $\mathfrak{D}$ is the UD of a model of A. For example, the wff

$$\sim(\exists x)Gxx \cdot (x)(\exists y)Gyx \cdot (x)(y)(z)[Gxy \cdot Gyz \supset Gxz]$$

is satisfiable in the domain of positive integers (let 'G' mean '① > ②') but can be shown not to be satisfiable in any finite domain. A wff A is said to be *valid in a domain* $\mathfrak{D}$ if A comes out true under every interpretation which has $\mathfrak{D}$ as UD, that is, if every interpretation of A in $\mathfrak{D}$ is a model of A. For example, the wff '$Fy \supset (\exists x)Fx$' is valid in every nonempty domain, and the wff '$\sim[Fx \cdot \sim Fy]$' is valid in any domain that has exactly one member. Clearly, a wff is satisfiable if and only if it is satisfiable in some nonempty domain or other, and a wff is valid if and only if it is valid in every nonempty domain. If in statements (1)–(5) we substitute 'satisfiable in the nonempty domain $\mathfrak{D}$' for 'satisfiable', and 'valid in the nonempty domain $\mathfrak{D}$' for 'valid', we obtain five obvious consequences of the above definitions.

48.1. Inflation Theorem

An important but less obvious consequence of the definition of satisfiability in a domain is the *inflation theorem*, which states that, if a wff A of LSQ is satisfiable in a nonempty domain $\mathfrak{D}$, then A is satisfiable in any domain that has at least as many members as $\mathfrak{D}$ has. Thus the wff '$(x)(\exists y)[Gyx \cdot (z)[Gzx \supset \sim Gyz]]$' is satisfiable in the domain of positive integers (for instance, let 'G' mean '① > ②'), so it follows from the inflation theorem that this wff is also satisfiable in the domain of real numbers because there are at least as many real numbers as there are positive integers. Note that the above wff comes out false under the interpretation in the domain of real numbers wherein 'G' means '① > ②'. This illustrates the fact that the inflation theorem does not claim that by giving predicate variables the same senses they were given in a model of a wff in one nonempty domain, one can obtain a model of the wff in a domain of equal or greater cardinality. It guarantees only that there is a model of a wff in a domain if there is a model of it in a nonempty domain with the same number of or fewer members.

The inflation theorem may be proved thus. Assume that there is a model Σ of wff A in a nonempty domain $\mathfrak{D}$. (That is, assume that Σ is a true interpretation of A whose UD is $\mathfrak{D}$.) First we show that there is a model of A in any domain of the same cardinality as $\mathfrak{D}$. Let $\mathfrak{D}'$ be a set of the same cardinality as $\mathfrak{D}$, and let ψ be a one-to-one mapping of $\mathfrak{D}$ onto $\mathfrak{D}'$. Let Σ' be the following interpretation of A with $\mathfrak{D}'$ as UD. Let V be any free variable of A. If V is a sentential variable, let Σ' assign to V whatever truth value

Σ assigns to V. If V is an individual variable, let Σ' assign $\psi(\alpha)$ to V, where α is the individual which Σ assigns to V and $\psi(\alpha)$ is the individual mapped with α by ψ. If V is an n-ary predicate variable and Σ assigns the set Δ of n-tuples of members of $\mathfrak{D}$ to V, let Σ' assign to V the set Δ' of n-tuples of members of $\mathfrak{D}'$, where an n-tuple $\langle \psi(\alpha_1), \ldots, \psi(\alpha_n) \rangle$ belongs to Δ' if and only if $\langle \alpha_1, \ldots, \alpha_n \rangle$ belongs to Δ. Clearly the value of A under Σ' is the same as its value under Σ. This completes the proof of the first part.

We will now show that, if $\mathfrak{D}$ is a proper nonempty subset of $\mathfrak{D}^*$ and if there is a model of a wff A in the domain $\mathfrak{D}$, then there is a model of A in the domain $\mathfrak{D}^*$. This result, together with the result of the preceding paragraph, entails the inflation theorem. By a *maximal interpretation* let us understand an interpretation that assigns a value to every variable (sentential, predicate, and individual) of LSQ. Clearly, every interpretation can be extended to a maximal interpretation in the sense that, given an interpretation I, there is a maximal interpretation $\bar{I}$ such that I and $\bar{I}$ have the same UD, $\bar{I}$ makes every value assignment made by I, and, for any wff B that has a truth value under I, the value of B under $\bar{I}$ is the same as the value of B under I. Let $\mathfrak{D}$ be a nonempty proper subset of $\mathfrak{D}^*$, and let Ω be the set of all maximal interpretations in the nonempty domain $\mathfrak{D}$. Clearly, Ω is nonempty. Let Γ be the set of things that belong to $\mathfrak{D}^*$ but not to $\mathfrak{D}$. So $\mathfrak{D}^* = \mathfrak{D} \cup \Gamma$. Let β be a particular member of $\mathfrak{D}$, and let ψ be the following mapping of $\mathfrak{D}^*$ onto $\mathfrak{D}$. If $\alpha \in \mathfrak{D}$, then $\psi(\alpha) = \alpha$, and if $\alpha \in \Gamma$, then $\psi(\alpha) = \beta$. With each member Σ of Ω we correlate every maximal interpretation Σ^* that is related to Σ in the following way. First, $\mathfrak{D}^*$ must be the UD of Σ^*. Second, Σ^* must make the same assignments to sentential variables that Σ makes. Third, if Σ^* assigns α to an individual variable b, then Σ must assign $\psi(\alpha)$ to b. Finally, to an n-ary predicate variable ϕ, Σ^* must assign the set Δ^* of n-tuples of members of $\mathfrak{D}^*$, where $\langle \alpha_1, \ldots, \alpha_n \rangle \in \Delta^*$ if and only if $\langle \psi(\alpha_1), \ldots, \psi(\alpha_n) \rangle \in \Delta$, where Δ is the value that Σ assigns to ϕ. (Note that at least one Σ^* is thus correlated with each Σ.) One can readily verify by mathematical induction on the number of occurrences of connectives and quantifiers in an arbitrary wff A of LSQ that, for each member Σ of Ω, the value of A under Σ is truth (falsehood) if and only if A comes out true (false) under every correlated interpretation Σ^*. Therefore, if $\mathfrak{D}$ is a nonempty subset of $\mathfrak{D}^*$ and there is a maximal model (that is, a true, maximal interpretation) of a wff A in $\mathfrak{D}$, then there is a maximal model of A in $\mathfrak{D}^*$. Any model can be extended to a maximal model, so it follows that there is a model of A in $\mathfrak{D}^*$ if there is a model of A in $\mathfrak{D}$.

48.2. Löwenheim Theorem; Spectrum Problem

Perhaps the most important result about satisfiability is the Löwenheim theorem. [For a proof of the Löwenheim theorem as a corollary of the proof of the Skolem–Gödel theorem given in Section 58, see Exercise (10) of Chapter 60.] The Löwenheim theorem states that, if a wff is satisfiable, then it is satisfiable in the domain of positive integers. From the Löwenheim and inflation theorems together, it follows that a satisfiable wff is satisfiable in any denumerable domain. (A set is said to be *denumerable* if its members can be put into one-to-one correspondence with the positive integers.) Another immediate consequence of the Löwenheim theorem is the nonexistence of a wff satisfiable in the domain of real numbers but not satisfiable in the domain of positive integers. Denumerable domains are the smallest infinite domains, so the net effect of the Löwenheim and inflation theorems is to lump all infinite domains together as far as satisfiability is concerned. That is, a wff of LSQ is satisfiable either in all infinite domains or in no infinite domain. There is no wff of LSQ that is satisfiable in some infinite domains but not in others.

For which nonzero cardinal numbers K, finite or infinite, does there exist a wff A_K of LSQ such that A_K is satisfiable in every domain with K or more members but is not satisfiable in any smaller nonempty domains? The foregoing problem has been called the *spectrum problem* and we now turn to its solution. Consider the following enumeration of wffs of LSQ:

(1) Fx_1

(2) $Fx_1 \cdot \sim Fx_2$

(3) $Fx_1 \cdot \sim Fx_2 \cdot Gx_1 \cdot Gx_2 \cdot \sim Gx_3$

(4) $Fx_1 \cdot \sim Fx_2 \cdot Gx_1 \cdot Gx_2 \cdot \sim Gx_3 \cdot Hx_1 \cdot Hx_2 \cdot Hx_3 \cdot \sim Hx_4.$

.

.

.

Inspection of the above sequence will show that wff (n) is satisfiable in a domain of n individuals but in no smaller nonempty domains.

Hence for any finite nonzero cardinal number K, there exists a wff of LSQ that is satisfiable in domains with K or more members but in no smaller nonempty domains. In addition, the wff '$\sim(\exists x)Gxx \cdot (x)(\exists y)Gyx \cdot (x)(y)(z)[Gxy \cdot Gyz \supset Gxz]$' mentioned in Section 48.0 is satisfiable in all infinite domains but in no finite ones. Hence, if $\aleph_0$ is the cardinal number of the positive integers, there is a wff satisfiable in a domain with $\aleph_0$ members but in no smaller nonempty domain. For any larger infinite cardinal K, however, we know from the Löwenheim theorem that any wff satisfiable in a domain with K members is also satisfiable in a domain with $\aleph_0$ members. Hence, for any such infinite cardinal K, there is no wff that is satisfiable in a domain of K members but in no smaller domains.

48.3. Generalized Inflation Theorem; Löwenheim–Skolem Theorem

The concepts of interpretation, model, satisfiability, validity, and so on, can easily be generalized to sets or classes of wffs. By an *interpretation of* a set Γ of wffs we understand a nonempty UD together with an appropriate assignment of values to at least every variable that occurs free in any member of Γ. By a *model of* a set Γ of wffs is meant an interpretation of Γ under which each member of Γ comes out true. For example, let Δ be the set of all the wffs $\ulcorner Gx_ix_j \urcorner$, where $i > j$, and let Σ be the interpretation in the domain of positive integers which construes 'G' as '① > ②' and which assigns to $\ulcorner x_k \urcorner$ the integer k. Clearly, Σ is a model of the infinite set Δ of wffs of LSQ. A class Γ of wffs is said to be *satisfiable* if there is a model of Γ. For example, the set Δ just mentioned is satisfiable, but the set $\{$'Fx','$\sim Fx$'$\}$ is not satisfiable even though each member of it is satisfiable. Finally, wffs A_1, ..., A_n shall be said to be *simultaneously satisfiable* if the set $\{A_1, ..., A_n\}$ is satisfiable. For example, 'Fx' and '$\sim Fy$' are simultaneously satisfiable, but 'Fx' and '$\sim Fx$' are not simultaneously satisfiable.

The determination that a class of wffs is satisfiable often constitutes the core of a consistency proof for a formal axiomatic system S. If one can prove that the set of theorems of S is satisfiable but that the set of all the wffs of S is not satisfiable, one may conclude that S is absolutely consistent. Such a consistency proof is called a *consistency proof by means of a model*. For example, an axiomatization of a non-Euclidean system of geometry within LSQ might be proved consistent by finding a Euclidean model of its theorems, that is, by so interpreting the wffs of LSQ that those wffs which are theorems of the axiomatic system all turn out to be true sentences of Euclidean geometry.

A class Γ of wffs is said to be *satisfiable in* a domain $\mathfrak{D}$ if some interpretation of Γ in $\mathfrak{D}$ (that is, which has $\mathfrak{D}$ as UD) is a model of Γ. A useful result about class satisfiability is the *generalized inflation theorem*, which says that, if a class Γ of wffs of LSQ is satisfiable in a nonempty domain $\mathfrak{D}$, then Γ is satisfiable in any domain that has at least as many members as $\mathfrak{D}$. (Proof of this metatheorem is assigned as an exercise in Chapter 49.) Thus the set Δ mentioned two paragraphs ago is satisfiable in the domain of the points of the Euclidean plane, because Δ is satisfiable in the domain of positive integers and there are more points in the Euclidean plane than there are positive integers.

But the most important metatheorem about class satisfiability is the so-called *Löwenheim–Skolem theorem*, which states that, if a class Γ of wffs of LSQ is satisfiable, then Γ is satisfiable in the domain of positive integers. The Löwenheim–Skolem theorem has some strange consequences. For example, one can write a finite number $A_1, \ldots, A_n$ of wffs of LSQ which contain only one free variable, the binary predicate variable 'F', such that when 'F' is taken to mean '① is a member of ②', the wffs $A_1, \ldots, A_n$ become the axioms of the system NBG (von Neumann–Bernays–Gödel) of set theory.[1] Assume that, in the appropriate domain, these axioms are all true. Assume, in other words, that the wffs $A_1, \ldots, A_n$ are simultaneously satisfiable. Clearly, then, their conjunction is a satisfiable wff. By the Löwenheim theorem, therefore, their conjunction is satisfiable in the domain of positive integers. But one of the wffs $A_1, \ldots, A_n$, called the *axiom of infinity*, asserts under the intended set-theoretical interpretation that there exists an infinite set. Moreover, the axioms $A_1, \ldots, A_n$ jointly imply a wff, known as *Cantor's theorem*, which asserts that the power set of a set has more members than the set. (The power set of a set Δ is

---

[1] See Elliot Mendelson, *Introduction to Mathematical Logic*, D. Van Nostrand Company, Inc., Princeton, N.J., 1964, pp. 159ff., for such a formulation of NBG. Actually, Mendelson uses function variables in addition to the symbols of LSQ, but these function variables can be eliminated in favor of the binary predicate variable 'F'.

the set of all subsets of Δ.) And another of the axioms A_1, ..., A_n asserts that every set has a power set. It follows that these axioms jointly entail that there are more sets than there are positive integers. Yet we have just seen that there is a model of these axioms in the domain of positive integers. Clearly the addition of a finite number of axioms to A_1, ..., A_n cannot remedy this situation, for if there is a true set-theoretical interpretation of the resulting axioms, the Löwenheim theorem entails that there is a model of them in the positive integers. Nevertheless, one might entertain the hope that the addition of an infinite set of wffs to the axioms A_1, ..., A_n of NBG would give a set of wffs that come out true under the set-theoretical interpretation but which have no model in the domain of positive integers. But even this hope is extinguished by the Löwenheim–Skolem theorem which guarantees a model in the domain of the positive integers. This discouraging state of affairs—that any set of wffs that are set-theoretical truths of NBG has a model in the positive integers—is known as the *Skolem paradox*. It is discouraging to learn that one cannot discriminate between sets and positive integers by writing axioms which can be interpreted as truths about the former but which cannot also be interpreted as truths about the latter. Proof of the Löwenheim–Skolem theorem is the topic of Exercise (10) in Chapter 60.

48.4. Implication and Truth-Functional Implication; Equivalence

A wff B shall be said to be a *consequence of* a set Γ of wffs of LSQ if every interpretation of the set $\Gamma \cup \{B\}$ which is a model of Γ is also a model of B. And we shall say that a wff A of LSQ *implies* a wff B of LSQ if B is a consequence of the set $\{A\}$. Wffs A_1, ..., A_n of LSQ shall be said *to jointly imply* a wff B of LSQ if the conjunction $\ulcorner A_1 \cdot \ldots \cdot A_n \urcorner$ implies B, that is, if B is a consequence of $\{A_1, \ldots, A_n\}$. Clearly wffs A_1, ..., A_n (jointly) imply a wff B if and only if the conditional $\ulcorner A_1 \cdot \ldots \cdot A_n \supset B \urcorner$ is valid. That is, (joint) implication amounts to validity of the conditional. It is also easily established that implication is reflexive and transitive but is not symmetrical.

Sometimes implication among wffs of LSQ is wholly a matter of truth-functional structure; that is, the implication does not turn on the presence of quantifiers. For example, that the wffs '$(x)Fx \supset Fy$' and '$\sim Fy$' imply the wff '$\sim (x)Fx$' turns on nothing more than the truth-functional structure of the given wffs. The notion of implication through truth functions will play an important role in the natural deduction system of Chapters 52ff., so it is imperative that we form a clear idea of it. The notion is exceedingly simple. A wff A of LSQ shall be said to *truth-functionally imply* a wff B of LSQ if the conditional $\ulcorner A \supset B \urcorner$ is tautologous. [For the notion of *tautologousness* of wffs of LSQ, see Exercise (9) of Chapter 47.] Similarly, wffs $A_1, \ldots, A_n$ shall be said *jointly to truth-functionally imply* a wff B if the conditional $\ulcorner A_1 \cdot \ldots \cdot A_n \supset B \urcorner$ is tautologous. According to these definitions, the wffs '$(x)(\exists y)Gxy \lor Fy$' and '$\sim(x)(\exists y)Gxy$' jointly truth-functionally imply 'Fy', because '$[(x)(\exists y)Gxy \lor Fy] \cdot \sim(x)(\exists y)Gxy \supset Fy$' is a tautologous wff. And the wff '$Fx \cdot \sim Fx$' truth-functionally implies the wff '$(\exists x)(y)Gxy$', because '$Fx \cdot \sim Fx \supset (\exists x)(y)Gxy$' is tautologous. It should be evident that there is a simple truth-tabular decision procedure for truth-functional (joint) implication.

A wff A is said to be *equivalent to* a wff B if, for every interpretation Σ of the set $\{A,B\}$, A and B have the same value under Σ. It is readily shown that equivalence is reflexive, symmetrical, and transitive among the wffs of LSQ. Furthermore, A is equivalent to B if and only if $\ulcorner A \equiv B \urcorner$ is valid. That is, equivalence amounts to validity of the biconditional. Moreover, A and B are equivalent if and only if each implies the other. That is, equivalence amounts to mutual implication.

49. EXERCISES

(1)   The *deflation theorem* states that, if a wff of LSQ is valid in a nonempty domain $\mathfrak{D}$, then it is valid in every nonempty domain that has the same number of or fewer members than $\mathfrak{D}$. Show that the inflation theorem entails the deflation theorem, and vice versa. (*Hint:* Remember that A is valid in $\mathfrak{D}$ if and only if $\ulcorner \sim A \urcorner$ is not satisfiable in $\mathfrak{D}$.)

(2)   An alternative version of the Löwenheim theorem says that, if a wff of LSQ is valid in the domain of positive integers, then it is valid. Show that this version of the Löwenheim theorem and the version given in Section 48.2 entail one another. (*Hint:* Make use of the inflation and deflation theorems.)

(3)   Prove the generalized inflation theorem. (*Hint:* The proof of the inflation theorem given in Section 48.1 is already almost a proof of this theorem.)

[4]   Prove that the wff

$$\sim(\exists x)Gxx \cdot (x)(\exists y)Gyx \cdot (x)(y)(z)[Gxy \cdot Gyz \supset Gxz]$$

is satisfiable in all infinite domains but in no finite nonempty domain. (*Hint:* Show that in any model of this wff, 'G' will determine an unending, nonrepetitious ordering of the members of the UD.)

(5)   For each positive integer k, show how to write a wff of LSQ that is valid in nonempty domains with k or fewer members but in no larger domains. (*Hint:* Make use of the solution to the spectrum problem given in Section 48.2.) Write a wff of LSQ that is valid in every finite domain but in no infinite domain. (*Hint:* See Exercise [4].)

(6)   Prove that a wff of LSQ is valid either in all infinite domains or in no infinite domains.

(7)   The *compactness theorem* for LSQ states that a class Γ of wffs of LSQ is satisfiable if and only if every finite subclass of Γ is satisfiable. Show that the compactness theorem is entailed by the statement that a wff A is a consequence of a set Δ of wffs of LSQ if and only if A is a consequence of some finite subset of Δ. Show that the compactness theorem also entails this statement. (*Hints:* For first part: Assume that every finite subset of Γ is satisfiable but that Γ is not. Then '$p \cdot \sim p$' is a consequence of Γ. By the given statement, then, '$p \cdot \sim p$' is a consequence of some finite subset of Γ, but this is impossible. Why? For second part: Assume that A is a consequence of Δ but of no finite subset of Δ. Let Δ_0 be any finite subset of Δ. Show that the set $\Delta_0 \cup \{\ulcorner\sim A\urcorner\}$ is satisfiable. Then use the compactness theorem to establish that $\Delta \cup \{\ulcorner\sim A\urcorner\}$ is satisfiable, from which it follows that A is not a consequence of Δ.)

(8) Which of the following are true statements about wffs of LSQ?

    (a) A valid wff is a consequence of every set of wffs.

    (b) Every wff is a consequence of a set of wffs that is not satisfiable.

    (c) If A is valid and B implies C, then A and B jointly imply C, and B implies $\ulcorner A \cdot C \urcorner$.

    (d) If Γ is satisfiable and A is a consequence of Γ, then A is satisfiable.

    (e) If A is satisfiable and is a consequence of Γ, then Γ is satisfiable.

(9) Determine whether the wffs at the left below (jointly) truth-functionally imply the wff at their right. [In each case the wff at the right is (jointly) implied by the wffs at its left.]

    (a) '$(x)[Fx \supset Gx]$', 'Fy'   'Gy'

    (b) '$(x)Fx \supset Gy$', '$(x)Fx$'   'Gy'

    (c) 'Fy'   '$(\exists x)Fx$'

    (d) '$\sim(\exists y)[Fy \vee Gy]$', '$(z)Hz$'   '$\sim\sim(z)Hz$'

    (e) '$(\exists x)[Fx \vee Gx]$', '$\sim(\exists x)Fx$'   '$(\exists x)Gx$'

    (f) 'Fy', '$(x)[Fx \equiv Gx]$'   'Gy'

    (g) '$(x)[Fy \supset (\exists z)Hz]$', '$Fy$'   '$(\exists z)Hz$'

    (h) '$(\exists x)(y)Gxy$'   '$(\exists y)Gyy$'

    (i) '$(x)(\exists y)Gxy$'   '$(\exists x)(\exists y)Gxy$'

(10) Prove that $A_1, \ldots, A_n$ jointly imply B if $A_1, \ldots, A_n$ jointly truth-functionally imply B. Show that not every implication is truth-functional implication. Develop a decision procedure for recognizing (joint) truth-functional implication.

(11) Prove that, if A contains no occurrences of the individual variable b, then $\ulcorner (a)A \urcorner$ is equivalent to $\ulcorner (b)S_b^a A| \urcorner$, and $\ulcorner (\exists a)A \urcorner$ is equivalent to $\ulcorner (\exists b)S_b^a A| \urcorner$. [See Exercise (5) of Chapter 47.]

(12) Show that each wff in the left-hand column is equivalent to the wff opposite it in the right-hand column.

    (a) $(x)Fx$ $\sim(\exists x)\sim Fx$

    (b) $(\exists x)Fx$ $\sim(x)\sim Fx$

    (c) $(x)Fx$ $(y)Fy$

    (d) $(\exists x)Fx$ $(\exists y)Fy$

(e) $(\exists x)[Fx \vee Gx]$	$(\exists x)Fx \vee (\exists x)Gx$
(f) $(x)[Fx \cdot Gx]$	$(x)Fx \cdot (x)Gx$
(g) $(\exists x)[p \vee Gx]$	$p \vee (\exists x)Gx$
(h) $(\exists x)[p \cdot Fx]$	$p \cdot (\exists x)Fx$
(i) $(x)[p \vee Fx]$	$p \vee (x)Fx$
(j) $(x)[p \cdot Fx]$	$p \cdot (x)Fx$
(k) $(\exists x)[Fx \supset p]$	$(x)Fx \supset p$
(l) $(x)[Fx \supset p]$	$(\exists x)Fx \supset p$
(m) $(\exists x)[p \supset Fx]$	$p \supset (\exists x)Fx$
(n) $(x)[p \supset Fx]$	$p \supset (x)Fx$
(o) $(x)[Fx \supset Gx]$	$\sim(\exists x)[Fx \cdot \sim Gx]$
(p) $(x)[Fx \supset \sim Gx]$	$\sim(\exists x)[Fx \cdot Gx]$

(13)   Prove the *principle of interchange of equivalents* for LSQ. That is, prove that if B is equivalent to C and if A_C results from the wff A_B by replacing zero or more (not necessarily all) occurrences of B in A_B by occurrences of C, then A_C is equivalent to A_B. (*Hint:* Pattern your proof after the proof of the principle of interchange of equivalents for LSP given in Section 22.1.)

(14)   Let $\Gamma_1, \ldots, \Gamma_n$ be sets of wffs of LSQ. Prove that if, for each i $(1 \leq i \leq n)$, A_i is a consequence of Γ_i, and if $A_1, \ldots, A_n$ jointly imply B, then B is a consequence of the union of the sets $\Gamma_1, \ldots, \Gamma_n$.

(15)   Prove that if $A_1, \ldots, A_n$ jointly imply B, then

$$\ulcorner A_1 \cdot \ldots \cdot A_n \supset B \urcorner$$

is valid. Prove also that if $A_1, \ldots, A_n$ jointly imply B, then $A_1, \ldots, A_k$ jointly imply $\ulcorner A_{k+1} \cdot \ldots \cdot A_n \supset B \urcorner$, where $1 \leq k < n$.

50. LOGICAL ANALYSIS OF ENGLISH DISCOURSE

50.0. Logical Truth and the Empty Domain

In Part One we found that validity is both a necessary and a sufficient condition of the logical truth of sentences of P-languages. We learned, too, that invalidity (contradictoriness) is a necessary and sufficient condition for the logical falsehood of sentences of P-languages. We will now investigate whether the same relationships obtain between validity and logical truth, and invalidity and logical falsehood, with regard to sentences of Q-languages.

By a *sentence of* a Q-language is meant a wff each free variable of which is invested with sense in that Q-language. Suppose that A is a sentence of a Q-language L and that A is valid. Is A logically true? Clearly A is logically true if it is tautologous. But what if A is not tautologous?

In Section 46.3 an empirical assumption slipped unremarked into the semantical theory of Q-languages through the stipulation that every UD or domain of individuals have at least one member. This stipulation contaminates the inductive definition of Section 46.4, which explains what the value of a wff is under a minimal interpretation. In a word, the semantical theory of Q-languages assumes or presupposes that there is at least one element in the UD of every Q-language.

Not every thinker considers the belief that there is something rather than nothing to be empirical. There are platonistic philosophers who believe that mathematical objects exist necessarily. Such philosophers might deem it a matter of logic that every UD has at least one member. In fact, most platonistic philosophers hold that an infinite number of things exist necessarily. These thinkers might even be prepared to countenance as analytic truths wffs that are valid in all infinite domains but that are not valid in some finite domains. We know from the deflation theorem that LSQ contains no such wffs. But the language schema obtained by adding to LSQ the identity sign ' $=$ ' as a predicate constant, the language schema that we will call LSQ *with identity* does contain such wffs. For example, the wff '$(\exists x)(\exists y)\sim(x = y)$', which asserts that there are at least two individuals, is valid in all infinite domains but not in all finite ones.

At the opposite extreme are finitistic thinkers who believe that there can be only a finite number of things altogether. These philosophers may accept as analytic truths wffs that are valid in every finite domain but in no infinite domain. We have already observed in Exercise (5) of Chapter 49 that LSQ contains such wffs.

Although the matter is disputed, we are of the opinion that whether there is something rather than nothing is an empirical or factual question, not a problem of meaning analysis. We hold, therefore, that (interpreted) wffs which are valid in every non-empty domain but which are not valid in the empty domain (UD with no members) are not, strictly speaking, logical truths.

If we permit the empty set to be the UD of an interpretation, we may draw from the inductive definition of Section 46.4 the following conclusions about the value of a wff under an interpretation in the empty domain:

(i) If A contains no free occurrences of b, then $\ulcorner(b)A\urcorner$ and $\ulcorner(\exists b)A\urcorner$ have the same value under an interpretation in the empty domain as A has.

(ii) If A contains free occurrences of b, then the value of $\ulcorner(b)A\urcorner$ under an interpretation Σ in the empty domain is truth, and the value of $\ulcorner(\exists b)A\urcorner$ under Σ is falsehood.

Note that if Σ is an interpretation of a wff B in the empty domain, then B contains no free occurrences of individual variables. For, if B contained free occurrences of an individual variable b, Σ would have to assign an individual to b as its value, but in the empty domain there are no individuals to be assigned. A wff that has no free occurrences of individual variables is said to be *closed*. Wffs that are not closed are said to be *open*. The point just made can be rephrased thus. Only closed wffs have interpretations in the empty domain. Thanks to (i) and (ii), it is a simple matter to determine the value of a closed wff under an interpretation in the empty domain. For example, the wff below comes out false under every interpretation of it in the empty domain.

$(x)[p \supset (\exists y)Fxy] \supset (\exists y)(x)[Gxy \equiv (\exists x)Fxx]$
  t [by (ii)]   f   f [by (ii)]

Let us call a closed wff *purely valid* if it is valid in all domains, the empty domain included. Obviously, every purely valid wff is valid. There are valid wffs, however, which are not purely valid. For example, the valid wff '$(x)Fx \supset (\exists x)Fx$' is not purely valid, for it comes out false under every interpretation of it in the empty domain. Unlike validity, being purely valid is both a necessary and sufficient condition of the logical truth of a sentence of a Q-language. It is, of course, only a sufficient condition of analytic truth. It is expedient, however, to weaken the notions of logical and analytic truth so that validity is a sufficient condition of both logical and analytic truth, and a necessary condition of logical truth. Accordingly, we will hereafter understand an analytic (logical) truth to be a sentence whose truth follows from the meaning of the (logical) words it contains together with the assumption that there is at least one individual.

50.1. Universes of Discourse of English Statements

We have already noticed that the meaning of a sentence in a language depends in part on the makeup of the UD of the language. For example, let Σ_1 be the interpretation of '$(x)(\exists y)Fyx$' in the domain of positive integers wherein 'F' means '① is a square root of ②', and let Σ_2 be like Σ_1 except that the UD of Σ_2 is the set of positive real numbers. Then '$(x)(\exists y)Fyx$' agrees so little in meaning under Σ_1 and Σ_2 that it has opposite values under them. Is '$(x)(\exists y)Fyx$' under Σ_1 synonymous with the English sentence 'Every number has a square root'? To answer that question one must settle a prior one: What is the UD of the English language? The obvious reply is that the set of everything there is forms the UD of English. The reader familiar with the antinomies of set theory, especially Cantor's antinomy, will appreciate the unsatisfactoriness of this reply, for it is easily proved that no such set exists. (Equally unsatisfactory, on somewhat different grounds, as the UD of English would be the universal class of one of the set theories that discriminate between *sets*, that is, classes that belong to classes, and *ultimate classes*, that is, classes that belong to no classes.)

It is comforting to know that we need never set out on the quixotic quest for an elusive set that really is, or will do satisfactorily as, the UD of the English language. For any purpose short of radical metaphysical speculation we can get along well enough with some modest set adopted for the occasion as the UD. When, for example, our interests do not go beyond the positive integers, we might choose them as the UD. Or when we are talking exclusively about people, we might take the set of human beings as the UD. By thus tailoring the UD to our immediate interests we can trim away considerable verbiage. For example, if we let 'F' mean '① is a square root of ②', we can express the falsehood that every positive integer has a square root in the positive integers by '$(x)(\exists y)Fyx$' provided that we take the set of positive integers as UD. But if the UD were the union of the set of positive integers and the set of rational numbers, we would need an additional predicate, such as 'H' meaning '① is a positive integer', to make the same statement by means of the wff '$(x)[Hx \supset (\exists y)[Fyx \cdot Hy]]$'.

It is quite pointless to ask whether an English sentence is synonymous with a sentence of a Q-language until some set has been specified as the UD of the English sentence. This set then functions as a semantic backdrop against which questions of meaning become meaningful. The task of specifying a set as the UD of an English sentence need not be conceived as the problem of discovering what the UD of the English sentence really is. It is rather the pragmatic task of selecting as UD a set that will efficiently serve whatever interests led us to consider the sentence in the first place. Henceforth, whenever we are comparing the sentences of a Q-language with certain English sentences, we shall take the UD of the English statements to be the same as the UD of the Q-language. This convention enables us to say without further ado that, under the interpretation Σ_1 mentioned in the first paragraph of the present section, the wff '$(x)(\exists y)Fyx$' means 'Every number has a square root'.

50.2. Translating English into Q-Languages

An English sentence may be shown to be analytically true by establishing its synonymy with a valid wff of some Q-language or other. This enterprise has two aspects. There is first the problem of recognizing synonymy among such sentences, the problem we now take up. We defer for a time the other problem, which has to do with the recognition of validity of wffs of LSQ.

We have dealt at length in Part One with the translation of truth-functional molecular structure, so we will concentrate on the translation of quantificational atomic structure. In English, universal quantification is indicated by words such as 'all', 'every', 'each', 'any', 'universally', 'always', 'invariably', and the like. For example, under the interpretation in the domain of human beings in which 'F' and 'G' mean, respectively, '① is Cretan' and '① is a liar', the sentence '$(x)[Fx \supset Gx]$' is synonymous with all the following:

> All Cretans are liars.
> Every Cretan is a liar.
> Any Cretan lies.
> Cretans are always liars.
> Cretans are liars.
> A Cretan is a liar
> Only liars are Cretans.
> Whoever is a Cretan is a liar.
> Invariably Cretans are liars.

Existential quantification in English is indicated by expressions such as 'some', 'at least one', 'sometimes', 'there is', 'there are', and so on. For example, '$(\exists x)[Fx \cdot Gx]$' is synonymous with the following:

> Some Cretans are liars.
> There are Cretans who are liars.
> At least one Cretan is a liar.

Depending on intent, the sentence 'Cretans lie' can mean either '$(x)[Fx \supset Gx]$' or '$(\exists x)[Fx \cdot Gx]$'. The indefinite article is similarly ambiguous between universal and existential quantification. For example, the statement 'A Cretan lies' might mean '$(\exists x)[Fx \cdot Gx]$', although it would ordinarily mean '$(x)[Fx \supset Gx]$'. The word 'any' can also indicate either existential or universal quantification. For example, the sentence 'If any Cretan is a liar, then any Cretan is a liar' would ordinarily mean '$(\exists x)[Fx \cdot Gx] \supset (x)[Fx \supset Gx]$'. These illustrations should serve as a reminder that translational rules are only rules of thumb. They are well applied only when applied cautiously and with an ear attuned to the subtleties and vagaries of English discourse. They are no substitute for, but merely an aid to, insight into intended meaning.

The sentence 'All Cretans lie' is synonymous not only with

'$(x)[Fx \supset Gx]$' but also with '$(y)[Fy \supset Gy]$' and '$(z)[Fz \supset Gz]$', and so on. That is, bound variables function as pronouns, so mere change of the bound variable of '$(x)[Fx \supset Gx]$' does not affect its meaning. In general, wffs that are alike except for inconsequential changes of bound variables are synonymous under interpretation. [Pairs of wffs such as '$(x)(\exists y)Fxy$' and '$(x)(\exists x)Fxx$', and '$(x)Gyx$' and '$(y)Gyy$', differ by consequential changes of bound variables. See Exercise (7) of Chapter 51.] But not all acceptable translations of 'All Cretans lie' are like '$(x)[Fx \supset Gx]$' except for inconsequential changes of bound variables. The wffs '$\sim(\exists y)[Fy \cdot \sim Gy]$' and '$(z)[\sim Fz \lor Gz]$' also mean 'All Cretans are liars'.

The word 'some' usually means 'at least one' but it sometimes means 'at least several'. For example, the sentence 'Richard Nixon is popular among some people' would probably be deemed false if Nixon were liked by only one person, but a single mendacious Cretan suffices to make 'Some Cretans are liars' true. By letting 'H' mean '① is identical with ②', we can say that several Cretans are liars by means of the wff '$(\exists x)(\exists y)[Fx \cdot Gx \cdot Fy \cdot Gy \cdot \sim Hxy]$'. It is a popular but false belief that 'some' is incompatible with 'all'. This misconception may derive from the fact that the communication-oriented character of natural languages obliges one to eschew a weaker statement when a stronger is justified. For example, someone who asserts 'Some Cretans lie' while knowing that all Cretans are liars should expect to be reprimanded for prevaricating, but only the fact that 'some' is compatible with 'all' makes this form of prevarication possible. Provided that it is well understood that there are Cretans, one who knows that all Cretans are liars is expected to say 'All Cretans lie', not 'Some Cretans lie'. The proviso that the existence of Cretans is taken for granted is essential, because '$(\exists x)[Fx \cdot Gx]$' is not implied by '$(x)[Fx \supset Gx]$' alone but in combination with '$(\exists x)Fx$'.

Suppose that the last mendacious Cretans lived two millenia ago. Wouldn't '$(\exists x)[Fx \cdot Gx]$' now be false, because it means that *there are*, as opposed to *there have been*, Cretans who lie? If we carefully inspect the inductive definition of Section 46.4, we see that the existential quantifier does not express the present existence of objects that satisfy its scope but expresses merely that some member of the UD satisfies its scope. Depending on the composition of the UD, such an object may be out of the remote past or from the distant future. If the UD is the set of all human beings who have ever lived, are now living, or will ever live (for brevity, we say simply *the set of human beings*), then '$(\exists x)[Fx \cdot Gx]$' is true if and only if at least one such person is (tenselessly) a Cretan liar. That is, '$(\exists x)[Fx \cdot Gx]$' is true if and only if there have been Cretan liars, or there are now Cretan liars, or there will be Cretan liars. In short, the existential quantifier expresses membership in the UD, not present existence. Accordingly, the expressions 'there is' and 'there are' should be understood tenselessly when they are used to translate existential quantifiers. Similar remarks apply to universal quantifiers which also express membership in the UD, not present existence. That is, '$(x)Fx$' does not mean that everything there now is is Cretan. It means rather that every member of the UD is Cretan.

Tense also obtrudes itself through predicates.[1] The predicate '$\textcircled{1}$ is a Cretan' can be understood tenselessly or as tensed. Suppose that the UD is the set of people (past, present, and future). Then the extension of '$\textcircled{1}$ is a Cretan', taken tenselessly, is the set of all persons who have ever been Cretan, are now Cretan, or will ever be Cretan. But taken as tensed, the predicate '$\textcircled{1}$ is a Cretan' has as its present extension the set of people now living who are Cretans. It will prove convenient to regard most predicates in the present tense as tenseless. If we mean them as tensed, we will add a temporal qualifier such as 'now'. Thus we will construe '$\textcircled{1}$ is a Cretan' as tenseless, but we will understand the extension of '$\textcircled{1}$ is now a Cretan' to be the set of Cretans now living. Our policy is to eschew temporal relations, whenever possible, by eschewing tenses. But, although there are no tenses in our Q-languages, we must occasionally deal with temporal relations when they are the primary topic of concern. Suppose, for example, that we wish to say in a Q-language that Hitler attacked England before invading Russia. We might take the set of all people and all moments (in some definite temporal reference system) as the UD, and let 'F', 'G', and 'H' mean '$\textcircled{1}$ is a time at which $\textcircled{2}$ attacks England' and '$\textcircled{1}$ is a time at which $\textcircled{2}$ invades Russia' and '$\textcircled{1}$ is before $\textcircled{2}$', respectively, and let 'w' denote Hitler. The sought-after translation then becomes '$(x)(y)[Fxw \cdot Gyw \supset Hxy] \cdot (\exists x)(\exists y)[Fxw \cdot Gyw]$'. Or suppose we want to say now (noontime July 14, 1968) that there will never be another king of France. We could add 'F_1', meaning

[1] See Appendix J, *Tense Logic*, for a fuller discussion of tense and of the ways it can be handled in formalized languages.

'①︎ is a king of France at time ②︎', and 'z' denoting noontime July 14, 1968, to the foregoing Q-language and produce '$(x)[(\exists y)F_1yx \supset Hxz]$' as our translation.

Words such as 'nothing' and 'no' express quantification under negation. For example, with the set of people as UD and with 'F' and 'G' meaning '①︎ is Cretan' and '①︎ is a liar', respectively, 'No Creatans are liars' means '$\sim(\exists x)[Fx \cdot Gx]$' or equivalently '$(x)[Fx \supset \sim Gx]$'. And 'Nothing is Cretan' goes into symbols as '$\sim(\exists x)Fx$' as does 'No one is Cretan', for we cannot discriminate 'no one' from 'nothing' when the UD is the set of people. But if we made the set of organisms the UD and added the predicate 'H' for '①︎ is a human being', we could translate 'No one is Cretan' by '$\sim(\exists x)[Hx \cdot Fx]$' while '$\sim(\exists x)Fx$' remains as our translation of 'Nothing is Cretan'.

Most of our examples have been quite simple, manifesting neither multiple nor nested quantification. So let us look at some cases where the quantificational structure is more complex, such as the translation of 'No square is prime' into a Q-language the UD of which is the set of positive integers and in which 'F' and 'G' mean '①︎ is prime' and '①︎ × ②︎ = ③︎', respectively. It is good practice to divide the work of translation into a series of small translational steps moving inward from overlying structures to underlying ones. For example, we might first reduce 'No square is prime' to '$(x)[x$ is square $\supset x$ is not prime]'. The portion 'x is square' then becomes '$(\exists y)Gyyx$', and the portion 'x is not prime' goes into symbols as '$\sim Fx$'. Putting these all together, we get '$(x)[(\exists y)Gyyx \supset \sim Fx]$' as our translation of 'No square is prime'. When translating English into a Q-language, one must be careful to award quantifiers their intended scopes. For example, it would be wrong to translate 'No square is prime' as '$\sim(\exists x)(\exists y)Gyyx \cdot Fx$' because the last occurrence of 'x' should clearly be bound to the quantifier '$(\exists x)$' to give the intended meaning '$\sim(\exists x)[(\exists y)Gyyx \cdot Fx]$'. Prudence dictates that the translator check a putative translation to ensure that quantifiers bind the variable occurrences they were intended to bind.

Let us add the predicate 'H', meaning '①︎ + ②︎ = ③︎', to the Q-language of the preceding paragraph and translate Goldbach's conjecture that every even number is the sum of two primes into it. Our first translational step yields

$(x)[x$ is even $\supset x$ is the sum of two primes].

The component 'x is even' then becomes '$(\exists y)Hyyx$', while the portion 'x is the sum of two primes' becomes '$(\exists y)(\exists z)[Fy \cdot Fz \cdot Hyzx]$'. Putting these pieces together we get

$$(x)[(\exists y)Hyyx \supset (\exists y)(\exists z)[Fy \cdot Fz \cdot Hyzx]]$$

as our translation of Goldbach's conjecture. Notice that the truth of '$(\exists y)(\exists z)[Fy \cdot Fz \cdot Hyzx]$' is compatible with x's being the sum of some prime added to itself. That is, the word 'two' in Goldbach's conjecture signifies pairhood, not diversity. But in a statement such as 'Lyndon B. Johnson has two daughters', the occurrence of 'two' signifies diversity. Consider a Q-language whose UD is the set of people and in which 'w' denotes Lyndon B. Johnson, 'F' means '① is a daughter of ②', and 'H_3' means '① is identical with ②'. Then we may translate the statement about Johnson as '$(\exists x)(\exists y)[\sim H_3xy \cdot Fxw \cdot Fyw]$' if we take it to mean that Johnson has at least two daughters. But if we take it to mean that he has exactly two daughters, we must translate it as

$$(\exists x)(\exists y)[\sim H_3xy \cdot Fxw \cdot Fyw \cdot (z)[Fzw \supset H_3zx \lor H_3zy]]$$

or some equivalent wff.

We will have many calls for a predicate variable synonymous with '① is identical with ②', so let us agree informally to reserve 'H_3' for this purpose and, when 'H_3' is so used, let us abbreviate wffs of the form $\ulcorner H_3b_1b_2 \urcorner$, where b_1 and b_2 are individual variables, as $\ulcorner (b_1 = b_2) \urcorner$. In virtue of these informal conventions the last wff mentioned in the preceding paragraph may be written '$(\exists x)(\exists y)[\sim(x = y) \cdot Fxw \cdot Fyw \cdot (z)[Fzw \supset (z = x) \lor (z = y)]]$'.

Some translations require considerable ingenuity. Consider, for example, the translation of 'Moses was an ancestor of Einstein' into a Q-language whose UD is the union of the set of people with the set of all sets of people, and in which 'F' means '① is a parent of ②', 'G' means '① is a member of the set ②', 'w' means 'Moses', and 'z' means 'Einstein'. An adequate translation would be '$(\exists x)[Fxz \cdot \sim Fxw] \cdot (x)\{Gzx \cdot (y)[(\exists z)(Gzx \cdot Fyz) \supset Gyx] \supset Gwx\}$'.

51.   EXERCISES

(1) Prove that there is only one value which can be assigned to a predicate variable in an interpretation in the empty domain. How many different value assignments to '$p \supset [q \vee (x)Fx]$' are there in the empty domain?

(2) Develop a decision procedure for recognizing validity of closed wffs in the empty domain.

(3) Why would it be wrong to translate the particular affirmative statement form 'Some F are G' of traditional logic as '$(\exists x)[Fx \supset Gx]$' rather than as '$(\exists x)[Fx \cdot Gx]$'? (For a brief introduction to so-called traditional logic, see Section 62.1.)

(4) In traditional logic the universal affirmative statement form 'All F are G' was thought to imply the particular affirmative statement form 'Some F are G'. Does implication obtain between their translations '$(x)[Fx \supset Gx]$' and '$(\exists x)[Fx \cdot Gx]$'? If not, try to find an alternative but plausible translation of 'All F are G' that does imply '$(\exists x)[Fx \cdot Gx]$'.

(5) Discuss the thesis of traditional logic that the universal negative statement form 'No F are G' implies the particular negative statement form 'Some F are not G'.

(6) Traditional logicians taught that 'All F are G' and 'Some F are not G' are contradictory in the sense that, under any interpretation, exactly one of them comes out true. Can this doctrine be reconciled with the traditional thesis mentioned in Exercise (4)?

(7) The relation of alphabetic variance may be defined thus:

    (i) If D comes from A by replacing zero or more particular occurrences of a well-formed subformula $\ulcorner(a)B\urcorner$ of A by an occurrence of $\ulcorner(b)S^a_b B|\urcorner$ where b is an individual variable that occurs free neither in B nor in the scope of any quantifier of B that contains b as its variable of quantification, then D is an alphabetic variant of A.

    (ii) [It is left to the reader to supply a clause analogous to (i) for existentially quantified subformulas of A.]

(iii) If A is an alphabetic variant of B and B is an alphabetic variant of C, then A is an alphabetic variant of C.

(iv) A wff A is an alphabetic variant of a wff B if and only if its being so follows from the preceding clauses.

We can now state precisely what was meant by the remark in Section 50.2 that certain wffs differ only by *inconsequential* change of bound variables: The two wffs are alphabetic variants of one another. Prove that alphabetic variance is reflexive, symmetrical, and transitive among the wffs of LSQ. For each pair of wffs in the list below, ascertain whether they are alphabetic variants of one another. Develop a decision procedure for recognizing alphabetic variance.

$(x)[(\exists y)Fxy \supset (\exists x)(z)Gxz]$ $(x)(y)[(\exists z)Fyz \lor (\exists z)Fxz]$

$(z)[(\exists y)Fzy \supset (\exists x)(z)Gxz]$ $(y)(x)[(\exists z)Fxz \lor (\exists z)Fyz]$

$(z)[(\exists y)Fzy \supset (\exists y)(x)Gyx]$ $(z)(x)[(\exists y)Fzy \lor (\exists y)Fxy]$

$(y)[(\exists y)Fyy \supset (\exists x)(z)Gxz]$ $(z)(x)[(\exists y)Fyz \lor (\exists y)Fyx]$

$(x)[(\exists x)Fxx \supset (\exists x)(z)Gxz]$ $(z)(x)[(\exists y)Fzy \lor (\exists y)Fxy]$

(8) Let the UD be the set of people and instants of time, and let 'F' mean '① is Cretan', 'G' mean '① is mendacious', 'H' mean '① is a time before ②', 'F_1' mean '① is alive at ②', and 'w' be synonymous with some term that denotes the present moment. Translate the following into the Q-language just described:

No Cretans now living are liars.

Alas, there have been mendacious Cretans.

Although some Cretans have been liars, none are now.

There will be Cretans who lie.

There always have been, there are now, and there always will be Cretans who are liars.

Liars there have always been and will always be.

When liars cease to exist, so will Cretans.

If there are two Cretans who are veracious, then no one is mendacious.

Cretans are always liars.

(9) Translate the following statements into the Q-language described below: UD is the set of people; 'F' means '① loves ② at least as much as ① loves ③', 'G' means '① respects ② at least as much as ① respects ③', 'H' means '① loves ②',

'F_1' means '① is male', 'G_1' means '① is beautiful', 'H_1' means '① is wise', 'F_2' means '① is a neighbor of ②', 'G_2' means '① deserves honor', and 'H_3' means '① = ②'.

None but the wise deserve honor.

Only lovers deserve honor.

If each loves his neighbor, then all are wise and honorable.

Everybody loves a beautiful woman.

Although the wise are never loved, they are always respected as much as anyone else.

A wise neighbor is respected as much as a beautiful one, but loved less.

The most respected person in the world happens to be beautiful.

The wise love their neighbors more than themselves.

He who loves his neighbor is worthy of honor.

No one else loves someone who loves himself over his neighbor.

Whoever fails to love his neighbor does not love himself.

Whoever has but one neighbor will love him, while whoever has two neighbors will love one more than the other.

There is exactly one woman who is loved by all men.

Though everyone loves someone, no one loves another as much as himself unless everyone who loves is loved in return.

Everyone loves someone more than anyone else.

The more loved are the more respected.

Better loved is better respected.

Unlike self-respect, self-love is universal.

Some people love themselves more than the person they most respect.

The only lovers who merit honor are those who are also wise.

Anyone who respects others less than himself loves himself more than others.

There are two and only two people who love everybody.

There are exactly three wise men.

(10)   Translate into idiomatic English each of the following sentences of the Q-language described in Exercise (9) and determine its truth value.

$(x)(\exists y)[F_2yx \cdot (z)(F_2zx \supset (z = y))]$
$(x)(y)Hxy \supset (\exists x)(y)Hyx$
$(\exists x)(y)Hyx \supset (x)(\exists y)Hxy$
$(x)(y)[(z)(Fzxy \cdot \sim Fzyx) \supset (\exists z)(Gzyx \cdot \sim Gzxy)]$
$(x)(y)[Hxy \cdot Hyx \supset (z)(\sim(z = x) \cdot \sim(z = y) \supset Fxyz)]$
$(\exists x)(y)(z)[\sim(x = z) \supset Gyxz]$
$(x)[(\exists y)(\sim F_1y \cdot G_1y \cdot Hxy) \supset \sim H_1x \vee (z)(F_2zx \supset G_2z)]$
$(\exists x)[(y)Gyxy \cdot (w)((y)Gywy \supset (w = x)) \cdot (z)((\exists y)Hzy \supset Hzx)]$

(11) Translate the following statements into the Q-language described below: UD is the set of natural numbers, 'F' means '① + ② = ③', 'G' means '① > ②', 'H' means '① × ② = ③', and 'H_3' means '① = ②'.

Addition and multiplication are commutative.

There is a zero element for addition, that is, an element that when added to any element gives the latter.

There is exactly one zero element for addition.

There is a unit element for multiplication, that is, an element that when multiplied by any element gives the latter.

There is a number smaller than or equal to every number.

There is exactly one unit element for multiplication.

There is no largest number.

Some numbers are prime, but not all.

Every nonzero element is smaller than its square.

Between some numbers are still other numbers.

The relation of being greater than is transitive, asymmetric, and irreflexive.

The relation being greater than or equal to is reflexive and transitive.

The smallest nonzero element that is not prime is larger than the smallest prime.

There is no largest prime.

There is exactly one even prime number.

Of two even numbers, at least one is not prime.

If the product of two numbers is greater than their sum, then at least one of them is greater than one. (*N.B.* The number one is the unit element for multiplication.)

The product of two numbers equals zero if and only if at least one of them is zero.

A pair of numbers have a unique sum and product.

Not every number divides a number (without remainder).

If Goldbach's conjecture is true, then between any prime greater than two and its square is another prime. (*N.B.* The number two is the only even prime.)

(12)   Translate into idiomatic English each of the following sentences of the Q-language described in Exercise (11), and determine its truth value:

$(x)(\exists y)(\exists z)[\sim(x = y) \cdot \sim(x = z) \cdot Hyzx] \supset$
$$(x)(\exists y)(\exists z)[\sim(x = y) \cdot \sim(x = z) \cdot Gxy \cdot Gxz]$$

$(x)\sim(\exists y)[Gyx \cdot (z)(Gzx \supset (z = y))]$

$(\exists x)(\exists y)[Gxy \cdot (z)(Gxz \supset (z = y))]$

$(\exists x)[(\exists y)[Gxy \cdot (z)(Gxz \supset (z = y))] \cdot$
$$(w)[(\exists y)(Gwy \cdot (z)(Gwz \supset (w = y))) \supset (w = x)]]$$

$(x)(\exists y)[Gyx \cdot (z)(Gzx \supset Gzy \vee (z = y))]$

$(\exists x)(\exists y)(\exists z)[Fxyz \cdot Hxyz]$

$(x)(y)[(\exists z)Fyzx \supset Gxy \vee (x = y)]$

$(x)(y)[\sim(\exists z)Fyzx \equiv Gyx]$

$(x)(y)[(z)Fxzz \cdot (z)Hyzz \supset Gyx]$

$(\exists x)(\exists y)[(z)Fxzz \cdot (w)((z)Fwzz \supset (w = x)) \cdot$
$$(z)Hyzz \cdot (w)((z)Hwzz \supset (w = y)) \cdot Gyx]$$

$(\exists x)(y)[Fxxy \equiv Hxxy]$

$(\exists x)[(y)(Fxxy \equiv Hxxy) \cdot (w)[(y)(Fwwy \equiv Hwwy) \supset (w = x)]]$

$(x)(y)[\sim(x = y) \supset Gxy \vee Gyx]$

$(x)(y)\{(\exists z)Hxzy \supset (\exists z)[Hxzy \cdot (w)(Hxwy \supset (w = z))] \vee$
$$(z)Fyzz\}$$

$(x)(y)(z)[(x = y) \cdot (y = z) \supset (x = z)]$

$(x)(x = x) \cdot \sim(\exists y)Gyy$

$(\exists x)(y)[\sim(x = y) \supset Gxy] \supset (x)(y)(x = y)$

$\sim(x)(y)[Gxy \vee Gyx] \cdot (x)(y)[(x = y) \vee Gxy \vee Gyx]$

$(x)(y)[Gxy \cdot (\exists z)Gyz \supset (\exists z)(\exists w)(\sim(z = w) \cdot Gxz \cdot Gxw)]$

$(\exists x)[(y)Fxyy \cdot (w)((y)Fwyy \supset (w = x)) \cdot$
$$(z)((\exists y)Gzy \supset \sim(z = x))]$$

(13)   Thomas Aquinas has been criticized for allegedly assuming, in his famous third proof for the existence of God, that 'Every contingent thing can not-be at some time or other' entails 'There is some time at which every contingent thing can not-be'. Translate these two sentences into the Q-

language below and show that the translation of the first statement does not imply the translation of the second. Let the UD be the set of moments of time and of contingent objects. Let 'F' mean '① can not-be at ②', 'G' mean '① is a contingent thing', and 'H' mean '① is a moment of time'.

(14) Two wffs that are alphabetic variants of one another are said to *differ only by alphabetic changes of bound variables*. Prove that wffs which differ only by alphabetic changes of bound variables are equivalent.

52. QUINE'S SYSTEM OF NATURAL DEDUCTION (I)

52.0. Instances

To show that a wff of LSQ is valid we have relied on *ad hoc* semantical arguments based on the inductive definition of Section 46.4. Unlike the truth-tabular method of proving validity of wffs of LSP, this semantic technique is neither simple nor systematic. We urgently need a simple, systematic method to establish the validity of wffs of LSQ. The next several sections will be devoted to the development of such a method. First, however, a few preliminaries.

A simple but important concept for the natural deduction system about to be developed is the notion of an *instance*. A wff A_b is said to be *an instance of* the wffs $\ulcorner(a)A_a\urcorner$ and $\ulcorner(\exists a)A_a\urcorner$ if A_b results from A_a through the substitution of b (called the *variable of instantiation*) for free occurrences of a in A_a, provided no free occurrence of a in A_a lies in the scope of a quantifier whose variable of quantification is b. (In the special case when a does not occur free in A_a, we shall say that there is no variable of quantification.) In other words, A_b is an instance of $\ulcorner(a)A_a\urcorner$ and $\ulcorner(\exists a)A_a\urcorner$ if and only if A_b is like A_a except perhaps in having free occurrences of the variable b wherever A_a has free occurrences of the variable a. For example, each wff in the left-hand column below is an instance of the wff opposite it in the right-hand column.

Fy	$(\exists x)Fx$
Fy	$(x)Fx$
$(\exists y)Gxy$	$(\exists x)(\exists y)Gxy$
$(\exists y)Gxy$	$(\exists z)(\exists y)Gzy$
$(\exists y)Gxy$	$(w)(\exists y)Gxy$
Gxy	$(x)Gxy$
Gyy	$(x)Gxy$
Gyy	$(\exists w)Gwy$
$Fy \supset Fy$	$(z)[Fz \supset Gz]$
$(\exists y)[Fwy \equiv Gyw]$	$(x)(\exists y)[Fxy \equiv Gyx]$

But no wff in the left-hand column below is an instance of the wff opposite it in the right-hand column.

Gxy	$(x)Gxx$
Gxy	$(\exists y)Gyy$
Gxy	$(\exists w)Gyw$
$(y)Gyy$	$(\exists x)(y)Gxy$

Obviously, if A_b is an instance of $\ulcorner(a)A_a\urcorner$, then $\ulcorner(a)A_a\urcorner$ implies A_b. Similarly, if A_b is an instance of $\ulcorner(\exists a)A_a\urcorner$, then A_b implies $\ulcorner(\exists a)A_a\urcorner$. There is, too, a simple decision procedure for recognizing whether one wff is an instance of another.

52.1.   Natural Deduction Systems versus Logistic Systems

One may regard a *formal system* as a set of rules for constructing finite sequences of wffs of the system. The finite sequences that can be permissibly constructed are called *proofs*. A proof is said to be a *proof of* the last wff in it, which is called a *theorem*. All the formal systems we have so far encountered have been *logistic systems*, that is, systems in which every initial subsequence of a proof is itself a proof. Not every formal system is a logistic system. Of those formal systems which lack the logistic property that every initial subsequence of a proof is a proof, some are known as *natural deduction systems* because their rules for constructing proofs resemble or reflect common informal rules for deriving or deducing a statement from other statements. The formal system now to be presented is a natural deduction system. Apart from minor modi-

fications in the rule of conditionalization (see below) and in the
device for keeping track of premises, the system is that of Quine's
textbook *Methods of Logic*[1] and will be called "system Q." We have
adopted Quine's system because it is the smoothest-running system
known to us.

To be more accurate, we do not construct plain sequences of
wffs in system Q but *annotated* sequences. That is, the proofs are
certain annotated finite sequences of wffs of LSQ. Some of the
annotation consists merely in the numbering of the wffs of a
sequence of wffs. In order to facilitate cross-reference, each wff
(line) is numbered as it is set down, the notation $\ulcorner (n) \urcorner$ being put
immediately to the left of the nth wff (line). We use the term 'line'
ambiguously, sometimes to refer to the entire annotated line and
sometimes to refer just to the wff that appears on the annotated
line. The context will determine which use is intended. System Q
contains seven rules for constructing finite sequences of lines. Any
finite sequence of lines set down in accordance with these seven
rules is called a *deduction*. Later we shall designate certain deductions as *proofs*. The vocabulary, formation rules, and semantics of
system Q are the same as for LSQ.

52.2.   Rule of Premiss

The first of the seven rules of system Q is the *rule of premiss* (RP).
RP states that *any wff may be set down as the nth line of a deduction
($n \geq 1$), provided*

(i)   *at the left of the new line we put* $\ulcorner *_n \urcorner$, *and*
(ii)   *at the right of the new line we write* 'RP'.

For example, we could initiate a deduction by using RP thus:

$*_1(1)$ $(x)Fx \supset (\exists y)Gy$ RP

The occurrence of 'RP' is written at the right to show which rule
was employed in setting down the line. The subscripted asterisks
at the left of a line are called *stars*. Stars determine the premisses
of a line in the following way. A line (k) is a *premiss of* a line (n) in
a deduction if $\ulcorner *_k \urcorner$ appears at the left of (n) in the deduction. In

---

[1] See W. V. O. Quine, *Methods of Logic*, Holt, Rinehart and Winston, Inc.,
New York, rev. ed., 1963.

the deduction below, for example, line (2) is the only premiss of line (2).

$*_1(1)$	$(\exists x)(\exists y)Fxy$	RP
$*_2(2)$	$p \vee (y)Hy$	RP
$*_3(3)$	$(y)[q \equiv Fy]$	RP

Note that any line set down in accordance with RP has itself as its only premiss. It follows trivially that any line set down in accordance with RP is implied by its premisses.

52.3. Rule of Truth Functions

The second of the seven rules of system Q is the *rule of truth functions* (TF). The rule TF states that *any wff which is (jointly) truth-functionally implied by some earlier lines $L_1, \ldots, L_k$ of a deduction may be set down as the nth line of the deduction $(n > 1)$, provided*

(i)   *at the left of the new line (n) we put an occurrence of every star that occurs at the left of any of the lines $L_1, \ldots, L_k$;*

(ii) *at the right of the new line (n) we put 'TF' followed by numerals referring to each of the lines $L_1, \ldots, L_k$.*

For example, using RP and TF we can construct the following deduction.

$*_1(1)$	$(x)Gx \vee (\exists y)Fy$	RP
$*_2(2)$	$\sim(x)Gx$	RP
$*_1*_2(3)$	$(\exists y)Fy$	TF(1)(2)
$*_1(4)$	$\sim(x)Gx \supset (\exists y)Fy$	TF(1)

Neither the order of the stars at the left of a line nor the order of the reference numerals at the right of a line is material. In the deduction above, for example, we could have written the third line in any of the following four ways.

$*_2*_1(3)$	$(\exists y)Fy$	TF(1)(2)
$*_2*_1(3)$	$(\exists y)Fy$	TF(2)(1)
$*_1*_2(3)$	$(\exists y)Fy$	TF(1)(2)
$*_1*_2(3)$	$(\exists y)Fy$	TF(2)(1)

The occurrence of 'TF' together with the reference numerals following it at the right of a line shows that the line was set down in accordance with TF on the grounds that the lines referred to by the reference numerals jointly truth-functionally imply the given line.

By a *starred* line of a deduction is meant a line at the left of which there appears at least one star. A starred line is said to be *sound in* a deduction if it is implied by its premises in that deduction. An unstarred line is said to be *sound in* a deduction if it is valid. (Only starred lines have appeared thus far in our sample deductions.) From the property of the consequence relation proved in Exercise (14) of Chapter 49, it follows that TF *preserves soundness in a deduction*, that is, that a line of a deduction set down in accordance with TF is sound in the deduction if all the earlier lines of the deduction are sound in the deduction. That RP also preserves soundness in a deduction is obvious, because any line of a deduction that is set down in accordance with RP is sound in that deduction.

52.4. Rule of Universal Instantiation

Our next rule is called *universal instantiation* (UI). The rule UI says that *any wff which is an instance of an earlier universally quantified line (k) of a deduction may be set down as the nth line of the deduction, provided*

(i) *at the left of (n) we put an occurrence of every star which occurs at the left of (k), and*

(ii) *at the right of (n) we write* $\ulcorner \mathrm{UI}(k) \urcorner$.

The following deduction illustrates the correct use of UI.

$*_1(1)$	$(x)Fx \cdot (y)Hy$	RP
$*_1(2)$	$(x)Fx$	TF(1)
$*_1(3)$	Fy	UI(2)
$*_1(4)$	$(y)Hy$	TF(1)
$*_1(5)$	Hy	UI(4)
$*_1(6)$	$Fy \cdot Hy$	TF(3)(5)

But the following pseudo-deduction illustrates a common mistake that is fostered by our abbreviative conventions.

$*_1(1)$	$(x)Fx \cdot (y)Hy$	RP
$*_1(2)$	$Fy \cdot (y)Hy$	UI(1) *WRONG!*

Line (2) is not an instance of line (1), although many neophytes mistake it for one. Line (1) does not even begin with a quantifier. It begins with a left bracket (dropped by convention) that is not a part of any quantifier.

In an application of UI the occurrence of $\ulcorner UI(k)\urcorner$ at the right of line (n) shows that (n) was set down in accordance with UI on the grounds that (n) is an instance of the universally quantified line (k). The net effect of proviso (i) in the formulation of UI is to make every premiss of (k) also a premiss of (n). As (k) implies (n), it readily follows from the property of the consequence relation proved in Exercise (14) of Chapter 49 that UI preserves soundness in a deduction.

52.5.   Rule of Existential Generalization

The fourth rule of system Q is called *existential generalization* (EG). It states that an *existentially quantified wff* $\ulcorner(\exists a)A_a\urcorner$ *may be set down as the nth line of a deduction if an instance of it* A_b *occurs as an earlier line* (k) *in the deduction, provided*

(i)   *at the left of* (n) *we put an occurrence of every star which occurs at the left of* (k), *and*

(ii)   *at the right of* (n) *we write* $\ulcorner EG(k)\urcorner$.

The following deduction illustrates how EG is correctly applied.

$*_1(1)$	$(x)[Fx \supset Gx]$	RP
$*_1(2)$	$Fy \supset Gy$	UI(1)
$*_3(3)$	$\sim Gy$	RP
$*_1*_3(4)$	$\sim Fy$	TF(2)(3)
$*_1(5)$	$(\exists x)[Fx \supset Gx]$	EG(2)
$*_1*_3(6)$	$(\exists z)\sim Fz$	EG(4)
$*_3(7)$	$(\exists y)\sim Gy$	EG(3)
$*_3(8)$	$(\exists x)(\exists y)\sim Gy$	EG(7)

The expression $\ulcorner EG(k)\urcorner$ at the right of a line (n) of a deduction shows that line (n) was put down via EG on the grounds that it is an existentially quantified wff that has the earlier line (k) as an instance. Again, the effect of proviso (i) in the rule EG is to make every premiss of (k) also a premiss of (n). And (k) implies (n), so it follows that, like UI, EG also preserves soundness in a deduction.

52.6.   Rule of Conditionalization

The next rule is called *conditionalization* (Cd) and is the only rule of system Q that allows us to get rid of stars. When any other rule is used to set down a new line of a deduction, either a new star is introduced (RP) or all the stars that appear at the left of the line or lines referred to by the reference numerals at the right of the new line are put at the left of the new line. But it is otherwise with Cd. The rule Cd permits us to omit, or, as we say, *conditionalize out* one of these stars.

The rule Cd states that *a conditional* $\ulcorner A \supset B \urcorner$ *may be set down as the nth line of a deduction if B is an earlier line* (k) *and A is a premiss* (j) *of* (k), *provided*

(i) *at the left of* (n) *we put an occurrence of every star, except* $\ulcorner *_j \urcorner$, *which occurs at the left of* (k), *and*

(ii) *at the right of* (n) *we write* $\ulcorner Cd*_j(k) \urcorner$.

The use of Cd is illustrated by the following two deductions.

$*_1(1)$	$(x)(y)Hxy$	RP
$*_1(2)$	$(y)Hxy$	UI(1)
$*_1(3)$	Hxx	UI(2)
$*_1(4)$	$(\exists z)Hzz$	EG(3)
(5)	$(x)(y)Hxy \supset (\exists z)Hzz$	Cd$*_1$(4)

$*_1(1)$	$(x)Fx$	RP
$*_2(2)$	$(y)Gy$	RP
$*_1(3)$	Fx	UI(1)
$*_2(4)$	Gx	UI(2)
$*_1*_2(5)$	$Fx \cdot Gx$	TF(3)(4)
$*_1*_2(6)$	$(\exists x)[Fx \cdot Gx]$	EG(5)
$*_2(7)$	$(x)Fx \supset (\exists x)[Fx \cdot Gx]$	Cd$*_1$(6)
(8)	$(y)Gy \supset [(x)Fx \supset (\exists x)(Fx \cdot Gx)]$	Cd$*_2$(7)
(9)	$(x)Fx \cdot (y)Gy \supset (\exists x)[Fx \cdot Gx]$	TF(8)

When a new line (n) is set down in accordance with Cd, the expression $\ulcorner Cd*_j(k) \urcorner$ at the right of (n) signifies that (n) was set down by Cd and that (n) is a conditional with line (j) as antecedent and line (k) as consequent, where (j) is a premiss of (k). By virtue of proviso (i), the premisses of (n) will consist of the premisses of (k) less the premiss (j), which is conditionalized out. Therefore, in view of the property of implication proved in Exercise (15) of Chapter 49, it follows that Cd preserves soundness in a deduction.

52.7.   The Five Soundness-Preserving Rules

We have already remarked that each of the rules RP, TF, UI, EG, and Cd preserves soundness in a deduction. Of these five rules only RP can get a deduction started; that is, RP is the only rule that can be used to set down the first line of a deduction. And, as any line introduced by RP is sound in the given deduction, it follows that every line of a deduction in which only these five rules are used is sound in the deduction. Now a deduction will be called *sound* if every line of it is sound in that deduction. The foregoing observations, therefore, amount to saying that any deduction in which only the rules RP, TF, UI, EG, or Cd are used is sound. We know about a sound deduction that an unstarred line is valid and that a starred line is implied by its premises in the deduction. Hence, to prove that a wff is valid, it suffices to construct a sound deduction in which it stands as an unstarred line. For example, we might prove that '$(x)Fx \cdot (y)Gy \supset (\exists x)[Fx \cdot Gx]$' is valid by constructing the deduction last exhibited above. The five soundness-preserving rules RP, TF, UI, EG, and Cd thus provide a simple, systematic method of showing validity that dispenses with semantical arguments based on the inductive definition of Section 46.4. But the method has a very serious drawback, incompleteness. The method is incomplete in the sense that there are valid wffs, some of them quite simple, which cannot be shown valid by the method. For example, the wff '$(x)[Fx \supset Fx]$' cannot be thus shown valid [see Exercise (13) of Chapter 53].

We observed that one may prove that a wff of LSQ is valid by constructing a sound deduction in which it stands as an unstarred line. Deductions can also establish implication. There are two ways of using the soundness-preserving rules RP, TF, UI, EG, and Cd to prove implication. One can prove that the wffs $A_1, \ldots, A_n$ (jointly) imply B by constructing a sound deduction in which B stands as a starred last line having the wffs $A_1, \ldots, A_n$ as its premises. For example, the sixth line of the last deduction above shows that '$(x)Fx$' and '$(y)Gy$' jointly imply '$(\exists x)[Fx \cdot Gx]$'. Or one can prove that $A_1, \ldots, A_n$ (jointly) imply B by constructing a sound deduction in which the conditional $\ulcorner A_1 \cdot \ldots \cdot A_n \supset B \urcorner$ stands as an unstarred line, because implication amounts to validity of the conditional. For example, the ninth line of the last deduction above shows that '$(x)Fx$' and '$(y)Gy$' jointly imply '$(\exists x)[Fx \cdot Gx]$'.

Because of the incompleteness of the five rules RP, TF, UI, EG, and Cd, our next order of business will be to frame additional rules that will furnish a complete method of proving validity, that is, a method adequate to establish the validity of all the valid wffs of LSQ.

53. EXERCISES

(1) Develop a decision procedure for recognizing whether one wff is an instance of another. Determine about the pairs of wffs listed below whether either member is an instance of the other.

    (a) $(\exists x)(\exists y)Fyx$, $(\exists y)Fyw$

    (b) $(\exists x)[Fx \supset (x)Gxx]$, $Fy \supset (x)Gxx$

    (c) $(\exists z)Fyz$, Fyy

    (d) $(\exists y)[Fy \lor (\exists x)Gxy]$, $Fx \lor (\exists x)Gxx$

    (e) Fyy, $(x)Fxx$

    (f) Fyy, $(x)Fxy$

    (g) $(x)[p \supset (\exists y)Fy]$, $p \supset (\exists y)Fy$

    (h) $(x)(y)Fxy$, $(y)Fxy$

    (i) $(y)Fyy$, Fyz

    (j) $(z)Fyz$, Fzz

    (k) Fyy, $(\exists x)Fyx$

    (l) Fyy, $(x)Fyx$

    (m) $(\exists x)(\exists y)Fy$, $(\exists y)Fy$

    (n) $(x)Fxy$, Fyx

(2) Prove that universally quantified wffs imply their instances whereas existentially quantified wffs are implied by their instances.

(3) Annotate each of the following sequences in such a way that a sound deduction with unstarred last line results:

    (1) $(x)Fxx$

    (2) Fzz

(3) $(\exists y)Fzy$

(4) $(\exists z)(\exists y)Fzy$

(5) $(x)Fxx \supset (\exists z)(\exists y)Fzy$

(1) $(x)[Fx \supset Gx]$

(2) $Fy \supset Gy$

(3) Fy

(4) Gy

(5) $(\exists x)Gx$

(6) $(x)[Fx \supset Gx] \supset (\exists x)Gx$

(7) $Fy \supset [(x)(Fx \supset Gx) \supset (\exists x)Gx]$

(8) $Fy \cdot (x)[Fx \supset Gx] \supset (\exists x)Gx$

(4)   Use the five soundness-preserving rules to construct deductions which show that

(a)   'Fy' implies '$(\exists x)Fx$';

(b)   '$(x)Fxx \supset (\exists x)Fxx$' is valid;

(c)   '$(x)[Fx \supset Gx]$' and '$\sim Gx$' jointly imply '$(\exists y)\sim Fy$';

(d)   '$(x)(\exists y)Gxy \supset (\exists x)(\exists y)Gxy$' is valid;

(e)   '$(y)[Gy \lor Hy]$', '$Hy \supset Fz$', and '$(x)\sim Fx$' jointly imply 'Gy';

(f)   '$(\exists x)(y)Gxy \supset (\exists x)(y)Gxy$' is valid;

(g)   '$Fy \lor \sim Fy$' is valid.

(5)   Mention two ways to use the five soundness-preserving rules to prove equivalence.

[6]   Let A be any wff of Q that does not contain any existential quantifiers. Prove that if A stands as an unstarred last line of a deduction in which only the five rules RP, TF, UI, EG, and Cd are used, then A also stands as an unstarred last line of a deduction in which only the four rules RP, TF, UI, and Cd are used. (*Hint:* Let L_1, ..., L_k be any deduction in which only RP, TF, UI, EG, and Cd are used. Let L'_1, ..., L'_k result from L_1, ..., L_k by replacement of each existential quantifier $\ulcorner(\exists c)\urcorner$ by $\ulcorner\sim(c)\sim\urcorner$. If L_j came from L_i by EG, insert the following three lines between L'_i (let L'_i be A_b) and L'_j [let L'_j be $\ulcorner\sim(a)\sim A_a\urcorner$]:

$*_m(m)$	$(a)\sim A_a$	RP
$*_m(m+1)$	$\sim A_b$	UI(m)
$(m+2)$	$(a)\sim A_a \supset \sim A_b$	Cd$*_m(m+1)$

Then renumber the wffs of the resulting sequence and annotate L'_j as derived from L'_i and $(m + 2)$ by TF. Show that this new sequence is a deduction in which only the four rules RP, TF, UI, and Cd are used.)

[7] Let S be the logistic system whose vocabulary is that of LSQ less the symbols 'v', '·', '≡', and which has appropriate formation rules. The axioms of S are given by the following four axiom schemata:

    (i) $(a)A_a \supset A_b$, where A_b is an instance of $\ulcorner (a)A_a \urcorner$.

    (ii) $A \supset [B \supset A]$.

    (iii) $[A \supset (B \supset C)] \supset [(A \supset B) \supset (A \supset C)]$.

    (iv) $[\sim A \supset \sim B] \supset [B \supset A]$.

And let S have only one rule of inference, *modus ponens*. A sequence $B_1, \ldots, B_k$ of wffs of S will be called a *proof of B_k from the hypotheses $A_1, \ldots, A_n$* if each B_i is an axiom, or one of the hypotheses $A_1, \ldots, A_n$, or derived by *modus ponens* from two earlier wffs in the sequence. Prove the deduction theorem for S; that is, prove that if $A_1, \ldots, A_n \vdash B$, then $A_1, \ldots, A_{n-1} \vdash \ulcorner A_n \supset B \urcorner$. See Section 30.0. (*Hint:* Pattern your proof after the one given in Section 30.0.)

[8] Let T be the natural deduction system whose vocabulary and formation rules are the same as in system S of Exercise [7]. Let the rules of T be RP, TF, UI, and Cd only, and let us understand by a *theorem of* T any wff that is an unstarred line of a deduction of T. Prove that S and T have the same theorems. (*Hint:* Make use of what you proved in Exercise [7].)

[9] Let Q' be the natural deduction system which is like Q except that Q' has only the five rules RP, TF, UI, EG, and Cd. (Remember, Q has seven rules, only five of which have been formulated thus far.) Let A be any wff of system Q' which is devoid of existential quantifiers. Prove that A is a theorem of Q' if and only if B is a theorem of T, where B results from A by eliminating occurrences of 'v', '·', and '≡' in A in favor of '$\sim$' and '$\supset$'. (By a *theorem of* Q' is meant any wff that stands as an unstarred line in a deduction of Q'.) (*Hint:* Make use of the results of Exercises [8] and [6].)

(10) Prove that no wff of the form $\ulcorner (a)A \urcorner$ is truth-functionally

implied by a finite number of wffs each of which has the form $\ulcorner (b)B \supset C \urcorner$.

[11] Prove that, if A is a theorem of system S of Exercise [7], then there is a finite number $D_1, \ldots, D_r$ of wffs of the form $\ulcorner (b)B \supset C \urcorner$ such that $D_1, \ldots, D_r$ jointly truth-functionally imply A. (*Hint:* Let $A_1, \ldots, A_n$ be a proof in system S and let $B_1, \ldots, B_k$ be a complete list of the instances of axiom schema (i) which occur in the sequence $A_1, \ldots, A_n$. Show that $B_1, \ldots, B_k$ jointly truth-functionally imply A_n.)

(12) Prove that '$(x)[Fx \supset Fx]$' is not a theorem of system S. (*Hint:* See Exercises (10) and [11].)

(13) Prove that the five rules RP, TF, UI, EG, and Cd are incomplete in the sense that some valid wffs of system Q do not stand as unstarred lines of deductions in which only the five rules RP, TF, UI, EG, and Cd are used. (*Hint:* Make use of the results of Exercises (12), [9], and [8].)

54. QUINE'S SYSTEM OF NATURAL DEDUCTION (II)

54.0. Conservative Instances

An instance A_b of a wff $\ulcorner (a)A_a \urcorner$ [or $\ulcorner (\exists a)A_a \urcorner$] is called *conservative* if there is a variable of instantiation b and it occurs free in A_b only where a occurs free in A_a, or if there is no variable of instantiation. (See the definition of *instance* and of the *variable of instantiation* in Section 52.0.) That is, A_b is a conservative instance of $\ulcorner (a)A_a \urcorner$ and $\ulcorner (\exists a)A_a \urcorner$ if and only if A_b is like A_a except perhaps for having free occurrences of b wherever and only wherever A_a has free occurrences of a. For example, '$(x)Fxz$' is a conservative instance of both '$(\exists z)(x)Fxz$' and '$(y)(x)Fxy$' with 'z' as the variable of instantiation in both cases. Similarly, '$(\exists y)Gxy$' is a conservative instance of both '$(\exists x)(\exists y)Gxy$' and '$(w)(\exists y)Gwy$' with '$x$' as the variable of instantiation in each case. But 'Fyy' is only an instance of '$(\exists x)Fxy$' and '$(x)Fxy$'; it is not a conservative instance of these two wffs. With one exception, conservative instances boast a variable of instantiation. The exception involves vacuous quantifiers. For example, although '$(\exists y)Gxy$' is a conservative instance of '$(\exists w)(\exists y)Gxy$', no variable of instantiation is involved.

The following account may help the reader to recognize instances and conservative instances quickly and easily. Take a wff $\ulcorner(\exists a)A_a\urcorner$ or $\ulcorner(a)A_a\urcorner$, drop the initial quantifier, and substitute b for all free occurrences of a. If none of the substituted occurrences of b are bound, the result is an instance of the original quantified wff. If, in addition, either b is the same as a or does not occur free in A_a, then the result is a conservative instance of the original wff, with b as the variable of instantiation.

54.1. Rule of Universal Generalization

Unlike the five rules of system Q already introduced, the two rules about to be formulated do not preserve soundness in a deduction. Most deductions that employ these two rules are *unsound* but, as we will shortly see, very useful nonetheless. The first of these two rules is known as *universal generalization* (UG). The rule UG states that *a universally quantified wff $\ulcorner(a)A_a\urcorner$ may be set down as the nth line of a deduction if a conservative instance A_b of it occurs as an earlier line* (k) *in the deduction, provided*

(i)   *at the left of* (n) *we put an occurrence of every star that occurs at the left of line* (k),

(ii) *at the right of* (n) *we put* $\ulcorner UG(k)\boxed{b}\urcorner$, *where b is the variable of instantiation (if any), and*

(iii) *provided the variable of instantiation b (if any) is not already flagged in the deduction.* (For an explanation of "flagging", see below.)

The use of UG is illustrated by the following two deductions.

$*_1(1)$	Fy	RP
$*_2(2)$	$\sim(\exists x)Fx$	RP
$*_1(3)$	$(\exists x)Fx$	EG(1)
(4)	$Fy \supset (\exists x)Fx$	Cd$*_1$(3)
$*_2(5)$	$\sim Fy$	TF(4)(2)
$*_2(6)$	$(x)\sim Fx$	UG(5)$\boxed{y}$
(7)	$\sim(\exists x)Fx \supset (x)\sim Fx$	Cd$*_2$(6)

$*_1(1)$	$(x)[Fx \cdot Gx]$	RP
$*_1(2)$	$Fy \cdot Gy$	UI(1)
$*_1(3)$	Fy	TF(2)
$*_1(4)$	$(x)Fx$	UG(3) 🏳
$*_1(5)$	$Fx \cdot Gx$	UI(1)
$*_1(6)$	Gx	TF(5)
$*_1(7)$	$(x)Gx$	UG(6) 🏳
$*_1(8)$	$(x)Fx \cdot (x)Gx$	TF(4)(7)
(9)	$(x)[Fx \cdot Gx] \supset (x)Fx \cdot (x)Gx$	Cd$*_1$(8)

Presently we shall designate certain deductions of system Q as *proofs*, and we will prove that the last line of a proof is valid. It will turn out that both of the above deductions are proofs. Each of them, therefore, establishes the validity of its last line.

The design '🏳' is called a *flag* and any variable that occurs on its field is said to be *flagged*. For example, 'y' is the only variable flagged in the first of the two deductions above. Proviso (ii) in the formulation of UG requires one to flag the variable of instantiation (if any) when going from a conservative instance to a universally quantified wff. Proviso (iii) prohibits one from flagging the same variable more than once within a deduction. Violation of the third proviso leads to patent absurdities. For example, the pseudo proof below, which violates only proviso (iii) of UG, purports to show that '$(x)[Fx \lor Gx] \supset (x)Fx \lor (x)Gx$' is valid.

$*_1(1)$	$(x)[Fx \lor Gx]$	RP
$*_1(2)$	$Fy \lor Gy$	UI(1)
$*_3(3)$	Fy	RP
$*_3(4)$	$(x)Fx$	UG(3) 🏳
(5)	$Fy \supset (x)Fx$	Cd$*_3$(4)
$*_6(6)$	Gy	RP
$*_6(7)$	$(x)Gx$	UG(6) 🏳 *WRONG!*
(8)	$Gy \supset (x)Gx$	Cd$*_6$(7)
(9)	$(x)[Fx \lor Gx] \supset [Fy \lor Gy]$	Cd$*_1$(2)
(11)	$(x)[Fx \lor Gx] \supset (x)Fx \lor (x)Gx$	TF(5)(8)(9)

When UG is used to set down a vacuously quantified line no variable is flagged, because there is then no variable of quantification. For example:

$*_1(1)$	$(x)Fx$	RP
$*_1(2)$	$(y)(x)Fx$	UG(1) 🏳
(3)	$(x)Fx \supset (y)(x)Fx$	Cd$*_1$(2)

54.2.   Rule of Existential Instantiation

The seventh and last rule of system Q is called *existential instantiation* (EI). The rule EI states that, *if an existentially quantified wff* $\ulcorner(\exists a)A_a\urcorner$ *occurs as line (k) of a deduction, then a conservative instance* A_b *of it may be set down as a later line (n) of the deduction, provided*

(i)   *at the left of (n) we put an occurrence of every star which appears at the left of (k),*

(ii) *at the right of (n) we write* $\ulcorner EI(k)\underset{\bullet}{\boxed{b}}\urcorner$, *where b is the variable of instantiation (if any), and*

(iii) *provided the variable of instantiation (if any) is not already flagged in the deduction.*

The two deductions below show how EI is applied.

*₁(1)	$(x)\sim Fx$	RP
*₂(2)	$\sim\sim(\exists x)Fx$	RP
*₂(3)	$(\exists x)Fx$	TF(2)
*₁(4)	$\sim Fy$	UI(1)
*₂(5)	Fy	EI(3) $\boxed{y}$
*₁*₂(6)	$Fy \cdot \sim Fy$	TF(4)(5)
*₁(7)	$\sim\sim(\exists x)Fx \supset Fy\cdot\sim Fy$	Cd*₂(6)
*₁(8)	$\sim(\exists x)Fx$	TF(7)
(9)	$(x)\sim Fx \supset \sim(\exists x)Fx$	Cd*₁(8)

*₁(1)	$(\exists x)Fx$	RP
*₁(2)	Fx	EI(1) $\boxed{x}$
*₁(3)	$Fx \vee Gx$	TF(2)
*₁(4)	$(\exists x)[Fx \vee Gx]$	EG(3)
(5)	$(\exists x)Fx \supset (\exists x)[Fx \vee Gx]$	Cd*₁(4)
*₆(6)	$(\exists x)Gx$	RP
*₆(7)	Gy	EI(6) $\boxed{y}$
*₆(8)	$Fy \vee Gy$	TF(7)
*₆(9)	$(\exists x)[Fx \vee Gx]$	EG(8)
(10)	$(\exists x)Gx \supset (\exists x)[Fx \vee Gx]$	Cd*₆(9)
(11)	$(\exists x)Fx \vee (\exists x)Gx \supset (\exists x)[Fx \vee Gx]$	TF(5)(10)

As the deductions above will turn out to be proofs in system Q, each shows the validity of its last line.

As with UG, one is not permitted to flag the same variable more than once when applying EI. Absurdity results when this flagging restriction is violated. For example, violation of it leads to the pseudo deduction below, which purports to show that

'$(\exists x)Fx \cdot (\exists x)Gx \supset (\exists x)[Fx \cdot Gx]$' is valid.

$*_1(1)$	$(\exists x)Fx \cdot (\exists x)Gx$	RP
$*_1(2)$	$(\exists x)Fx$	TF(1)
$*_1(3)$	Fy	EI(2)
$*_1(4)$	$(\exists x)Gx$	TF(1)
$*_1(5)$	Gy	EI(4) *WRONG!*
$*_1(6)$	$Fy \cdot Gy$	TF(3)(5)
$*_1(7)$	$(\exists x)[Fx \cdot Gx]$	EG(6)
(8)	$(\exists x)Fx \cdot (\exists x)Gx \supset (\exists x)[Fx \cdot Gx]$	Cd$*_1$(7)

And, as with UG, there is only one circumstance in which use of EI does not cause a variable to be flagged—when EI is used to drop a vacuous existential quantifier. In this circumstance there is no variable of instantiation. For example:

$*_1(1)$	$(\exists x)p$	RP
$*_1(2)$	p	EI(1)
(3)	$(\exists x)p \supset p$	Cd$*_1$(2)
$*_4(4)$	p	RP
$*_4(5)$	$(\exists x)p$	EG(4)
(6)	$p \supset (\exists x)p$	Cd$*_4$(5)
(7)	$p \equiv (\exists x)p$	TF(3)(6)

54.3. Rationale Behind Universal Generalization and Existential Instantiation

There is an obvious correspondence of the five soundness-preserving rules of system Q to intuitive rules of correct reasoning. For example, Cd corresponds to a rule of which we have made frequent use in proving metatheorems that have the form of conditionals. Namely, we may assume the antecedent as a premiss (a procedure corresponding to RP), derive the consequent from it, and infer therefrom that the conditional is logically true. Neither UG nor EI is soundness-preserving, but nevertheless each corresponds to intuitive rules of correct reasoning. The rule UG corresponds to the rule that permits one to infer that all objects of a given kind have a certain property from the proposition that an arbitrary object of that kind has that property. For example, one might let A be an arbitrary wff of LSQ, observe that A implies itself, and infer therefrom that every wff of LSQ implies itself. In applications of this intuitive counterpart of UG it is essential that the object considered be really an arbitrary object of the relevant kind, or else a fallacy of reasoning may ensue. Consider, for example, this piece of fallacious reasoning. Let $\{A,B\}$ be a satisfiable set of wffs of LSQ. Let Σ be any maximal model (that is, true maximal interpretation) of A which is also a model of B. From our assumption about $\{A,B\}$ it follows that there are models like Σ. Now the conditional $\ulcorner A \supset B \urcorner$ comes out true under Σ. And, as Σ is an arbitrary maximal model of A, it follows that $\ulcorner A \supset B \urcorner$ comes out true under every model of A that is an interpretation of B. Hence A implies B. Hence any two wffs of LSQ that are simultaneously satisfiable imply one another. The prohibition against multiple flagging of the same variable, together with the metarules to be given presently that define which deductions of system Q are proofs, preclude UG's giving rise to fallacious inferences such as the one above.

The rule EI corresponds to the intuitive rule that permits one to introduce a name for an object of a certain kind when one has proved or assumed that such objects exist, and then to reason about the named presumptive object. Suppose, for example, that someone has assumed that there are singulary connectives of LSP which are functionally complete. He might then let $\otimes$ be such a connective; that is, he might introduce '$\otimes$' as a name of a singulary connective which is functionally complete. By reasoning about $\otimes$, he may be able to show that it does not serve to define '$\supset$', from which he infers that $\otimes$ is not functionally complete. Thereupon he will infer the falsehood of his original assumption from the contradiction to which it led. When applying the intuitive counterpart of EI, one may not introduce as a name an expression already pre-empted as a name. In the above illustration, for example, if '$\otimes$' had already been introduced as a name for Sheffer's stroke, it would have been improper to construe it as a name of a functionally complete singulary connective. Fallacies that might have arisen through improper employment of existential instantiation are precluded by the restriction on multiple flagging of the same variable, together with the metarules that define proofs.

54.4. Finished Deductions; Proofs; Metatheorems

A deduction that fulfills both of the following conditions is said to be *finished:*

C1. No variable that is flagged in the deduction may occur free in the last line or in any premiss of the last line.

C2.   There must be an ordering b_1, ..., b_n of all the flagged variables of the deduction such that no variable in the ordering occurs free in any line where any variable that comes later in the ordering is flagged.

All the deductions so far constructed have been finished. The deduction below is unfinished, however, because it violates C1.

$*_1(1)$ Fy RP
$*_1(2)$ $(x)Fx$ UG(1) $\boxed{y}$

But we can finish it by appending two additional lines:

(3) $Fy \supset (x)Fx$ $Cd*_1(2)$
(4) $(\exists y)[Fy \supset (x)Fx]$ EG(3)

What has just been illustrated is true of all unfinished deductions that violate C1 but satisfy C2: They can be finished by use of Cd and EG. These deductions, therefore, are finishable. But a deduction that violates C2 is not only unfinished but unfinishable. For example, no matter how one appends additional lines to the unfinished deduction below, the result will be an unfinished deduction which, like the original, violates C2.

$*_1(1)$ $(x)(\exists y)Gyx$ RP
$*_1(2)$ $(\exists y)Gyz$ UI(1)
$*_1(3)$ Gwz EI(2) $\boxed{w}$
$*_1(4)$ $(x)Gwx$ UG(3) $\boxed{z}$
$*_1(5)$ $(\exists y)(x)Gyx$ EG(4)
(6) $(x)(\exists y)Gyx \supset (\exists y)(x)Gyx$ $Cd*_1(5)$

There are only two orderings of the flagged variables of the above deduction, $\langle 'w','z' \rangle$ and $\langle 'z','w' \rangle$. As 'w' occurs free in the line where 'z' is flagged and 'z' occurs free in the line where 'w' is flagged, neither ordering has the property that C2 calls for. Therefore, the deduction violates C2 and is accordingly unfinished. Furthermore, because any continuation of the deduction would also violate C2, the deduction is unfinishable. Obviously once a deduction violates C2 every continuation of it will also violate C2. That is why such deductions are unfinishable.

Unfinishable deductions hold no interest for us, because the proofs of system Q will all be finished deductions. Accordingly, when constructing deductions we should guard against violations of C2 because they render a deduction unfinishable. Therefore, whenever we flag a variable in a deduction that already contains flagged variables, we should immediately check to see whether C2 is satisfied. If C2 is not satisfied, we should erase the line which had just been set down and which precipitated the violation.

By a *proof* in system Q we shall understand a finished deduction with unstarred last line. A proof is said to be a *proof of* its last line. For example, the proof below is a proof of '$Fy \supset (\exists x)Fx$'.

$*_1(1)$	Fy	RP
$*_1(2)$	$(\exists x)Fx$	EG(1)
(3)	$Fy \supset (\exists x)Fx$	Cd$*_1$(2)

By a *theorem* of system Q is meant any wff of which there is a proof. Thus '$Fy \supset (\exists x)Fx$' is a theorem of system Q. Many of the illustrative deductions that have been constructed in preceding sections are proofs. Their last lines, therefore, are theorems of system Q.

Theorems derive their importance from two principal metatheorems about system Q, the consistency theorem and the completeness theorem, which state that system Q is consistent and complete with respect to validity, that is, that a wff of system Q (or LSQ) is valid if and only if it is a theorem of system Q.

Every theorem of system Q is valid (consistency theorem).
Every valid wff of system Q is a theorem of system Q (completeness theorem).

The consistency theorem is proved in Section 54.5. A proof of the completeness theorem will be found in Chapter 58.

Finished deductions that are not proofs, such as the one below, are nonetheless valuable for establishing implication.

$*_1(1)$	$(x)Fx$	RP
$*_1(2)$	Fx	UI(1)
$*_3(3)$	$(x)Gx$	RP
$*_3(4)$	Gx	UI(3)
$*_1*_3(5)$	$Fx \cdot Gx$	TF(2)(4)
$*_1*_3(6)$	$(x)[Fx \cdot Gx]$	UG(5)

Let Ω be a finished deduction that is not a proof and let (n) be the last line of Ω. By repeated use of Cd and TF, one can append new lines in such a way that the result is a proof whose last line is a conditional which has (n) as consequent and whose antecedent is a conjunction of the premises of (n). For example, appending the following lines to the finished deduction above gives a proof of the conditional whose consequent is line (6) and whose antecedent is a conjunction of lines (1) and (3).

$*_1(7)$	$(x)Gx \supset (x)[Fx \cdot Gx]$	$Cd*_3(6)$
(8)	$(x)Fx \supset [(x)Gx \supset (x)(Fx \cdot Gx)]$	$Cd*_1(7)$
(9)	$(x)Fx \cdot (x)Gx \supset (x)[Fx \cdot Gx]$	$TF(8)$

From the consistency theorem and the fact that joint implication amounts to validity of the conditional, it follows that a starred last line of a finished deduction is jointly implied by its premises. Hence, to prove that $A_1, \ldots, A_n$ jointly imply B, it suffices to produce a finished deduction that has B as its last line (k), with $A_1, \ldots, A_n$ as the premises of (k). And from the completeness theorem it follows that, if $A_1, \ldots, A_n$ jointly imply B, then there is a finished deduction whose last line is B with $A_1, \ldots, A_n$ as premises thereof.

Let Ω be a finished deduction and let $A_1, \ldots, A_k$ be the premises (if any) of the last line B of Ω. We shall speak of Ω as a *proof of B from the premises $A_1, \ldots, A_n$*. And we let '$A_1, \ldots, A_n \vdash B$' mean 'there is proof of B from the premises $A_1, \ldots, A_n$'. Obviously, $A_1, \ldots, A_n$ jointly imply B if and only if $A_1, \ldots, A_n \vdash B$. Moreover, A is a theorem of system Q if and only if $\vdash A$, that is, if and only if there is a proof of A from no premises.

Where Δ is a set of wffs of system Q, we let the expression '$\Delta \vdash A$' mean 'there is a proof of A from a finite number of members of Δ as premises'. And a set Δ of wffs of system Q will be said to be *consistent* if there is no wff B such that $\Delta \vdash B$ and $\Delta \vdash \ulcorner \sim B \urcorner$. There is an important lemma about system Q which is known as the *Skolem–Gödel theorem*. This lemma states that *if a class of wffs is consistent, then it is satisfiable*. The Skolem–Gödel theorem is proved in Chapter 58. The completeness theorem, the compactness theorem (see Exercise $\langle 7 \rangle$ of Chapter 49), and the so-called *strong completeness theorem* can all be derived as corollaries of the Skolem–Gödel theorem.

A wff A is a consequence of a set Δ of wffs of system Q if and only if $\Delta \vdash A$ (strong completeness theorem)

To appreciate the significance of the strong completeness theorem, suppose that some infinite class Δ of wffs of system Q has been laid down as the axioms of a theory T. We intuitively think of the theorems of a theory as the set of wffs that are the consequences of its axioms. If the rules of system Q form an adequate logic, the theorems of T will be identical with the set of wffs A such that $\Delta \vdash A$. From the consistency theorem we know that, if $\Delta \vdash A$, then A is a consequence of Δ and is therefore a theorem of T. And from the completeness theorem we know that, if A is a consequence of a finite subset of Δ, then $\Delta \vdash A$. But perhaps there is a wff B which is a consequence of Δ but is a consequence of no finite subset of Δ. If so, there would be no proof of B from Δ and the rules of system Q would be somewhat inadequate to develop the theory T. But the strong completeness theorem entails that there are no wffs like B. Hence the rules of system Q are adequate to the development of any theory T.

54.5. Proof of the Consistency Theorem

Before proving the consistency theorem for system Q we pause to establish several useful lemmas.

> **Lemma 1.**   If A_b implies C and b does not occur free in C, then $\ulcorner(\exists b)A_b\urcorner$ implies C.

To prove lemma 1, suppose that A_b implies C, that b does not occur free in C, and that $\ulcorner(\exists b)A_b\urcorner$ does not imply C. Then there is a false minimal interpretation Σ of $\ulcorner(\exists b)A_b \supset C\urcorner$. Let Σ_1 be the minimal interpretation of $\ulcorner(\exists b)A_b\urcorner$ determined by Σ. Clearly $\ulcorner(\exists b)A_b\urcorner$ comes out true under Σ_1. By the semantics of the existential quantifier, therefore, we know that there is a true minimal interpretation Σ_2 of A_b which is exactly like Σ_1 except perhaps that Σ_2 assigns some individual β to b whereas Σ_1 makes no assignment to b. Let Σ' be like Σ except that Σ' assigns β to b while Σ makes no assignment to b. Clearly C comes out with the same value (falsehood) under both Σ and Σ', and A_b has the same value under Σ' as A_b has under Σ_2—truth. Thus $\ulcorner A_b \supset C\urcorner$ comes out false under Σ', which entails that A_b does not imply C. But this contradicts our initial supposition. By indirect proof, therefore, we infer that lemma 1 is true.

> **Lemma 2.**   If A_b implies C, and b does not occur free in C, and $\ulcorner(\exists b)A_b\urcorner$ is valid, then C is valid.

Lemma 2 follows almost immediately from lemma 1. If A_b implies

C and b does not occur free in C, we know from lemma 1 that $\ulcorner(\exists b)A_b\urcorner$ implies C. And, as valid wffs imply only valid wffs, we may infer that C is valid if $\ulcorner(\exists b)A_b\urcorner$ is valid.

> **Lemma 3.** If A_b is a conservative instance of $\ulcorner(a)A_a\urcorner$ with b as the variable of instantiation, then $\ulcorner(\exists b)[A_b \supset (a)A_a]\urcorner$ is valid.

Note that $\ulcorner(\exists a)[A_a \supset (a)A_a]\urcorner$ is equivalent to $\ulcorner(\exists b)[A_b \supset (a)A_a]\urcorner$, because these two wffs differ only by alphabetic change of a bound variable. Hence it suffices to prove that the former wff is valid. Suppose, then, that $\ulcorner(\exists a)[A_a \supset (a)A_a]\urcorner$ is not valid. Then there is a false minimal interpretation Σ of it. Let Σ_1 be any minimal interpretation of $\ulcorner A_a \supset (a)A_a\urcorner$ which is like Σ except perhaps for the value assigned to a. (Σ makes no assignment to a.) From the semantics of the existential quantifier we know that $\ulcorner A_a \supset (a)A_a\urcorner$ comes out false under Σ_1. Hence $\ulcorner(a)A_a\urcorner$ comes out false under Σ_2, where Σ_2 is the minimal interpretation of $\ulcorner(a)A_a\urcorner$ determined by Σ_1. Note that Σ_2 and Σ are identical. Hence $\ulcorner(a)A_a\urcorner$ comes out false under Σ. From the semantics of the universal quantifier, we then know that $\ulcorner A_a\urcorner$ comes out false under at least one minimal interpretation Σ_3 which is like Σ except perhaps for the value assigned to a. Hence $\ulcorner A_a \supset (a)A_a\urcorner$ comes out true under Σ_3. But then $\ulcorner(\exists a)[A_a \supset (a)A_a]\urcorner$ comes out true under Σ, which contradicts the supposition that Σ is a false minimal interpretation of this wff. The lemma follows, therefore, by indirect proof.

> **Lemma 4.** If A_b is a conservative instance of $\ulcorner(\exists a)A_a\urcorner$ with b as the variable of instantiation, then $\ulcorner(\exists b)[(\exists a)A_a \supset A_b]\urcorner$ is valid.

The reader may construct a proof of this lemma along the lines of the proof of lemma 3.

We are now ready to prove the consistency theorem, that is, to prove that the last line of any proof is valid. We will proceed by mathematical induction on the number of uses of UG and EI in a proof Ω.

Induction Basis. Suppose that there are zero uses of UG and EI in Ω. Then only the five soundness-preserving rules RP, TF, UI, EG, and Cd are used in Ω. But we observed in Section 52.7 that an unstarred line of such a deduction is valid. Now the last line of Ω is unstarred, because Ω is a proof. Hence the last line of Ω is valid. This completes the induction basis.

Induction Step. Assume that the last lines of proofs which contain n uses of UG and EI are valid. Let Ω be a proof with $n + 1$ uses of UG and EI, and let $b_1, \ldots, b_m, b$ be an ordering of the flagged variables of Ω which satisfies the ordering requirement C2 of Section 54.4. We consider two subcases according as the line of Ω wherein b is flagged, say line (k), was introduced by UG or by EI.

First subcase. Suppose that line (k), the line of Ω wherein b is flagged, is set down by UG. Then (k) has the following form:

$\ldots(k) \quad (a)A_a$ UG(j) $\boxed{b}$

Line (k) will be a conservative instance A_b of line (k). Increase by one each numeral in Ω and put the following line at the top of the new sequence:

$*_1(1) \quad A_b \supset (a)A_a$ RP

Change old line (k), now line $(k + 1)$, as follows:

$*_1\ldots(k + 1) \quad (a)A_a$ TF(1)$(j + 1)$

[Remember, line $(j + 1)$ is old line (j).] Throughout the new sequence put '$*_1$' before any line that requires it in order to be properly set down. The last line of this new sequence will be the following, where B is the last line (unstarred) of Ω:

$?(r) \quad B$ $\ldots$

If there is no star at the left of (r), the new sequence will be a proof with n uses of UG and EI. By the hypothesis of induction, therefore, B will be valid. If there are any stars at the left of (r), there will be only the one star '$*_1$'. The new sequence will be a finished deduction with starred last line. Append to it the following line:

$(r + 1) \quad [A_b \supset (a)A_a] \supset B$ Cd$*_1(r)$

The result will be a proof with n uses of UG and EI. (The reader should verify that both conditions C1 and C2 of Section 54.4 are satisfied; the ordering $b_1, \ldots, b_m$ will do for C2.) By the hypothesis of induction, therefore, $\ulcorner[A_b \supset (a)A_a] \supset B\urcorner$ is valid. Hence $\ulcorner A_b \supset (a)A_a\urcorner$ implies B. Ω was a proof, so b does not occur free in B, as b is a flagged variable of Ω. By lemma 3, $\ulcorner(\exists b)[A_b \supset (a)A_a]\urcorner$ is valid. Therefore, by lemma 2, B is valid. B is the last line of Ω, so this terminates the first subcase.

Second Subcase. The case where line (k) of Ω is set down by EI may be treated similarly and is left to the reader.

By mathematical induction, therefore, we conclude that the last line of any proof is valid. In other words, we have shown that every theorem of system Q is valid (consistency theorem for system Q).

55.   EXERCISES

(1)   For each of the pairs of wffs of Exercise (1) of Chapter 53, determine whether either member of the pair is a conservative instance of the other. Develop a decision procedure for recognizing conservative instances and for picking out the variable of instantiation (if any).

(2)   In the constructions below, flag the appropriate variables.

$*_1(1)$	$Fy \supset p$	RP
$*_1(2)$	$(x)[Fx \supset p]$	UG(1)

$*_1(1)$	Hxy	RP
$*_1(2)$	$(x)Hxy$	UG(1)

$*_1(1)$	$(\exists y)Gxy$	RP
$*_1(2)$	Gxz	EI(1)

$*_1(1)$	$(\exists x)(\exists y)Gxy$	RP
$*_1(2)$	$(\exists y)Gxy$	EI(1)

(3)   Annotate the sequences below in such a way that proofs (finished deductions with unstarred last lines) result.

(1) $(\exists x)[Fx \vee Gx]$
(2) $Fy \vee Gy$
(3) $(\exists x)[Fx \vee Gx] \supset [Fy \vee Gy]$
(4) Fy
(5) $(\exists x)Fx$
(6) $Fy \supset (\exists x)Fx$
(7) Gy
(8) $(\exists x)Gx$
(9) $Gy \supset (\exists x)Gx$
(10) $(\exists x)[Fx \vee Gx] \supset (\exists x)Fx \vee (\exists x)Gx$

(1) $(x) \sim Fxx$
(2) $(x)(y)(z)[Fxy \cdot Fyz \supset Fxz]$
(3) $(y)(z)[Fxy \cdot Fyz \supset Fxz]$
(4) $(z)[Fxy \cdot Fyz \supset Fxz]$
(5) $Fxy \cdot Fyx \supset Fxx$
(6) $\sim Fxx$
(7) $Fxy \supset \sim Fyx$
(8) $(y)[Fxy \supset \sim Fyx]$
(9) $(x)(y)[Fxy \supset \sim Fyx]$
(10) $(2) \supset (9)$
(11) $(1) \supset [(2) \supset (9)]$
(12) $(1) \cdot (2) \supset (9)$

(4)   Prove that an unfinished deduction which satisfies C2 can be finished. Prove that no deduction which violates C2 can be finished. Can a deduction with at most one flagged variable violate C2?

(5)   Assuming both the consistency and completeness theorems for system Q, prove that A is equivalent to B if and only if $A \vdash B$ and $B \vdash A$. On the same assumptions, prove that A is equivalent to B if and only if $\vdash \ulcorner A \equiv B \urcorner$. Explain how one can use system Q to establish equivalence.

(6)   Derive the completeness theorem for system Q from the Skolem–Gödel theorem. (See the first paragraph of Section 30.3.)

(7)   Derive the compactness theorem for system Q from the Skolem–Gödel theorem. (See Section 30.4.)

[8]   Derive the strong completeness theorem from the Skolem–Gödel theorem. (*Hint:* To show that $\Delta \vdash A$ if A is a consequence of Δ, assume that A is a consequence of Δ but that it is not the case that $\Delta \vdash A$. Then show, for each finite subset Δ_0 of Δ, that the set $\Delta_0 \cup \{ \ulcorner \sim A \urcorner \}$ is satisfiable because consistent. From the compactness theorem it then follows that $\Delta \cup \{ \ulcorner \sim A \urcorner \}$ is satisfiable, which entails that A is not a consequence of Δ.)

(9)   Derive the completeness theorem for system Q from the strong completeness theorem.

(10) Derive the compactness theorem for system Q from the strong completeness theorem. (*Hint:* If Δ is not satisfiable, then, for any wff B, both B and $\ulcorner \sim B \urcorner$ are consequences of Δ.)

(11)   Derive the Skolem–Gödel theorem from the strong completeness theorem. [*Hint:* See hint of Exercise (10).]

(12)   Throughout the second deduction of Section 54.2 substitute 'w' for all free occurrences of 'x', substitute 'z' for all free occurrences of 'y', and flag 'w' and 'z' where 'x' and 'y' are flagged, deleting the flags for 'x' and 'y'. Is the result a proof of '$(\exists x)Fx \vee (\exists x)Gx \supset (\exists x)[Fx \vee Gx]$'?

[13]   Let the deduction $L_1, \ldots, L_k$ be a proof of B from the premisses $A_1, \ldots, A_n$, let $c_1, \ldots, c_m$ be a complete list of the distinct flagged variables of the deduction, and let $d_1, \ldots, d_m$ be individual variables that occur nowhere in the deduction. For each i, let L_i' be the result of substituting $d_1, \ldots, d_m$ for free occurrences of $c_1, \ldots, c_m$, respectively in L_i. Also, wherever c_j occurs on a flag, replace that occurrence of c_j by one of d_j. Prove that the resulting sequence $L_1', \ldots, L_k'$ is also a proof of B from the premisses $A_1, \ldots, A_n$. [*Hint:* See exercise (12).]

[14]   Prove that if $A_1, \ldots, A_n \vdash B$ and $A_1, \ldots, A_n$ are all theorems of system Q, then B is a theorem of system Q. (*Hint:* Let Ω be a proof of B from the premisses $A_1, \ldots, A_n$, and, for each i, let Ω_i be a proof of A_i. Use the result of [13] to show that, for each $i \leq n$, there is a proof Ω_i' of A_i in which no variables are flagged which occur anywhere in Ω or in Ω_j', $j \neq i$. Then show that $\Omega_1', \ldots, \Omega_n'$ is a proof of B.)

(15)   Prove that if $A_1, \ldots, A_n, B_1, \ldots, B_k \vdash B$ and, for each i $(1 \leq i \leq k)$, $A_1, \ldots, A_n \vdash B_i$, then $A_1, \ldots, A_n \vdash B$. (*Hint:* Make use of what was proved in Exercise [14].)

[16]   Let system Q⁺ be like system Q except for having these two additional rules:

Rule NE: *If* $\ulcorner \sim(\exists a)A_a \urcorner$ *occurs as an earlier line* (k) *of a deduction, one may set down* $\ulcorner (a)\sim A_a \urcorner$ *as line* (n), *provided that at the left of* (n) *is put an occurrence of every star that appears at the left of* (k), *and provided that at the right of* (n) *is put* $\ulcorner NE(k) \urcorner$.

Rule NU: *If* $\ulcorner \sim(a)A_a \urcorner$ *occurs as an earlier line* (k) *of a deduction, one may set down* $\ulcorner (\exists a)\sim A_a \urcorner$ *as line* (n), *provided that at the left of* (n) *is put an occurrence of every star that appears at the left of* (k), *and provided that at the right of* (n) *is put* $\ulcorner NU(k) \urcorner$.

Prove that systems Q and Q⁺ have the same theorems. Prove also that $A_1, \ldots, A_n \vdash B$ in system Q if and only if $A_1, \ldots, A_n \vdash B$ in system Q⁺. (*Hint:* Let Ω be a proof of B in Q⁺. Show how to convert Ω into a proof of B in Q by making appropriate insertions in front of each line of Ω which is set down in accordance with NE or NU. What insertions are appropriate may be divined from an examination of the following two deduction schemata:

*₁(1)	$\sim(\exists a)A_a$	RP
*₂(2)	A_b	RP
*₂(3)	$(\exists a)A_a$	EG(2)
(4)	$A_b \supset (\exists a)A_a$	Cd*₂(3)
*₁(5)	$\sim A_b$	TF(1)(4)
*₁(6)	$(a)\sim A_a$	UG(5)

*₁(1)	$\sim(a)A_a$	RP
*₂(2)	A_b	RP
*₂(3)	$(a)A_a$	UG(2)
(4)	$A_b \supset (a)A_a$	Cd*₂(3)
*₁(5)	$\sim A_b$	TF(1)(4)
*₁(6)	$(\exists a)\sim A_a$	EG(5)

(17) When using system Q to show validity, considerable repetition can be avoided by capitalizing upon the result of Exercise [14]. How? Also explain how some labor can be saved by capitalizing upon the result of Exercise [16].

(18) Prove that if $A_1, \ldots, A_n \vdash B$ and $A_1, \ldots, A_n, B \vdash C$, then $A_1, \ldots, A_n \vdash C$.

(19) Let A be any tautologous wff of system Q. Show that the following three-line-long sequence is a proof of A:

*₁(1)	A	RP
(2)	$A \supset A$	Cd*₁(1)
(3)	A	TF(2)

(20) Rule NE allows one to pass in a deduction from a negated existentially quantified wff $\ulcorner\sim(\exists a)A\urcorner$ to the wff $\ulcorner(a)\sim A\urcorner$. Similarly, NU allows one to pass from a negated universally quantified wff $\ulcorner\sim(a)A\urcorner$ to $\ulcorner(\exists a)\sim A\urcorner$. Formulate an analogous rule EN which allows one to pass from $\ulcorner(\exists a)\sim A\urcorner$ to $\ulcorner\sim(a)A\urcorner$, and a rule UN which allows one to pass from

⌜$(a) \sim A$⌝ to ⌜$\sim(\exists a)A$⌝. Show that the addition of the four rules NE, NU, EN, and UN to system Q would issue in no new theorems. Explain how one might use these four rules to reduce the tedium of proving theorems in system Q. Show that $A_1, \ldots, A_n \vdash B$ in this augmented system if and only if $A_1, \ldots, A_n \vdash B$ in system Q. (*Hint:* See Exercise [16].)

56. APPLYING THE NATURAL DEDUCTION SYSTEM

56.0. Deductive Strategies

Suppose we are told that a wff A is valid and are asked to exhibit a proof of A in system Q. From the completeness theorem we know that there exist proofs of A. Hence, if we were to enumerate the proofs of system Q one after another (see Exercise [6] of Chapter 31) we would eventually come across a proof of A. But such a strategy would be outrageously prodigal of time; thousands of years might be consumed by the search for a proof of a theorem as elementary as '$(x)Fx \cdot (x)Gx \supset (x)(Fx \cdot Gx)$'. Fortunately there are a few simple strategies for constructing proofs which lead quickly and efficiently to proofs of many theorems of system Q. Whoever masters them will experience little difficulty in proving the important theorems of Q that are commonly found in logic textbooks.

The first of our strategies for constructing proofs is called the *strategy of the conditional*. It applies whenever we are trying to derive a conditional wff ⌜$A \supset B$⌝. In such a case the strategy of the conditional directs us to set the antecedent A down as a premiss and then to try to derive B from it; if successful, we are then to use Cd to obtain a derivation of ⌜$A \supset B$⌝. For example, if we were seeking a proof of '$(x)Fx \cdot (x)Gx \supset (x)(Fx \cdot Gx)$', this strategy would direct us to set '$(x)Fx \cdot (x)Gx$' down as a premiss and then to try to derive '$(x)(Fx \cdot Gx)$' from it. (In isolation, neither the strategy of the conditional nor any of the other strategies often takes us all the way to the sought-after proof. The concurrence of several strategies is usually required for this.)

Our next strategy is called *quantifier strategy*. It is really a multiple strategy consisting of several substrategies. The first substrategy applies when we are trying to derive from wffs A_1, ..., A_n a wff B that begins with a quantifier. If B is an existentially quantified wff $\ulcorner(\exists a)C_a\urcorner$, this substrategy directs us to try to derive an instance C_b of B from A_1, ..., A_n; if successful, we are then to use EG on C_b to obtain B, that is, $\ulcorner(\exists a)C_a\urcorner$. Or if B is a universally quantified wff $\ulcorner(a)C_a\urcorner$, this substrategy directs us to try to derive a conservative instance C_b of B from A_1, ..., A_n; if successful, we are then to use UG on C_b to obtain B, that is, $\ulcorner(a)C_a\urcorner$. For example, if we were trying to derive '$(x)(Fx \cdot Gx)$' from '$(x)Fx \cdot (x)Gx$', this first substrategy would have us try to derive a conservative instance of the former, say '$Fy \cdot Gy$', from the latter. The partial sketch of a deduction given below illustrates the application of the strategy of the conditional and of so much of the quantifier strategy as has been already presented to the problem of constructing a proof of '$(x)Fx\cdot(x)Gx \supset (x)(Fx \cdot Gx)$'.

$*_1(1)$	$(x)Fx \cdot (x)Gx$	RP
$*_1(k)$	$Fy \cdot Gy$	?
$*_1(k+1)$	$(x)(Fx \cdot Gx)$	UG(k) ▨
$(k+2)$	$(x)Fx\cdot(x)Gx \supset (x)(Fx \cdot Gx)$	Cd$*_1(k+1)$

To explain the second substrategy of the quantifier strategy we need another special term. An occurrence of a quantifier in a wff is said to be *prenex in* that wff if there are nothing but quantifiers to its left in that wff. For example, the first occurrence of '(x)' and the first occurrence of '$(\exists y)$' are the only prenex quantifiers in the wff '$(x)(\exists y)[(x)Fx \supset (\exists y)Gxy]$'. The second occurrence of '(x)' is not prenex in that wff because, in addition to quantifiers, there is a left bracket to its left. Now, the second substrategy applies whenever we are trying to derive a wff from some wffs A_1, ..., A_n. It directs us to use UI and EI to eliminate all prenex quantifiers from A_1, ..., A_n. Notice that this substrategy does not yet apply to the problem represented by the outline sketch of a deduction above, because there are no prenex quantifiers in '$(x)Fx \cdot (x)Gx$', as the reader will perceive on unabbreviating it. The substrategy becomes relevant to this problem only after the strategy of truth functions has been applied.

The *strategy of truth functions* is another multiple strategy. One of its substrategies concerns cases where we are working toward a wff from wffs some of which are conjunctions. In such a case this substrategy directs us to use TF to break up the conjunctions into their conjuncts and then to work from the latter toward the target wff. For example, application of this substrategy, together with the overall quantifier strategy, to the problem above yields this much of what will ultimately be a proof:

$$
\begin{array}{lll}
*_1(1) & (x)Fx \cdot (x)Gx & \text{RP} \\
*_1(2) & (x)Fx & \text{TF(1)} \\
*_1(3) & (x)Gx & \text{TF(1)} \\
*_1(4) & Fy & \text{UI(2)} \\
*_1(5) & Gy & \text{UI(3)} \\
\\
*_1(k) & Fy \cdot Gy & ? \\
*_1(k+1) & (x)(Fx \cdot Gx) & \text{UG}(k)\,\boxed{y}\; \\
(k+2) & (x)Fx \cdot (x)Gx \supset (x)(Fx \cdot Gx) & \text{Cd}*_1(k+1)
\end{array}
$$

Another substrategy of the strategy of truth functions directs us to check whether $A_1, \ldots, A_n$ jointly truth-functionally imply B whenever we are working toward a wff B from wffs $A_1, \ldots, A_n$. If $A_1, \ldots, A_n$ do truth-functionally imply B we are to set B down as derived from $A_1, \ldots, A_n$ by TF. This substrategy enables us finally to dispatch the above problem thus:

$$
\begin{array}{lll}
*_1(1) & (x)Fx \cdot (x)Gx & \text{RP} \\
*_1(2) & (x)Fx & \text{TF(1)} \\
*_1(3) & (x)Gx & \text{TF(1)} \\
*_1(4) & Fy & \text{UI(2)} \\
*_1(5) & Gy & \text{UI(3)} \\
*_1(6) & Fy \cdot Gy & \text{TF(4)(5)} \\
*_1(7) & (x)(Fx \cdot Gx) & \text{UG(6)}\,\boxed{y}\; \\
(8) & (1) \supset (7) & \text{Cd}*_1(7)
\end{array}
$$

(Note that to save space we have used the numeral of a line as an abbreviation for it.) When we are working toward a conjunction $\ulcorner A \cdot B \urcorner$, another substrategy of the strategy of truth functions directs us to work toward each of the conjuncts A and B. If successful in deriving both A and B, we are then to use TF to set down $\ulcorner A \cdot B \urcorner$. (For an illustration of the application of this substrategy, the reader should inspect the second deduction presented in Section 54.1.) Still another substrategy of truth functions applies when we are trying to derive a wff C from a disjunction $\ulcorner A \vee B \urcorner$. This substrategy directs us to try to derive C from A alone and from B alone. If successful, we are to use Cd twice to obtain $\ulcorner A \supset C \urcorner$ and $\ulcorner B \supset C \urcorner$, which jointly truth-functionally imply $\ulcorner A \vee B \supset C \urcorner$. (For an illustration, see the second deduction in Section 54.2.) The last of the substrategies of the strategy of truth functions is commonly presented as an independent strategy called *indirect proof*. It applies in cases where one is getting nowhere using the other strategies in trying to derive a wff B from wffs $A_1, \ldots, A_n$. In such a case this substrategy directs us to try to derive a truth-functional contradiction C from $A_1, \ldots, A_n$ and $\ulcorner {\sim} B \urcorner$. If successful, we are then to use Cd to get $\ulcorner {\sim} B \supset C \urcorner$, which truth-functionally implies B. (For an illustration, see the first deduction in Section 54.2.)

In many simple cases straightforward application of the above strategies leads quickly and easily to the sought-after deductions. In other cases their *intelligent* application will lead to the same.

56.1.   Time-Savers

In doing Exercise [14] of Chapter 55 you showed that if $A_1, \ldots, A_n$ are all theorems of system Q and if $A_1, \ldots, A_n \vdash B$, then B is also a theorem of Q. In showing this you relied upon a mechanical procedure which, when supplied with proofs of each A_i and a proof of B from $A_1, \ldots, A_n$ as input, generates a proof of B as output. This suggests a short-cut method of establishing that a wff A is a theorem of system Q. To establish that A is a theorem of system Q, it suffices to exhibit a proof of A from previously established theorems as premises. We demand that the proof of A be from *previously established* theorems rather than just from theorems. If we made only the latter demand, someone could justifiably object that we had not established that some of the alleged theorems used as premises are actually theorems of Q. Henceforth, therefore, when asked to establish by deductions that some wff is a theorem, we shall regard the request as satisfied when we have produced a proof of that wff from previously established theorems as premisses. For example, we would offer the following as a proof by deduction that '$\sim(\exists x)Fx \equiv (x)\sim Fx$' is a theorem of Q.

$*_1(1)$	$\sim(\exists x)Fx \supset (x)\sim Fx$	RP(Th)
$*_2(2)$	$(x)\sim Fx \supset \sim(\exists x)Fx$	RP(Th)
$*_1*_2(3)$	$\sim(\exists x)Fx \equiv (x)\sim Fx$	TF(1)(2)

Considerable time can also be saved by capitalizing upon the result of Exercises [16] and (20) of Chapter 55. There you proved that the addition of the four rules NE, NU, EN, and UN to system Q did not yield any new theorems. That is, you proved that whatever can be proved in system Q with these rules can also be proved in system Q without them. Accordingly, we will use these four rules as though they actually were rules of system Q. For example, we might present the following deduction to show that

$$\sim(x)Fx \equiv (\exists x)\sim Fx$$

is a theorem of Q.

$*_1(1)$	$\sim(x)Fx$	RP
$*_1(2)$	$(\exists x)\sim Fx$	NU(1)
(3)	$\sim(x)Fx \supset (\exists x)\sim Fx$	Cd$*_1$(2)
$*_4(4)$	$(\exists x)\sim Fx$	RP
$*_4(5)$	$\sim(x)Fx$	EN(4)
(6)	$(\exists x)\sim Fx \supset \sim(x)Fx$	Cd$*_4$(5)
(7)	$\sim(x)Fx \equiv (\exists x)\sim Fx$	TF(3)(6)

56.2.   Identity

Because of its extreme simplicity and topic neutrality the concept of identity is commonly regarded as a logical notion. Heretofore we have used $\ulcorner a = b \urcorner$ as an abbreviation for $\ulcorner H_3ab \urcorner$ with the express stipulation that 'H_3' be taken to mean '① is identical with ②'. Hereafter we will regard the identity sign '$=$' as a primitive symbol, specifically as a binary predicate *constant*, and we will call system Q *with identity* (system QI) the system that results when '$=$', together with the formation and deduction rules for identity, are added to system Q. The identity sign is called a *predicate constant* because, whatever meaning be given to other symbols, '$=$' is always taken to mean '① is identical with ②'. We leave it to the reader to modify the formation rules of system Q so as to accommodate '$=$'. For the sake of naturalness, we let $\ulcorner(a = b)\urcorner$

be an abbreviation for $\ulcorner = ab \urcorner$, and we let $\ulcorner (a \neq b) \urcorner$ abbreviate $\ulcorner \sim (a = b) \urcorner$.

System QI contains two deduction rules for identity. The first is the *rule of self-identity* (RI). The rule of self-identity states that *the wff '$(x)(x = x)$' may be set down as an unstarred line of a deduction provided that 'RI' is written at the right*. The use of RI is illustrated below:

(1)	$(x)(x = x)$	RI
(2)	$z = z$	UI(1)
(3)	$(\exists y)(y = z)$	EG(2)
(4)	$(x)(\exists y)(y = x)$	UG(3)⬚

The second rule for identity mentions universal closures of wffs. A wff $\ulcorner (a_1) \ldots (a_n) A \urcorner$ is said to be a *universal closure* of a wff A if $a_1, \ldots, a_n$ is a complete list of the distinct free individual variables of A. For example, '$(x)(y)(\exists z)Fxyz$' and '$(y)(x)(\exists z)Fxyz$' are the universal closures of '$(\exists z)Fxyz$', and '$(x)Fx$' has itself as its only universal closure. The second rule for identity is known as the *rule of the substitutivity of identity* (RS). RS states that *any universal closure of a wff of the form $\ulcorner A_a \cdot (a = b) \supset A_b \urcorner$, where A_b is like A_a except that A_b may contain free occurrences of b at one or more places at which A_a contains free occurrences of a, may be set down as an unstarred line of a deduction provided that 'RS' is written at the right*. The use of RI and RS is illustrated by the three deductions below.

(1)	$(x)(y)[(x = x) \cdot (x = y) \supset (y = x)]$	RS
(2)	$(x = x) \cdot (x = y) \supset (y = x)$	UI(1) twice
(3)	$(x)(x = x)$	RI
(4)	$x = x$	UI(3)
(5)	$(x = y) \supset (y = x)$	TF(2)(4)
(6)	$(x)(y)[(x = y) \supset (y = x)]$	UG(5)⬚⬚twice

(1)	$(x)(y)(z)[(x = y) \cdot (y = z) \supset (x = z)]$	RS

*₁(1)	$(\exists z)[(z = x) \cdot (z = y)]$	RP
*₁(2)	$(z = x) \cdot (z = y)$	EI(1)⬚
(3)	$(x)(y)(z)[(z = y) \cdot (z = x) \supset (x = y)]$	RS
(4)	$(z = y) \cdot (z = x) \supset (x = y)$	UI(3) thrice
*₁(5)	$x = y$	TF(2)(4)
(6)	$(1) \supset (5)$	Cd*₁(5)
(7)	$(x)(y)\{(\exists z)[(z = x) \cdot (z = y)] \supset (x = y)\}$	UG(6)⬚⬚twice

Except for the provisions already noted which concern the identity sign, system QI is exactly like system Q. Not only are the syntactical concepts such as proof and finished deduction unchanged, but the semantical concepts such as interpretation, validity, and consequence also remain unchanged, except for the stipulation that the identity sign is always taken to mean '① is identical with ②'. Thus '$(x)(x = x)$' and '$(\exists y)(x = y)$' are valid wffs of system QI because they come out true under all interpretations in all nonempty domains. The question naturally arises whether system QI is consistent or complete with respect to validity. The answer to both parts of that question is affirmative. It is easily shown that every theorem of system QI is valid [consistency theorem for system QI: see Exercise (11) of Chapter 57]. And it can be shown that every valid wff of system QI is a theorem of system QI (completeness theorem for system QI). (See Section 56.4 for a proof of the completeness theorem for system QI.) Moreover, it can even be shown [Exercise (14) of Chapter 57] that a wff B is a consequence of a set Δ of wffs of system QI if and only if there is a proof of B from Δ in system QI (strong completeness theorem for system QI). That is, B is a consequence of Δ if and only if $\Delta \vdash B$. (When system QI is under discussion, we use the turnstile '$\vdash$' to refer to proofs in system QI.)

But the reader should not think that every metatheoretic statement that is true of system Q also holds for system QI. Many important model-theoretic statements fail to hold for system QI. For example, neither the inflation theorem nor the deflation theorem is true of system QI. To see that the deflation theorem fails, notice that '$(x)(y = x)$' is satisfiable in domains of one individual but in no larger domains. And to see that the deflation theorem fails, observe that '$(\exists y)(x \neq y)$' is valid in all domains with two or more members but in no smaller domains. Even the Löwenheim theorem fails, for there are satisfiable wffs such as '$(x)(y = x)$' which are not satisfiable in the domain of positive integers. Nevertheless one may prove a *modified* Löwenheim theorem for system QI: If a wff is satisfiable, then it is satisfiable in a nonempty subset of the positive integers (see Section 56.4). Finally, we observe that the spectrum problem has a stronger solution for system QI than for system Q. For each positive integer k, there are wffs of system QI that are satisfiable in domains of k individuals but in no other domains. For example '$(x \neq y) \cdot (z)[(x = z) \lor (y = z)]$' is satisfiable in domains of two individuals but in no other domains.

Unlike system Q, system QI boasts wffs that contain no free variables *of any type*. Examples of such wffs are '$(x)(x = x)$' and '$(\exists x)(y)(x = y)$'. Truth values accrue to such wffs as soon as a domain of individuals has been selected, because the meaning of the identity sign is held constant. For example, the second wff above is true in the domain that contains just the planet Mercury but is false in the domain of all the planets. For wffs without free variables of any kind, validity in a domain and satisfiability in a domain amount to the same thing. Such a wff is both valid and satisfiable in a domain if it is true in that domain; if it is not true in that domain, it is neither valid nor satisfiable in it.

56.3. Postulate Systems; Calculus of Individuals[1]

Any set Δ of wffs of system QI may be designated as a set of *postulates*. A wff is said to be a Δ-*theorem* if it is a consequence of Δ. From the strong completeness theorem for system QI it follows that a wff A is a Δ-theorem if and only if $\Delta \vdash A$. Hence to show that a wff is a Δ-theorem it plainly suffices to exhibit a proof of it from members of Δ as premises, and if it is a Δ-theorem such proofs exist.

To illustrate postulate systems we present the *calculus of individuals* (hereafter COI), which was advanced as a philosophically useful supplement to set theory by the philosophers Henry S. Leonard and Nelson Goodman. The COI is a postulate system in which the concept of *being discrete from* is taken as the only unexplained notion. The part-whole relation plays a role in the COI somewhat akin to that which the membership relation plays in set theory. The part-whole relation, like all other concepts introduced in the COI, is explained in terms of the discreteness relation. Only one predicate variable is endowed with meaning in the COI; the binary predicate variable 'F' is construed to mean '① is discrete from ②' in the intuitive sense that things are discrete if and only

[1] For the present adaptation of the Leonard–Goodman calculus of individuals I am greatly indebted to my colleague Herbert E. Hendry. The reader interested in the philosophical significance of the calculus of individuals should consult Henry S. Leonard and Nelson Goodman, "The Calculus of Individuals and Its Uses," *Journal of Symbolic Logic*, vol. 5 (1940), pp. 45–55.

if they have no parts in common. For convenience of presentation and ease of comprehension, four abbreviative conventions (definitions) are set forth:

D1. $(a < b) =_{Df} (c)[Fcb \supset Fca]$, where c is the first individual variable in lexicographical order after a and b.

In virtue of D1, for example, '$(x < y)$' abbreviates '$(z)[Fzy \supset Fzx]$'. We will read $\ulcorner(a < b)\urcorner$ as $\ulcorner a$ is a part of $b\urcorner$, a reading that is justified by the meaning given to 'F' in the COI.

D2. $(a \ll b) =_{Df} (a < b) \cdot (a \neq b)$.

We read $\ulcorner(a \ll b)\urcorner$ quite naturally as $\ulcorner a$ is a proper part of $b\urcorner$.

D3. $Oab =_{Df} (\exists c)[(c < a) \cdot (c < b)]$, where c is as in D1.

We read $\ulcorner Oab\urcorner$ as $\ulcorner a$ overlaps $b\urcorner$, because intuitively we understand overlapping things to be things having parts in common.

D4.   Atom $a =_{Df} \sim(\exists b)(b \ll a)$, where b is the first individual variable in lexicographical order after a.

Not surprisingly, we read $\ulcorner$Atom $a\urcorner$ as $\ulcorner a$ is an atom$\urcorner$. The concept of an atom formulated in D4 should not be confused with the chemical-physical concept of an atom. It is at least conceivable that no D4 atoms are spatially extended, or that qualia are the only D4 atoms, or even perhaps that there are no D4 atoms at all. These philosophical matters do indeed bear upon the use and interpretation of the COI, but they do not affect the development of the COI as a postulate system. The working out of the consequences of the postulates of the COI by means of deductions is completely independent of such semantical and philosophical issues.

The postulates of the COI are given by two postulates and one postulate schema.

P1. $(x)(y)[(x < y) \cdot (y < x) \supset (x = y)]$

This first postulate affirms the identity of individuals that are parts of one another.

P2. $(x)(y)[Oxy \equiv \sim Fxy]$

Postulate P2 states that individuals overlap if and only if they are not discrete from one another.

P3.   Any universal closure of a wff of the following form is a postulate.

$(\exists a)A_a \supset (\exists b)(c)[Fbc \equiv (a)(A_a \supset Fca)]$, where b and c are the first two individual variables in lexicographical order after all the individual variables in $\ulcorner(\exists a)A_a\urcorner$.

The gist of P3 is roughly that whenever there are individuals of a certain kind, then there is an individual which has all things of that kind as its parts. For example, if there are red things, then there is something which is the "fusion" of all red things. In our familiar world this rather bizarre individual would have, among other things, red balloons and red Volkswagens as parts.

Deducing Δ-theorems from a postulate set Δ can be very tedious. Fortunately much of the tedium can be eliminated. It is easily shown that if $A_1, \ldots, A_n$ are all Δ-theorems and if $A_1, \ldots, A_n \vdash B$ in system QI, then B is also a Δ-theorem. [See Exercise (15) of Chapter 57.] Hence, to show that a wff B is a Δ-theorem, it suffices to exhibit a proof of B from premisses all of which are Δ-theorems. The more Δ-theorems we prove, therefore, the easier it becomes to establish others. And we should not forget that all theorems of system Q and of system QI are Δ-theorems, no matter how the set Δ may be constituted.

Listed below are forty interesting theorems of the COI which the reader should prove in the order in which they are given. To help the reader get started, we have supplied proofs of some of them and hints for finding proofs of most of the others.

T1. $(x)(y)(z)[(x < y)\cdot(y < z) \supset (x < z)]$.

Let us begin by eliminating abbreviations from T1:

$(x)(y)(z)[(z)(Fzy \supset Fzx)\cdot(w_1)(Fw_1z \supset Fw_1y) \supset (w_1)(Fw_1z \supset Fw_1x)]$

Now let us apply the strategies of Section 56.0 to get a proof of unabbreviated T1 from the postulates of the COI.

$*_1(1)$	$(z)(Fzy \supset Fzx)$	RP
$*_2(2)$	$(w_1)(Fw_1z \supset Fw_1y)$	RP
$*_1(3)$	$Fwy \supset Fwx$	UI(1)
$*_2(4)$	$Fwz \supset Fwy$	UI(2)
$*_1*_2(5)$	$Fwz \supset Fwx$	TF(3)(4)
$*_1*_2(6)$	$(w_1)(Fw_1z \supset Fw_1x)$	UG(5)$\boxed{w}$
(7)	$(1) \supset [(2) \supset (6)]$	Cd$*_1*_2$(6) twice
(8)	$(1)\cdot(2) \supset (6)$	TF(7)
(9)	$(x)(y)(z)[(1)\cdot(2) \supset (6)]$	UG(8)$\boxed{z}\boxed{y}\boxed{x}$

T1 merely abbreviates line (9), so the deduction above establishes that T1 is a theorem of the COI, that is, that T1 is a Δ-theorem where Δ is the set of postulates of the COI. Notice that T1 does not depend essentially on the postulates of the COI or even on the rules for identity but is already a theorem of system Q. The abbreviative conventions of the COI create the illusion that T1 depends on the postulates of the COI.

T2. $(x)(x < x)$.

Eliminating abbreviations, we find that T2 abbreviates

$(x)(y)(Fyx \supset Fyx)$,

which is obviously a logical theorem, that is, a theorem of system QI. (It is even a theorem of system Q.)

$*_1(1)$	Fyx	RP
(2)	$Fyx \supset Fyx$	Cd$*_1(1)$
(3)	$(x)(y)(Fyx \supset Fyx)$	UG(2) 🔲 🔲

T3. $(x) \sim (x \ll x)$. (*Hint:* Unabbreviate.)
T4. $(x)(y)[(x \ll y) \supset \sim(y \ll x)]$.

Partial unabbreviation of T4 yields

'$(x)(y)\{(x < y) \cdot (x \neq y) \supset \sim[(y < x) \cdot (y \neq x)]\}$'.

$*_1(1)$	$(x < y) \cdot (x \neq y)$	RP
$*_2(2)$	$(y < x) \cdot (y \neq x)$	RP
$*_3(3)$	$(x)(y)[(x < y) \cdot (y < x) \supset (x = y)]$	RP(P1)
$*_3(4)$	$(x < y) \cdot (y < x) \supset (x = y)$	UI(3) twice
$*_1 *_2 *_3(5)$	$x = y$	TF(4)(1)(2)
$*_6(6)$	$(x)(y)[(x = y) \supset (y = x)]$	RP(Th)
$*_6(7)$	$(x = y) \supset (y = x)$	UI(6) twice
$*_1 *_2 *_3 *_6(8)$	$y = x$	TF(5)(7)
$*_1 *_3 *_6(9)$	$(y < x) \cdot (y \neq x) \supset (y = x)$	Cd$*_2(8)$
$*_1 *_3 *_6(10)$	$\sim[(y < x) \cdot (y \neq x)]$	TF(9)
$*_3 *_6(11)$	$(1) \supset (10)$	Cd$*_1(10)$
$*_3 *_6(12)$	$(x)(y)[(1) \supset (10)]$	UG(11) 🔲 🔲

T5. $(x)(y)[(x \ll y) \supset (x < y)]$. (*Hint:* Unabbreviate.)
T6. $(x)(y)(z)[(x \ll y) \cdot (y \ll z) \supset (x \ll z)]$.

Partial unabbreviation yields '$(x)(y)(z)[(x < y) \cdot (x \neq y) \cdot (y < z) \cdot (y \neq z) \supset (x < z) \cdot (x \neq z)]$'.

$*_1(1)$	$(x < y) \cdot (x \neq y) \cdot (y < z) \cdot (y \neq z)$	RP
$*_2(2)$	$(x)(y)(z)[(x < y) \cdot (y < z) \supset (x < z)]$	RP(T1)
$*_2(3)$	$(x < y) \cdot (y < z) \supset (x < z)$	UI(2) thrice
$*_1*_2(4)$	$x < z$	TF(1)(3)
$*_5(5)$	$x = z$	RP
$*_6(6)$	$(x)(y)(z)[(x < y) \cdot (x = z) \supset (z < y)]$	RS
$*_6(7)$	$(x < y) \cdot (x = z) \supset (z < y)$	UI(6) thrice
$*_1*_5*_6(8)$	$(z < y) \cdot (y < z)$	TF(1)(7)(5)
$*_9(9)$	$(x)(y)[(x < y) \cdot (y < x) \supset (x = y)]$	RP(P1)
$*_9(10)$	$(z < y) \cdot (y < z) \supset (z = y)$	UI(9) twice
$*_1*_5*_6*_9(11)$	$z = y$	TF(10)(8)
$*_{12}(12)$	$(x)(y)[(x = y) \supset (y = x)]$	RP(Th)
$*_{12}(13)$	$(z = y) \supset (y = z)$	UI(12) twice
$*_1*_5*_6*_9*_{12}(14)$	$y = z$	TF(13)(11)
$*_1*_6*_9*_{12}(15)$	$(x = z) \supset (y = z)$	Cd$*_5$(14)
$*_1*_2*_6*_9*_{12}(16)$	$(x < z) \cdot (x \neq z)$	TF(4)(15)(1)
$*_2*_6*_9*_{12}(17)$	$(1) \supset (16)$	Cd$*_1$(16)
$*_2*_6*_9*_{12}(18)$	$(x)(y)(z)[(1) \supset (16)]$	UG(17) 📷 📷 📷

T7. $(x)(y)(z)[(x \ll y) \cdot (y \ll z) \supset (x < z)]$.

$*_1(1)$	$(x)(y)(z)[(x \ll y) \cdot (y \ll z) \supset (x \ll z)]$	RP(T6)
$*_1(2)$	$(x \ll y) \cdot (y \ll z) \supset (x \ll z)$	UI(1) thrice
$*_3(3)$	$(x)(y)[(x \ll y) \supset (x < y)]$	RP(T5)
$*_3(4)$	$(x \ll z) \supset (x < z)$	UI(3) twice
$*_1*_3(5)$	$(x \ll y) \cdot (y \ll z) \supset (x < z)$	TF(2)(4)
$*_1*_3(6)$	$(x)(y)(z)[(x \ll y) \cdot (y \ll z) \supset (x < z)]$	UG(5) 📷 📷 📷

T8.	$(x)(y)(z)[(x \ll y) \cdot (y < z) \supset (x < z)]$.	Use T1 and T5
T9.	$(x)(y)(z)[(x \ll y) \cdot (y < z) \supset (x \ll z)]$.	
		Use T8, T5, P1, and T3
T10.	$(x)(y)(z)[(x < y) \cdot (y \ll z) \supset (x \ll z)]$.	
T11.	$(x)(y)(z)[(x < y) \cdot (y \ll z) \supset (x < z)]$.	
T12.	$(x)(y)[Oxy \equiv Oyx]$.	Unabbreviate
T13.	$(x)(y)[Fxy \equiv Fyx]$.	Use P2 and T12
T14.	$(x)(y)[(x < y) \supset Oxy]$.	Use D3 and T2
T15.	$(x)(y)[(x \ll y) \supset Oxy]$.	Use T14 and T5
T16.	$(x)Oxx$.	Use D3 and T2

T17. $(x) \sim Fxx.$ Use T16 and P2

T18. $(x)(y)[(x < y) \supset (x \ll y) \vee (x = y)].$ Use D2

T19. $(x)(y)[(x < y) \supset (x \ll y) \vee (y < x)].$

Use T18 and identity

T20. $(x)(y)(z)[(x < y) \cdot Fyz \supset Fxz].$ Use D1 and T13

T21. $(x)(y)(z)[(x < y) \cdot Oxz \supset Oyz].$ Use D3 and T1

T22. $(x)(y)(z)[(x \ll y) \cdot Oxz \supset Oyz].$

T23. $(x)(y)[(z)(Fzx \equiv Fzy) \supset (x = y)].$ Use D1 and P1

T24. $(x)(y)[(z)(Ozx \equiv Ozy) \supset (x = y)].$ Use P2 and T23

T25. $(x)(y)[(z)[(z < x) \equiv (z < y)] \supset (x = y)].$

Use P1 and T2

T26. $(x)(y)[(z)[(x < z) \equiv (y < z)] \supset (x = y)].$

T27. $(x)(y)[\sim \text{Atom } x \cdot Oyx \supset (\exists z)[(z \ll x) \cdot Oyz]].$

Use D4, D3, T5, T15, and T18

T28. $(x)(y)[\sim \text{Atom } x \cdot (z)[(z \ll x) \supset (z \ll y)] \supset$
$(z)(Ozx \supset Ozy)].$

T29. $(x)(y)[\sim \text{Atom } x \cdot (z)[(z \ll x) \equiv (z \ll y)] \supset (x = y)].$

Use T28 and T24

T30. $(\exists x)(y) \sim Fxy.$

Use T17 and the following instance of P3:
$(\exists x)(x = x) \supset (\exists y)(z)\{Fyz \equiv (x)[(x = x) \supset Fzx]\}$

T31. $(\exists x)(y)Oxy.$ Use T30 and P2

T32. $(x)[(y) \sim Fxy \equiv (y)Oxy].$ Use P2

T33. $(x)(y)[(z)(z < x) \cdot (z)(z < y) \supset (x = y)].$ Use P1

T34. $\sim (\exists y)(x)Fxy.$ Use T17

T35. $(x)(y)(\exists z)(w)[Fzw \equiv Fxw \cdot Fyw].$

Use T13 and the following instance of P3:
$(x)(y)\{(\exists z)[(z = x) \vee (z = y)] \supset (\exists w_1)(x_1)[Fw_1x_1 \equiv$
$(z)[(z = x) \vee (z = y) \supset Fx_1z]]\}$

T35 asserts the existence of a *sum individual* for every pair of individuals, that is, an individual composed of the two individuals as parts.

T36. $(x)(y)(z_1)(z_2)[(w)(Fz_1w \equiv Fxw \cdot Fyw) \cdot$
$(w)(Fz_2w \equiv Fxw \cdot Fyw) \supset (z_1 = z_2)].$

T36 asserts that there is at most one sum individual for each pair of individuals. To prove T36, use T23 and T13.

T37. $(x)(y)(z)[(w)(Fwz \equiv Fwx \cdot Fwy) \supset (x < z)].$ Use D1

T38. $(x)(y)[Oxy \supset (\exists z)(w)[(w < z) \equiv (w < x) \cdot (w < y)]]$.
Use D3 and the following instance of P3:
$(x)(y)\{(\exists z)[(z < x) \cdot (z < y)] \supset (\exists w_1)(x_1)[Fw_1x_1 \equiv$
$(z)[(z < x) \cdot (z < y) \supset Fx_1z]]\}$

T38 asserts the existence of a *product individual* for overlapping pairs of individuals, that is, an individual identical with their overlap.

T39. $(x)(y)[(z) \sim Fxz \cdot (z) \sim Fyz \supset (x = y)]$.
Use T12, T24, and T32
T40. $(\exists x)(y)(y < x)$.
Use T30, T13, and D1

An individual that has every individual as a part might aptly be styled a *universe*. Thus T40 asserts that a universe exists. T33, on the other hand, asserts that there is at most one universe. Taken together then, T40 and T33 affirm the existence of exactly one universe.

That abbreviative conventions can be hazardous may be appreciated by inspecting our proof of T6 above. Actually line (10) cannot be got from line (9) by UI alone, as becomes evident when these lines have been unabbreviated:

(9) $(x)(y)[(z)(Fzy \supset Fzx) \cdot (z)(Fzx \supset Fzy) \supset (x = y)]$
(10) $(w_1)(Fw_1y \supset Fw_1z) \cdot (w_1)(Fw_1z \supset Fw_1y) \supset (z = y)$

Nonetheless we can get (10) from (9) by using several deduction rules and without flagging any variables that appear in the given "proof". Our omission of such steps should be considered another timesaving device.

56.4. Completeness Theorem for System QI

The postulate systems of Section 56.3 all have system QI as their underlying logic. But we can also treat sets of wffs of system Q as postulate sets with system Q as the underlying logic. [So that systems Q and QI have exactly the same symbols, let us add ' = ' as a binary predicate *variable* to system Q. In system Q, then, unlike in system QI, we do not demand that ' = ' be always taken to mean '⓵ is identical with ⓶'.] Let $\mathfrak{J}$ be the set of wffs that RI and RS allow one to set down as unstarred lines of deductions. We observe first that there is a proof of A from $\mathfrak{F}$ in system Q if and only if A is a theorem of system QI. (Proof of this observation is left to the reader.) Therefore, by virtue of the strong completeness theorem for system Q, A is a consequence of $\mathfrak{F}$ if and only if A is a theorem of system QI. By a *normal interpretation* or *N-interpretation* of a wff or of a class of wffs of system Q let us understand an interpretation in which '$=$' is assigned the extension of '① is identical with ②' as its value.[2] And let us call a wff of system Q *N-valid* if it comes out true under all N-interpretations of it. Notice that a wff of system Q is N-valid if and only if it is valid in system QI. The completeness theorem for system QI follows easily from the above results in conjunction with the following lemma:

> Lemma.   Let Γ be a class of wffs of system Q. Then, if there is a model of $\Gamma \cup \mathfrak{F}$, then there is an N-model of $\Gamma \cup \mathfrak{F}$, that is, a true N-interpretation of $\Gamma \cup \mathfrak{F}$.

To see that the completeness theorem for system QI follows from this lemma, suppose that a wff A of system Q is N-valid. If A happens to be a consequence of $\mathfrak{F}$, then A is a theorem of system QI and nothing remains to be proved. So suppose also that A is not a consequence of $\mathfrak{F}$. Then there is a model of $\mathfrak{F} \cup \{\ulcorner{\sim}A\urcorner\}$. Whence, by the lemma, there is an N-model of $\mathfrak{F} \cup \{\ulcorner{\sim}A\urcorner\}$. But then $\ulcorner{\sim}A\urcorner$ comes out true under at least one N-interpretation and, therefore, A is not N-valid. But this contradicts our assumption about A. Therefore, A is a consequence of $\mathfrak{F}$, from which it follows that A is a theorem of system QI. But A is N-valid if and only if it is valid in system QI. Therefore, if A is valid in system QI, then A is a theorem of system QI (completeness theorem for system QI).

We shall now prove the lemma. Let $\mathfrak{D}$ be the domain of a maximal model $\Sigma_{\mathfrak{F}}$ of $\mathfrak{F}$. (See Section 48.1 concerning maximal interpretations and maximal models.) Let $\Delta_{\mathfrak{F}}$ be the extension that $\Sigma_{\mathfrak{F}}$ assigns to '$=$'. A subclass $\mathfrak{D}'$ of $\mathfrak{D}$ shall be called a *cell* if it satisfies these three conditions:

(i) $\mathfrak{D}'$ is nonempty.

(ii)   If $\alpha \in \mathfrak{D}'$ and $\langle \alpha, \beta \rangle \in \Delta_{\mathfrak{F}}$, then $\beta \in \mathfrak{D}'$.

(iii)   If $\alpha \in \mathfrak{D}'$ and $\beta \in \mathfrak{D}'$, then $\langle \alpha, \beta \rangle \in \Delta_{\mathfrak{F}}$.

---

[2] That is, the set of all ordered pairs $\langle \alpha, \alpha \rangle$, where α is a member of the UD, is assigned to '$=$' as its extension.

By appealing to the assumption that $\Sigma\mathfrak{J}$ is a model of $\mathfrak{J}$, one can show that the set of all the cells is a partition of $\mathfrak{D}$ into nonempty, mutually exclusive, and jointly exhaustive subsets. That is, one can readily demonstrate that every cell is nonempty, that no member of $\mathfrak{D}$ belongs to more than one cell, and that every member of $\mathfrak{D}$ belongs to at least one cell. For example, to prove that every member of $\mathfrak{D}$ belongs to at least one cell, one could reason thus. Let μ be an arbitrary member of $\mathfrak{D}$ and let $\mathfrak{D}_\mu$ be the set of all members η of $\mathfrak{D}$ such that $\langle\mu,\eta\rangle \in \Delta\mathfrak{J}$. $\Sigma\mathfrak{J}$ is a model of $\mathfrak{J}$ and '$(x)(x = x)$' belongs to $\mathfrak{J}$, so it follows that, for every member α of $\mathfrak{D}$, the ordered pair $\langle\alpha,\alpha\rangle$ is a member of $\Delta\mathfrak{J}$. Hence, $\langle\mu,\mu\rangle \in \Delta\mathfrak{J}$. Thus we see from the description of $\mathfrak{D}_\mu$ that μ belongs to $\mathfrak{D}_\mu$ and that, consequently, $\mathfrak{D}_\mu$ satisfies condition (i). Now let α be any member of $\mathfrak{D}_\mu$ and let β be any member of $\mathfrak{D}$ such that $\langle\alpha,\beta\rangle \in \Delta\mathfrak{J}$. From the description of $\mathfrak{D}_\mu$ it follows that $\langle\mu,\alpha\rangle \in \Delta\mathfrak{J}$. And, as $\Sigma\mathfrak{J}$ is a model of $\mathfrak{J}$ and '$(x)(y)(z)[(x = y)\cdot(y = z) \supset (x = z)]$' belongs to $\mathfrak{J}$, it follows that $\langle\mu,\beta\rangle \in \Delta\mathfrak{J}$. Thus $\beta \in \Delta_\mu$, and we see that condition (ii) is satisfied. Now, finally, let α and β be any members of $\mathfrak{D}_\mu$. From the description of $\mathfrak{D}_\mu$ it follows that both $\langle\mu,\alpha\rangle$ and $\langle\mu,\beta\rangle$ belong to $\Delta\mathfrak{J}$. As '$(x)(y)(z)[(z = x)\cdot(z = y) \supset (x = y)]$' belongs to $\mathfrak{J}$ and $\Sigma\mathfrak{J}$ is a model of $\mathfrak{J}$, it follows that $\langle\alpha,\beta\rangle$ belongs to $\Delta\mathfrak{J}$. Thus we see that condition (iii) is also satisfied by $\mathfrak{D}_\mu$. We have shown that an arbitrary member μ of $\mathfrak{D}$ belongs to at least one set $\mathfrak{D}_\mu$, which is a cell. We leave it to the reader to show that no member of $\mathfrak{D}$ belongs to more than one cell.

Let Ω be the set of all maximal models of $\mathfrak{J}$ in the domain $\mathfrak{D}$. We now correlate with each member Σ of Ω a maximal normal interpretation Σ^* as follows. We let the domain of Σ^* be the set of cells described above. (Note that the cardinality of the domain of Σ^* is equal to or smaller than the cardinality of the domain of Σ.) To a sentential variable b, we let Σ^* assign the same truth value that Σ assigns to b. Let $cell(\alpha)$ be the cell to which the element α of $\mathfrak{D}$ belongs. We let Σ^* assign $cell(\alpha)$ to an individual variable b, where α is the value that Σ assigns to b. To an n-ary predicate variable ϕ, we let Σ assign the set of all n-tuples $\langle cell(\alpha_1), \ldots, cell(\alpha_n)\rangle$ such that $\langle\alpha_1, \ldots, \alpha_n\rangle$ belongs to the extension that Σ assigns to ϕ. It can be readily shown that Σ^* is a normal maximal interpretation. Let B be an arbitrary wff of system Q and let Σ be an arbitrary member of Ω. By appealing to the fact that Σ is a model of $\mathfrak{J}$, one can prove by strong mathematical induction on the number of occurrences of connectives and quantifiers in B that B has the same value under both Σ and Σ^*. Any model of $\mathfrak{J}$ can be extended to a maximal model of $\mathfrak{J}$, so it follows that there is a model of a class $\mathfrak{J} \cup \Gamma$ of wffs of system Q in a given domain only if there is a normal model of $\mathfrak{J} \cup \Gamma$ in a domain of equal or smaller cardinality. This terminates our proof of the lemma.

The modified Löwenheim theorem for system QI follows directly from the results above. Note that we actually proved a stronger statement than the lemma: We proved that if $\mathfrak{J} \cup \Gamma$ has a model, then it has an N-model of equal or smaller cardinality. Suppose, then, that B is satisfiable in system QI, that is, with '$=$' interpreted as the identity sign. Then $\mathfrak{J} \cup \{B\}$ has a model in system Q. By the Löwenheim–Skolem theorem, $\mathfrak{J} \cup \{B\}$ has a model in the positive integers. Together with the strengthened lemma, this entails that $\mathfrak{J} \cup \{B\}$ has a finite or denumerable N-model or, what comes to the same, that B has a finite or denumerable model in system QI. Therefore, if B is satisfiable in system QI, then B is satisfiable in a finite or denumerable domain in system QI (modified Löwenheim theorem).

57. EXERCISES

(1)   Let $\ulcorner a \in b \urcorner$ abbreviate $\ulcorner Gab \urcorner$. Show by deductions in system Q that

(a) $\vdash \sim(\exists x)(y)(y \in x \equiv \sim y \in y)$

(b) $\vdash \sim(\exists x)(y)[y \in x \equiv \sim(\exists z)(y \in z \cdot z \in y)]$

(c)   '$(\exists y)(x)[x \in y \equiv (x = x)]$'   and   '$(x)(\exists y)(z)[z \in y \equiv z \in x \cdot \sim z \in z]$' are incompatible, that is, that the negation of their conjunction is valid. Find a model of each of these two wffs.

(d)   The so-called *pairing axiom*
'$(x)(y)(\exists z)\{x \in z \cdot y \in z \cdot (w)[w \in z \supset (w = x) \vee (w = y)]\}$'
implies the wff '$(x)(\exists y)(x \in y)$', which denies that there are any ultimate classes, that is, classes which are members of no classes.

(e) The wff
'$(\exists y)(x)\{x \in y \equiv (\exists z)[(w)(z \in w \equiv x \in w)\cdot \sim z \in x]\}$'
is self-contradictory or invalid.

(f) '$(y)(z)[(x)(x \in y \equiv x \in z) \supset (w)(y \in w \equiv z \in w)]$'
is equivalent to
'$(y)(z)(w)[(x)(x \in y \equiv x \in z)\cdot y \in w \supset z \in w]$'.
Both are forms of the so-called *Bestimmheit axiom* of
standard set theory.

(2) Prove by a deduction in system Q that no one loves all and
only those people who do not love themselves.

{3} Show by a deduction that '$(x)[F_1x \supset (Gx \equiv H_1x)]$' and
'$(x)[F_2x \supset (Gx \equiv H_2x)]$' imply '$(x)[F_1x\cdot F_2x \supset (H_1x \equiv H_2x)]$'.
Now, some philosophers have suggested that a dispositional
concept G, such as 'soluble', be *defined* by laying down several *bilateral reduction sentences* such as the first two wffs of
this exercise. What relevance does the result of this exercise
have for such a proposal?

{4} In their deductive-nomological model of scientific explanation, Carl G. Hempel and Paul Oppenheim argue that to
explain an event is to subsume it under covering laws via,
perhaps, initial conditions that do not themselves entail the
event to be explained. But consider that y's being black
might be "explained" thus, where 'F' means '① is a crow'
and 'G' means '① is black':

$(x)[Fx \supset Gx]$	Law
$Fy \vee Gy$	Initial condition
$\overline{Gy}$	Explained event

Show that the indicated law and initial condition imply 'Gy'
and that 'Gy' implies the initial condition. What embarrass-
ment, if any, do these facts cause for the Hempel–Oppenheim
model?

[5] Show by a deduction that '$(\exists x)(\exists y)(z)[(Fz \equiv Fx) \vee (Fz \equiv Fy)]$'
is valid.

{6} Show by deductions that
'$(x)(y)[\sim(Fxy \cdot Fyx) \supset (Fxy \cdot \sim Fyx)]$'
is equivalent to '$(x)(y)Fxy$' but incompatible with
'$Fxy \cdot \sim Fyx$'.
But the third wff is apparently a confirmational instance of

the first. What relevance, if any, does this have for a theory of confirmation?

(7) Show that the following are theorems of system QI:

$(x)(y)[(x = y) \supset (z)[(z = x) \equiv (z = y)]]$

$(x)(y)[Fx \cdot {\sim}Fy \supset (\exists z)(\exists w)(z \neq w)]$

$(x)(y)(x = y) \equiv (x)(y)(z)[(z = x) \mathbf{v} (z = y)]$

$(x)(y)(x = y) \equiv (\exists x)(y)(x = y)$

$(\exists x)(\exists y)(z)[(z = x) \mathbf{v} (z = y)] \equiv$

$$(x)(y)(z)[(x \neq y) \supset (x = z) \mathbf{v} (y = z)]$$

(8) By a deduction in system Q show that
'$(x)(x = x) \cdot (x)(y)[Fy \cdot (y = x) \supset Fx]$'
implies '$(y)\{Fy \equiv (\exists x)[(x = y) \cdot Fx]\}$'.

(9) Show how, for every positive integer k, to write a wff of system QI which is satisfiable in domains of k individuals but in no other domains.

(10) Let $\mathfrak{J}$ be the set of wffs that RI and RS allow one to set down as unstarred lines. Prove that A is a theorem of system QI if and only if there is a proof of A from $\mathfrak{J}$ in system Q.

(11) Prove that system QI is consistent with respect to validity. [*Hint:* Make use of the result of Exercise (10) and the fact that the members of $\mathfrak{J}$ are all valid in system QI, that is, when '$=$' is interpreted as the identity sign.]

(12) Where Σ and Σ^* are as in the proof of the lemma of Section 56.4, prove that a wff B of system Q has the same value under Σ^* as under Σ.

(13) Let $\mathfrak{J}$ be as in Exercise (10) and let Γ be any set of wffs of system Q. Show that a wff A is a consequence of Γ in system QI if and only if A is a consequence of $\mathfrak{J} \cup \Gamma$ in system Q.

(14) Prove that in system QI a wff A is a consequence of a set Γ of wffs if $\Gamma \vdash A$ (strong completeness theorem for system QI). [*Hint:* Where $\mathfrak{J}$ is as in Exercise (10), show that $\mathfrak{J} \cup \Gamma \vdash A$ in system Q if and only if $\Gamma \vdash A$ in system QI. Then appeal to the strong completeness theorem for system Q and to the result of Exercise (13).]

(15) Let Δ be any postulate set of wffs of system QI, and let $A_1, \ldots, A_n$ all be Δ-theorems. Prove that, if $A_1, \ldots, A_n \vdash B$ in system QI, then B is also a Δ-theorem.

(16) Explain what timesaving convention we have employed in writing 'twice' or 'thrice' after 'UI' or 'EG' as in the proof of '$(x)(y)[(x = y) \supset (y = x)]$' in Section 56.2.

(17) Consider the postulate system in system QI whose postulates are the following six wffs:

P1. $(x)(y)[Fx \cdot Fy \supset (\exists z)(Gz \cdot Hxz \cdot Hyz)]$.

P2. $(w)(x)(y)(z)[Fw \cdot Fx \cdot Gy \cdot Gz \cdot Hwy \cdot Hxy \cdot$
$$Hwz \cdot Hxz \cdot (w \neq x) \supset (y = z)].$$

P3. $(\exists x)Fx$.

P4. $(x)[Gx \supset (\exists y)(Fy \cdot \sim Hyx)]$.

P5. $(x)(y)[Gy \cdot Hxy \supset Fx]$.

P6. $(x)(y)[Fx \cdot Gy \cdot \sim Hxy \supset (\exists w_1)[Gw_1 \cdot Hxw_1 \cdot$
$$(z)(Hzw_1 \supset \sim Hzy) \cdot (w_2)[Gw_2 \cdot Hxw_2 \cdot$$
$$(z)(Hzw_2 \supset \sim Hzy) \supset (w_1 = w_2)]]].$$

Prove that the following wffs are theorems of the above postulate system.

T1. $(x)[Fx \supset (\exists y)(\exists z)(Gy \cdot Gz \cdot (y \neq z) \cdot Hxy \cdot Hxz)]$.

T2. $(x)[Gx \supset (\exists y)(\exists z)((y \neq z) \cdot Fy \cdot Fz \cdot Hyx \cdot Hzx)]$.

T3. $(x)(y)[Gx \cdot Gy \cdot (z)(Hzx \equiv Hzy) \supset (x = y)]$.

T4. $(\exists w)(\exists x)(\exists y)(\exists z)[Fw \cdot Fx \cdot Fy \cdot Fz \cdot (w \neq x) \cdot$
$$(w \neq y) \cdot (w \neq z) \cdot (x \neq y) \cdot (x \neq z) \cdot (y \neq z)].$$

Find a model of the above postulates in the domain of the points and straight lines of the Euclidean plane. (*Hint:* Let 'H' mean '① lies on ②' in the sense in which points are said to lie on lines.) Find a model of the postulates in a domain of ten individuals. Find a model of the postulates in a domain of six individuals. Do there exist models of the postulates in any smaller domains? Prove that each of the six postulates is independent in the sense that its omission would have diminished the set of theorems of the postulate system.

58. PROOF OF THE COMPLETENESS THEOREM FOR SYSTEM Q

58.0.   Corollaries of the Skolem–Gödel Theorem

In doing the exercises of Chapter 55 the reader has already shown that the completeness theorem, the compactness theorem, and the strong completeness theorem for system Q all follow as corollaries from the powerful Skolem–Gödel theorem, which states that every consistent class of wffs of system Q is satisfiable. The Skolem–Gödel theorem can itself be derived as a corollary of the following lemma.

> Lemma.   Let Γ be any set of wffs (of system Q) that contain no occurrences of the variables 'w_1', 'w_2', ... If Γ is consistent, then Γ is satisfiable.

To derive the Skolem–Gödel theorem from this lemma, suppose that Δ is any consistent class of wffs of system Q. Let Φ be the following mapping of the individual variables of system Q onto the variables 'x_1', 'x_2', ...

$$w \quad x \quad y \quad z \quad w_1 \quad \cdots$$
$$x_1 \quad x_2 \quad x_3 \quad x_4 \quad x_5 \quad \cdots$$

where Φ maps each variable in the upper row with the variable directly beneath it. Where A is a wff of system Q, let $\Phi(A)$ be the result of simultaneously replacing each individual variable b in A by $\Phi(b)$. For example, if A is '$(x)[Fwx \supset (\exists y)Gwy]$', then $\Phi(A)$ is '$(x_2)[Fx_1x_2 \supset (\exists x_3)Gx_1x_3]$'. And where Γ is any class of wffs of system Q, let $\Phi(\Gamma)$ be the class that results from Γ by supplanting each member A of Γ by $\Phi(A)$. Clearly $\Phi(\Gamma)$ is consistent if and only if Γ is consistent. Therefore, $\Phi(\Delta)$ is consistent because, by assumption, Δ is consistent. By the lemma, therefore, there is a model Σ of $\Phi(\Delta)$. Let Σ' be the following interpretation of Δ with the same domain as Σ. If b is a predicate variable or sentential variable, let Σ' assign to b whatever Σ assigns to b. If b is an individual variable, let Σ' assign to b the individual that Σ assigns to $\Phi(b)$. Obviously the value of a wff A under Σ' is the same as the value of $\Phi(A)$ under Σ. It follows that each member of Δ comes out true under Σ', because each member of $\Phi(\Delta)$ comes out true under Σ. Hence Σ' is a model of Δ. Thus we have shown that every consistent class of wffs of system Q is satisfiable (Skolem–Gödel theorem) if the above lemma is true. It remains only to prove the lemma.

58.1. Maximal, Consistent, ω-Complete Classes

A class Γ of wffs of system Q is called *maximal* if for every wff B that does not belong to Γ, the class $\Gamma \cup \{B\}$ is inconsistent. And a class Γ of wffs of system Q is said to be *ω-complete* if, for every existentially quantified member $\ulcorner(\exists a)A_a\urcorner$ of Γ, there is an instance A_b of it which is also a member of Γ. Let $\bar{\Gamma}$ be any maximal, consistent, ω-complete class. It can be shown that the following statements are all true of $\bar{\Gamma}$:

(a) $B \in \bar{\Gamma}$ if and only if $\ulcorner\sim B\urcorner \notin \bar{\Gamma}$.

(b) $\ulcorner A \cdot B\urcorner \in \bar{\Gamma}$ if and only if both A and B are members of $\bar{\Gamma}$.

(c) $\ulcorner A \vee B\urcorner \in \bar{\Gamma}$ if and only if A or B or both are members of $\bar{\Gamma}$.

(d) $\ulcorner A \supset B\urcorner \notin \bar{\Gamma}$ if and only if $A \in \bar{\Gamma}$ but $B \notin \bar{\Gamma}$.

(e) $\ulcorner A \equiv B\urcorner \in \bar{\Gamma}$ if and only if both A and B belong to $\bar{\Gamma}$ or neither belongs to $\bar{\Gamma}$.

(f) $\ulcorner(\exists a)A_a\urcorner \in \bar{\Gamma}$ if and only if some instance A_b of $\ulcorner(\exists a)A_a\urcorner$ is a member of $\bar{\Gamma}$.

(g) $\ulcorner(a)A_a\urcorner \in \bar{\Gamma}$ if and only if every instance A_b of $\ulcorner(a)A_a\urcorner$ is a member of $\bar{\Gamma}$.

It is left to the reader to show that clauses (a) through (e) are true. [See Exercise (2) of Chapter 60.] To prove (f), we first observe that if A_b is an instance of $\ulcorner(\exists a)A_a\urcorner$, then $A_b \vdash \ulcorner(\exists a)A_a\urcorner$. Hence, by the result of Exercise (1) of Chapter 60, if $A_b \in \bar{\Gamma}$, then $\ulcorner(\exists a)A_a\urcorner \in \bar{\Gamma}$. To prove the converse, we suppose that $\ulcorner(\exists a)A_a\urcorner \in \bar{\Gamma}$. From the definition of ω-completeness it follows that some instance A_b of $\ulcorner(\exists a)A_a\urcorner$ is also a member of $\bar{\Gamma}$. To prove (g), we first observe that $\ulcorner(a)A_a\urcorner \vdash A_b$ for every instance A_b of $\ulcorner(a)A_a\urcorner$. Hence every instance A_b of $\ulcorner(a)A_a\urcorner$ belongs to $\bar{\Gamma}$ if $\ulcorner(a)A_a\urcorner$ belongs to $\bar{\Gamma}$. To prove the converse, we suppose that every instance A_b of $\ulcorner(a)A_a\urcorner$ is a member of $\bar{\Gamma}$ but that $\ulcorner(a)A_a\urcorner \notin \bar{\Gamma}$. By clause (a), $\ulcorner\sim(a)A_a\urcorner \in \bar{\Gamma}$. But $\ulcorner\sim(a)A_a\urcorner \vdash \ulcorner(\exists a)\sim A_a\urcorner$. Hence $\ulcorner(\exists a)\sim A_a\urcorner \in \bar{\Gamma}$. By clause (f), then, some instance $\ulcorner\sim A_b\urcorner$ of $\ulcorner(\exists a)\sim A_a\urcorner$ is a member of $\bar{\Gamma}$. But then both A_b and $\ulcorner\sim A_b\urcorner$ belong to $\bar{\Gamma}$, which entails that $\bar{\Gamma}$ is inconsistent. Therefore, if every instance A_b of $\ulcorner(a)A_a\urcorner$ belongs to $\bar{\Gamma}$, $\ulcorner(a)A_a\urcorner$ also belongs to $\bar{\Gamma}$.

Clauses (a) through (g) enable us to show that every maximal, consistent, ω-complete class $\bar{\Gamma}$ is satisfiable. Consider the following interpretation Σ of $\bar{\Gamma}$ in the domain of the individual variables of system Q, that is, with the individual variables themselves taken as the individuals. To an individual variable b, let Σ assign b itself as value. To a sentential variable b, let Σ assign t or f according as $b \in \bar{\Gamma}$ or $b \notin \bar{\Gamma}$. To an n-ary predicate variable ϕ, let Σ assign as its extension the set Δ of n-tuples of individual variables, where $\langle b_1, \ldots, b_n \rangle \in \Delta$ if and only if $\ulcorner\phi b_1 \ldots b_n\urcorner \in \bar{\Gamma}$. We claim that, for any wff A of system Q, A comes out t or f under Σ according as $A \in \bar{\Gamma}$ or $A \notin \bar{\Gamma}$. If this claim is true, $\bar{\Gamma}$ is satisfiable, because Σ is then a model of $\bar{\Gamma}$. We prove the claim by strong mathematical induction on the number of occurrences of connectives and quantifiers in A. If there are zero occurrences, then A is an atomic wff and the claim is obviously true. Assume that the claim is true of all wffs with n or fewer occurrences of connectives and quantifiers, and let A contain $n+1$ occurrences. Then A has one of seven forms: $\ulcorner\sim B\urcorner$, $\ulcorner B \cdot C\urcorner$, $\ulcorner B \vee C\urcorner$, $\ulcorner B \supset C\urcorner$, $\ulcorner B \equiv C\urcorner$, $\ulcorner(\exists a)B_a\urcorner$, or $\ulcorner(a)B_a\urcorner$. Suppose A is $\ulcorner\sim B\urcorner$. If A is true under Σ, then B is false under Σ. By the hypothesis of induction, then, $B \notin \bar{\Gamma}$. By clause (a) above, $\ulcorner\sim B\urcorner \in \bar{\Gamma}$, that is, $A \in \bar{\Gamma}$. But if A is false under Σ, then B is true under Σ. By the hypothesis of induction, then, $B \in \bar{\Gamma}$. So by clause (a), $\ulcorner\sim B\urcorner \notin \bar{\Gamma}$. That is, $A \notin \bar{\Gamma}$. So in the event A is $\ulcorner\sim B\urcorner$, the claim is true. It is left to the reader to show that the claim is true in the event that A has any of the forms $\ulcorner B \cdot C\urcorner$, $\ulcorner B \vee C\urcorner$, $\ulcorner B \supset C\urcorner$, or $\ulcorner B \equiv C\urcorner$. Suppose, however, that A is $\ulcorner(\exists a)B_a\urcorner$. If $\ulcorner(\exists a)B_a\urcorner$ comes out false under Σ, then every instance B_b of it also comes out false under Σ. And by the hypothesis of induction none of these instances B_b belong to $\bar{\Gamma}$. By clause (f), then, $\ulcorner(\exists a)B_a\urcorner \notin \bar{\Gamma}$. But suppose $\ulcorner(\exists a)B_a\urcorner$ is true under Σ. Let Σ^* be the minimal interpretation of $\ulcorner(\exists a)B_a\urcorner$ determined by Σ. $\ulcorner(\exists a)B_a\urcorner$ is true under Σ, so there is an individual c (remember the individual variables are the individuals) such that, if we enlarge Σ^* by adding the assignment of c to the individual variable a, the enlarged interpretation Σ^{**} is a model of B_a. Let $b_1, \ldots, b_k$ be a complete list of the distinct bound variables of B_a, and let $d_1, \ldots, d_k$ be a list of distinct individual variables none of which occurs in B_a or is identical with c. And let B_a' be the result of replacing each bound occurrence of b_i in B_a by an occurrence of d_i. Then B_a has the same value under Σ^{**} as B_a does, namely truth, because B_a' differs from B_a only by alphabetic changes of bound variables. Let B_c' result from B_a' by substitution of c for a. Then the value of B_c' under Σ is the same as the value of B_a' under Σ^{**}, namely truth, because Σ assigns c to c. By the hypothesis of induction, then, $B_c' \in \bar{\Gamma}$. But $B_c' \vdash \ulcorner(\exists a)B_a\urcorner$. [See Exercise (12) of Chapter 60.] Hence $\ulcorner(\exists a)B_a\urcorner \in \bar{\Gamma}$. This completes the proof of the claim for the case when A is $\ulcorner(\exists a)B_a\urcorner$. We leave the case when A is $\ulcorner(a)B_a\urcorner$ to the reader, because a proof very similar to the one just presented may be given for this last case.

We have shown above that every maximal, consistent, ω-complete class is satisfiable. In fact, we have shown something stronger: that every maximal, consistent, ω-complete class is satisfiable in the domain of the individual variables. There are just as many positive integers as individual variables, so it follows from the generalized inflation theorem that every maximal, consistent, ω-complete class is satisfiable in the domain of the positive integers.

58.2. Proof of the Lemma of Section 58.0

Let Γ be any consistent set of wffs of system Q which contain no occurrences of the variables 'w_1', 'w_2', $\ldots$. If we can show that Γ is a subset of some maximal, consistent, ω-complete class $\bar{\Gamma}$, we can derive the lemma of Section 58.0 from the results of Section 58.1, because any model of $\bar{\Gamma}$ will also be a model of Γ. Let $A_1, A_2, A_3, \ldots$ be an enumeration without repetitions of all the wffs of system Q which is such that, if any member A_i is an existentially quantified wff $\ulcorner(\exists a)B_a\urcorner$, then the next wff A_{i+1} is some conservative instance B_b of A_i, where b is one of the variables $w_1, w_2, \ldots$ and where the variable of instantiation b occurs in no earlier wff of the enumeration. Clearly such enumerations exist. [See Exercise (3) of Chapter 60.) Let Γ_0 be Γ, and for each natural number k let Γ_{k+1} be $\Gamma_k \cup \{A_{k+1}\}$ if that union is consistent; if $\Gamma_k \cup \{A_{k+1}\}$ is not consistent, let Γ_{k+1} be the same as Γ_k. And, finally, let $\bar{\Gamma}$ be the union of all the sets $\Gamma_0, \Gamma_1, \Gamma_2, \ldots$. Obviously Γ is a subset of the class $\bar{\Gamma}$ which we shall now show to be a maximal, consistent, ω-complete class.

To show that $\bar{\Gamma}$ is consistent, we begin by supposing that it is not consistent. There is, then, a finite number $C_1, \ldots, C_m$ of members of $\bar{\Gamma}$ such that, for some wff D, both $C_1, \ldots, C_m \vdash D$ and $C_1, \ldots, C_m \vdash \ulcorner{\sim}D\urcorner$. But $C_1, \ldots, C_m$ all belong to some class Γ_r. [See Exercise (4) of Chapter 60.] Thus Γ_r is also inconsistent. But, by the way they are formed, all the classes Γ_i are consistent. Hence Γ_r is both consistent and inconsistent. By indirect proof, therefore, we conclude from this contradiction that $\bar{\Gamma}$ is consistent.

To prove that $\bar{\Gamma}$ is maximal, we also use indirect proof and begin by assuming that $\bar{\Gamma}$ is not maximal. From the definition of a maximal class and the fact that $\bar{\Gamma}$ is consistent it follows that there is at least one wff A_j in the enumeration of wffs which is not a member of $\bar{\Gamma}$ but which is such that $\bar{\Gamma} \cup \{A_j\}$ is consistent. But then $\Gamma_{j-1} \cup \{A_j\}$ is also consistent, because Γ_{j-1} is a subclass of $\bar{\Gamma}$. Accordingly, Γ_j is $\Gamma_{j-1} \cup \{A_j\}$. But Γ_j is also a subclass of $\bar{\Gamma}$, so it follows that the alleged nonmember A_j is a member of $\bar{\Gamma}$. From this contradiction we conclude that $\bar{\Gamma}$ is maximal.

It remains only to show that $\bar{\Gamma}$ is ω-complete. Consider that any existentially quantified member $\ulcorner(\exists a)B_a\urcorner$ of $\bar{\Gamma}$ will occur somewhere in the above-described enumeration of wffs, say as A_i. So $A_i \in \Gamma_i$. By the way the enumeration was formed, A_{i+1} will be some conservative instance B_b of A_i, where b occurs in no member of Γ_i. If $B_b \in \Gamma_{i+1}$, then $\bar{\Gamma}$ is ω-complete and our point is proved. So suppose $B_b \notin \Gamma_{i+1}$. By the way Γ_{i+1} was formed, it then follows that $\Gamma_i \cup \{B_b\}$ is inconsistent. So $\Gamma_i \vdash \ulcorner{\sim}B_b\urcorner$. Let $L_1, L_2, \ldots, L_k$ be a proof of $\ulcorner{\sim}B_b\urcorner$ from Γ_i. Add to that proof the following line:

$$(k + 1) \quad (a){\sim}B_a \hspace{4cm} \text{(k)UG}\boxed{b}$$

The result is a proof of $\ulcorner(a){\sim}B_a\urcorner$ from Γ_i. Hence $\bar{\Gamma} \vdash \ulcorner(a){\sim}B_a\urcorner$. But then $\ulcorner(a){\sim}B_a\urcorner \in \bar{\Gamma}$. Moreover $\ulcorner(a){\sim}B_a\urcorner \vdash \ulcorner{\sim}(\exists a)B_a\urcorner$. Hence $\ulcorner{\sim}(\exists a)B_a\urcorner \in \bar{\Gamma}$. But $\ulcorner(\exists a)B_a\urcorner \in \bar{\Gamma}$. Thus $\bar{\Gamma}$ is inconsistent, which contradicts the fact that $\bar{\Gamma}$ is consistent, as shown above. Hence $B_b \in \bar{\Gamma}$ and $\bar{\Gamma}$ is ω-complete. This completes the proof of the lemma of Section 58.0.

59.   QUANTIFICATION WITH FUNCTION VARIABLES

59.0.   Function Variables; Terms

Although any extant mathematical theory can be formalized in system QI, most mathematical theories are more naturally and smoothly formalized in a system that boasts function variables, that is, variables which take functions from individuals to individuals as their values. By an *n-ary function on a domain* $\mathfrak{D}$ *of individuals* we understand a function which, when applied to n individuals of $\mathfrak{D}$ in a particular order as arguments, yields a member of $\mathfrak{D}$ as value. For example, addition is a binary function on the domain of positive integers; it yields 7 as value when applied to 3 and 4 as arguments. We will shortly enrich system QI with function variables that take as values functions on the domain of individuals.

In Section 42.2 we used circled numerals to transform sentences into predicates or, as they might have been called, *extension designators*, because an n-ary predicate was taken to designate or refer to an extension (set of n-tuples of individuals). Circled numerals can also be used to convert certain referring singular terms into function designators, that is, expressions which designate or refer to functions. Referring singular terms are of two kinds: proper names and definite descriptions. For example, where the domain is the set of positive integers, '5', '3 + 2', and 'the successor of 4' are all referring singular terms that denote the integer five. Let t be a referring singular term. Supplanting referring singular terms within t by circled numerals will often yield a function designator. For example, we can in this manner convert '3 + 2' into three function designators: '①+①', '①+②', and '②+①'. The first designates the singulary function which, when applied to a positive integer k, yields $2k$; the second and third denote the binary functions which, when applied to k and m in order, yield $k + m$ and $m + k$, respectively. Because addition is commutative, both '①+②' and '②+①' happen to designate the same function.

The system that results when system QI is enriched with function variables will be called Q *with identity and function variables* (QIF). For each positive integer n, system QIF contains an infinite supply of n-ary function variables $\ulcorner f^n \urcorner$, $\ulcorner g^n \urcorner$, $\ulcorner h^n \urcorner$, $\ulcorner f_1^n \urcorner$, and so on, which take n-ary functions on the domain of individuals as values. To accommodate them, some changes in the formation rules of system QI are required. But first we must explain the notion of a *term* of system QIF, and we do so by an inductive definition:

(i)   Individual variables are terms.

(ii)   If ϕ is an n-ary function variable and t_1, $\ldots$, t_n are terms, then $\ulcorner \phi t_1 \ldots t_n \urcorner$ is a term.

(iii) A formula is a term if and only if it can be constructed by a finite number of applications of rules (i) and (ii).

For example, the formulas below are all terms of system QIF:

$$f^3xyx \qquad f^2xg^2xy \qquad f^1g^1f^2yy$$

Unlike the superscripts on predicate variables, the superscripts on function variables cannot always be dropped without introducing ambiguity. For example, the first of the three terms above could be unambiguously abbreviated as '$fxyx$', but the second cannot be written as '$fxgxy$' without ambiguity, because this expression might abbreviate either 'f^2xg^2xy' or 'f^3xg^1xy'. Accordingly, we shall dispense with superscripts on function variables only when no ambiguity can thereby result.

To accommodate function variables, the formation rule for predicate variables must be rewritten as follows:

If ϕ is an n-ary predicate variable and t_1, $\ldots$, t_n are terms, then $\ulcorner \phi t_1 \ldots t_n \urcorner$ is an (atomic) wff.

The following are examples of wffs of system QIF:

$$(x)(y)(fxy = fyx) \qquad\qquad (x)[Fx \supset Gg^2xx]$$
$$(x)[(\exists y)(y = fx) \equiv (\exists z)Fxz] \qquad (y)Ffy$$

To accommodate function variables, the semantics of system QI must also be modified. This may be done by presenting an inductive definition of the value of a *term or wff A under a minimal interpretation* Σ. Let ϕ be an n-ary function variable, t_1, $\ldots$, t_n be terms and Σ be a minimal interpretation of $\ulcorner \phi t_1 \ldots t_n \urcorner$. The aforementioned inductive definition will contain a clause to the following effect: The value of $\ulcorner\phi t_1\ldots t_n\urcorner$ under Σ is the individual α, where α is the result of applying to $\alpha_1,\ldots,\alpha_n$ (in that order) the function which Σ assigns to ϕ, where each α_i is the value of t_i under Σ. For example, let the domain of Σ be the set of positive integers and let Σ assign to 'f' the function designated by '① $+$ ②' and to 'x' and 'y' the numbers three and five, respectively; then the value of the term 'fxf^2xy' under Σ is the number eleven.

59.1. Natural Deduction Rules for System QIF

If we liberalize slightly the notion of an instance of a quantified wff, we can take over unchanged into system QIF eight of the nine deduction rules of system QI. The ninth rule, RS, will still require a minor modification. To explain this liberalized notion of an instance, we must first introduce the concepts of free and bound occurrences of terms in wffs. An occurrence of a term t in a wff A is said to be *bound in A* if any variable occurrences in that occurrence of t are bound in A. For example, both occurrences of the term 'gxy' are bound in the wff '$(x)Fg^2xy \supset (\exists x)(y)Gg^2xy$', but only the first occurrence of that term is bound in '$(\exists y)Fg^2xy \vee Fg^2xy$'. An occurrence of a term t in a wff A is said to be *free in A* if that occurrence of t is not bound in A. For example, the second occurrence of the term 'gxy' is free in the wff last mentioned. A wff A_t shall be said to be an *instance of the wff* $\ulcorner(a)A_a\urcorner$ [or $\ulcorner(\exists a)A_a\urcorner$] if A_t is the result of substituting the term t for all free occurrences of the variable a in A provided that each of the substituted occurrences of the term t is free in A_t. Put otherwise, A_t is an instance of $\ulcorner(a)A_a\urcorner$ [or $\ulcorner(\exists a)A_a\urcorner$] if and only if A_t is like A_a except for having free occurrences of the term t wherever A_a has free occurrences of a. For example, each wff in the left column below is an instance of the wff opposite it in the right column:

Fg^2yy	$(x)Fg^2xx$
$Fg^2f^1xf^1x$	$(\exists x)Fg^2xx$
$Ffy \equiv (w)Gwfy$	$(\exists y)[Fy \equiv (w)Gwy]$
$gw = gw$	$(z)(z = gw)$

Unlike that of an instance, the concept of a conservative instance is carried over unchanged into system QIF.

We can now state the rule RS for system QIF:

RS (modified).   Any universal closure of a wff of the form
$\ulcorner A_s \cdot (s = t) \supset A_t \urcorner$, where A_t is like A_s except for having free occurrences of the term t
at one or more places where A_s has free occurrences of the term s, may be set down as an
unstarred line of a deduction provided that
'RS' is written at the right.

All other concepts and rules are carried over from system QI unchanged into system QIF.

Like systems Q and QI, system QIF is both consistent and complete with respect to validity. The Skolem–Gödel theorem and the
strong completeness theorem also hold for system QIF. For hints
as to how to prove these and other important metatheorems about
system QIF, see the exercises of Chapter 60.

59.2.   Peano Arithmetic

To illustrate how smoothly and naturally familiar mathematical
theories can be formalized in system QIF, we shall present a
postulate set for ordinary arithmetic and derive some of its basic
theorems. The postulates are known as *Peano's postulates* after the
celebrated Italian mathematician Giuseppe Peano, who borrowed
them from Richard Dedekind.[1] The postulate system as a whole
has come to be known as *Peano arithmetic* (PA).

The set of natural numbers constitutes the domain of individuals
of the intended interpretation of PA. We let 'z_6' denote the number
zero, and we let the singulary function variable 'f' mean 'the successor of ①'; that is, we assign to 'f' as its value the function which,
when applied to a natural number k, yields the natural number
$k + 1$. For the sake of perspicuity, we let the numerals '0', '1',
'2', ... abbreviate 'z_6', 'fz_6', 'ffz_6', ..., respectively. And, where t
is any term, we let $\ulcorner t' \urcorner$ abbreviate $\ulcorner ft \urcorner$. We round out the intended
interpretation of PA by letting the binary function variables 'g'
and 'h' mean '① + ②' and '① × ②' ('the product of ① and ②'),

---

[1] For an historical account of Peano's postulates, the reader might consult
Hao Wang, "The Axiomatization of Arithmetic," *Journal of Symbolic Logic*,
vol. 22 (1957), pp. 145–158.

respectively. Again for perspicuity, we let $\ulcorner(t + s)\urcorner$ and $\ulcorner(t \otimes s)\urcorner$ abbreviate $\ulcorner gts\urcorner$ and $\ulcorner hts\urcorner$, where t and s are any terms. Four additional abbreviative conventions are presented below as labeled definitions. (For the sake of readability, we shall omit grouping indicators freely when no genuine ambiguity results.)

D1. $t < s =_{\mathrm{Df}} (\exists a)[(a \neq 0) \cdot (t + a = s)]$, where a is the first individual variable in lexicographical order after all the individual variables in the terms t and s.

D2. $t \leq s =_{\mathrm{Df}} (t < s) \mathrel{\mathbf{v}} (t = s)$.

D3. $t > s =_{\mathrm{Df}} s < t$.

D4. $t \geq s =_{\mathrm{Df}} s \leq t$.

Peano's postulates consist of six postulates and one postulate schema.

P1. $(x)(0 \neq x')$.

P2. $(x)(y)[(x' = y') \supset (x = y)]$.

P3. $(x)(x + 0 = x)$.

P4. $(x)(y)[x + y' = (x + y)']$.

P5. $(x)(x \otimes 0 = 0)$.

P6. $(x)(y)[x \otimes y' = (x \otimes y) + x]$.

P7. Any wff of the following form is a postulate: $\ulcorner A_0 \cdot (a)[A_a \supset A_{a'}] \supset (a)A_a \urcorner$, where $A_{a'}$ and A_0 are like A_a except for having free occurrences of $\ulcorner a'\urcorner$ and '0', respectively, wherever A_a has free occurrences of the variable a.

The schema P7 is called the *induction postulate* because it is a reflection in PA of the rule of inference of weak mathematical induction. A number of theorems of PA are given below. Proofs of some have been supplied, but proofs of most have been left to the reader.

T1. $(x)(x \neq x')$.

$*_1(1)$ $(0 \neq 0') \cdot (x)[(x \neq x') \supset (x' \neq x'')] \supset (x)(x \neq x')$

 RP(P7)

$*_2(2)$ $(x)(0 \neq x')$ RP(P1)

$*_2(3)$ $0 \neq 0'$ UI(2)

$*_4(4)$ $x \neq x'$ RP

$*_5(5)$ $(x)(y)[(x' = y') \supset (x = y)]$ RP(P2)

$*_5(6)$ $(x' = x'') \supset (x = x')$ UI(5) twice

$*_4*_5(7)$ $x' \neq x''$ TF(6)(4)

$*_5(8)$ $(x \neq x') \supset (x' \neq x'')$ Cd$*_4$(7)

$*_5(9)$ $(x)[(x \neq x') \supset (x' \neq x'')]$ UG(8)⊠

$*_1*_2*_5(10)$ $(x)(x \neq x')$ TF(1)(3)(9)

Lines (1), (2), and (5) are all postulates of PA, so the deduction above shows that T1 is a theorem of PA.

T2. $(x)(0 + x = x)$.

$*_1(1)$ $(0 + 0 = 0) \cdot (x)[(0 + x = x) \supset (0 + x' = x')] \supset$
$$(x)(0 + x = x)$$
RP(P7)

$*_2(2)$ $(x)(x + 0 = x)$ RP(P3)

$*_2(3)$ $0 + 0 = 0$ UI(2)

$*_4(4)$ $0 + x = x$ RP

(5) $(x)(x = x)$ RI

(6) $(0 + x)' = (0 + x)'$ UI(5)

(7) $(x)\{[(0 + x)' = (0 + x)'] \cdot [0 + x = x] \supset$
$$[(0 + x)' = x']\}$$
RS

(8) $[(0 + x)' = (0 + x)'] \cdot [0 + x = x] \supset [(0 + x)' = x']$
UI(7)

$*_4(9)$ $(0 + x)' = x'$ TF(8)(6)(4)

$*_{10}(10)$ $(x)(y)[x + y' = (x + y)']$ RP(P4)

$*_{10}(11)$ $0 + x' = (0 + x)'$ UI(10) twice

(12) $(x)\{[0 + x' = (0 + x)'] \cdot [(0 + x)' = x'] \supset$
$$[0 + x' = x']\}$$
RS

(13) $[0 + x' = (0 + x)'] \cdot [(0 + x)' = x'] \supset [0 + x' = x']$
UI(12)

$*_4*_{10}(14)$ $0 + x' = x'$ TF(13)(11)(9)

$*_{10}(15)$ $(0 + x = x) \supset (0 + x' = x')$ Cd$*_4$(14)

$*_{10}(16)$ $(x)[(0 + x = x) \supset (0 + x' = x')]$ UG(15)⊠

$*_1*_2*_{10}(17)$ $(x)(0 + x = x)$ TF(1)(3)(16)

T3. $(x)(y)[x' + y = (x + y)']$.

T4. $(x)(y)(x + y = y + x)$.

T5. $(x)(y)(z)[(x + y) + z = x + (y + z)]$.

T6. $(x)(y)(z)[x \otimes (y + z) = (x \otimes y) + (x \otimes z)]$.

T7. $(x)(0 \otimes x = 0)$.

T8. $(x)(y)[x' \otimes y = (x \otimes y) + y]$.

T9. $(x)(y)(x \otimes y = y \otimes x)$.

T10. $(x)(y)(z)[(x \otimes y) \otimes z = x \otimes (y \otimes z)]$.

If t is a term, we let $\ulcorner t^2 \urcorner$ abbreviate $\ulcorner t \otimes t \urcorner$.

T11. $(x)(y)[(x + y)^2 = x^2 + (x \otimes y) + (x \otimes y) + y^2]$.

T12. $(x)[x + x = 2 \otimes x]$.

T13. $(x)(y)[(x + y)^2 = x^2 + 2 \otimes (x \otimes y) + y^2]$.

T14. $(x)[(x \neq 0) \supset (\exists y)(x = y')]$.

T15. $\sim(\exists x)(x < 0)$.

T16. $(x)(y)[(x < y') \cdot \sim(x < y) \supset (x = y)]$.

T17. $(x)[(x \neq 0) \supset (0 < x)]$.

T18. $(x)(0 \leq x)$.

T19. $(\exists x)(y)[(x \neq y) \supset (x < y)]$.

T20. $(x)(y)[(x < y) \supset (x < y')]$.

T21. $(x)(x < x')$.

T22. $(x)(\exists y)(y > x)$.

T23. $1 > 0$.

T24. $(x)(y)[(x = y) \supset (x < y')]$.

T25. $(x)(y)[(x < y) \supset (x' < y')]$.

T26. $(x)(y)[(x < y) \vee (x = y) \vee (x > y)]$.

T27. $(x)(y)(\exists z)[(x + z = y) \vee (x = y + z)]$.

T28. $(x)(y)[(x + y = 0) \supset (x = 0) \cdot (y = 0)]$.

T29. $(x)(y)(z)[(x < y) \cdot (y < z) \supset (x < z)]$.

T30. $(x)(y)(z)[(x > y) \cdot (y > z) \supset (x > z)]$.

T31. $(x)(y)(z)[(x < y) \supset (x < y + z)]$.

T32. $(x)(y)(z)[(x \leq y) \cdot (y \leq z) \supset (x \leq z)]$.

T33. $(x)(y)(z)[(x \geq y) \cdot (y \geq z) \supset (x \geq z)]$.

T34. $(x)(y)[(x' < y) \supset (x < y)]$.

T35. $(x)(y)[(x \otimes y = 0) \supset (x = 0) \vee (y = 0)]$.

T36. $(x)\{(y)[(y < x) \supset Fy] \supset Fx\} \supset (x)Fx$.

T37. $(x)(y)[(x \leq y') \cdot \sim(x \leq y) \supset (x = y')]$.

T38. $(x)(y)[(x \leq y) \vee (x > y)]$.

T39. $(x)(y)[(x \leq y) \cdot \sim(x' \leq y) \supset (x = y)]$.

T40. $(x)(y)[(x < y) \supset \sim(x' > y)]$.

T41. $F0 \cdot (x)\{(y)[(y \leq x) \supset Fy] \supset Fx'\} \supset (x)Fx$.

T42. $(\exists x)Fx \supset (\exists x)[Fx \cdot (y)[Fy \supset (y \geq x)]]$.

T43. $(x)(y)(z)[(x + z = y + z) \supset (x = y)]$.

T44. $(x)(y)(z)[(x \otimes z = y \otimes z) \cdot (z \neq 0) \supset (x = y)]$.

T45. $(x)(y)(z)[(x > y) \supset (x + z > y)]$.

T46. $(x)(y)[(x \neq 0) \supset (x + y > y)]$.

T47. $\sim(\exists x)(x < x)$.

T48. $(x)(y)[(x > y) \supset (x \neq y) \cdot \sim(x < y)]$.

T49. $(x)(y)[(x' < y') \supset (x < y)]$.

T50. $(x)\sim(\exists y)[(x < y) \cdot (y < x')]$.

T51. $\sim(x)(y)[(x < y) \supset (\exists z)[(x < z) \cdot (z < y)]]$.

T52. $(x)(y)(z)[(x < y) \supset (x + z < y + z)]$.

T53. $(w)(x)(y)(z)[(w < x) \cdot (y < z) \supset (w + y < x + z)]$.

T54. $\sim(\exists x)(y)(x > y)$.

T55. $(x)(y)(z)[(x > y) \supset (x + z > y + z)]$.

T56. $(w)(x)(y)(z)[(w > x) \cdot (y > z) \supset (w + y > x + z)]$.

T57. $(x)(y)[(y \neq 0) \supset (x \leq x \otimes y)]$.

T58. $(x)(y)[(x \neq 0) \cdot (y > 1) \supset (x < x \otimes y)]$.

T59. $(x)[(x > 1) \supset (x < x^2)]$.

T60. $(x)(y)(z)[(x < y) \cdot (z \neq 0) \supset (x \otimes z < y \otimes z)]$.

T61. $(x)(y)(z)[(x < y) \supset (x \otimes z \leq y \otimes z)]$.

T62. $(x)[1 \otimes x = x]$.

T63. $(x)[(y)(y + x = y) \supset (x = 0)]$.

T64. $(x)[(y)(y \otimes x = 0) \supset (x = 0)]$.

T65. $(x)[(y)(x \otimes y = y) \supset (x = 1)]$.

T66. $(x)(y)(z)[(x \otimes z \leq y \otimes z) \cdot (z \neq 0) \supset (x \leq y)]$.

T67. $(x)(x' = x + 1)$.

T68. $(x)(y)[(x < y) \supset (x^2 < y^2)]$.

T69. $(x)\{(\exists y)(x = y^2) \supset (\exists y)[(x = y^2) \cdot (w)[(x = w^2) \supset (w = y)]]\}$.

T70. $(x)(y)[(x \neq 0) \cdot (x < y) \supset (\exists z)(x \otimes z > y)]$.

Although most mathematical theories are more smoothly and naturally formalized in system QIF than in system QI, any theory formalizable in the former can also be formalized in the latter by letting special $(n + 1)$-ary predicates do the work of n-ary function variables. Roughly speaking, for each interpreted n-ary function variable ϕ we introduce an interpreted $(n + 1)$-ary predicate ψ such that the function assigned to ϕ yields the individual α when applied to the individuals $\alpha_1, \ldots, \alpha_n$ if and only if $\langle \alpha_1, \ldots, \alpha_n, \alpha \rangle$ belongs to the extension of ψ. For example, to formalize arithmetic in system QI we might let binary 'F' and ternary 'G' and 'H' mean 'the successor of ① is ②', '① + ② = ③', and '① × ② = ③', respectively. In addition to analogues of all the postulates of PA, we would lay down these three postulates:

$(x)(\exists y)\{Fxy \cdot (z)[Fxz \supset (z = y)]\}$

$$(x)(y)(\exists z)\{Gxyz \cdot (w)[Gxyw \supset (w = z)]\}$$
$$(x)(y)(\exists z)\{Hxyz \cdot (w)[Hxyw \supset (w = z)]\}$$

For illustration we present analogues of the postulates P1, P2, and P4 of PA:

$$(x) \sim Fx0$$
$$(x)(y)(z)[Fxz \cdot Fyz \supset (x = y)]$$
$$(w)(x)(y)(z)(x_1)[Fyw \cdot Gxyz \cdot Gxwx_1 \supset Fzx_1]$$

We leave it to the reader to supply analogues of the other postulates of PA.

60. EXERCISES

(1) Let $\bar{\Gamma}$ be any maximal, consistent class of wffs of system Q. Prove that if $A_1, \ldots, A_n$ all belong to $\bar{\Gamma}$ and $A_1, \ldots, A_n \vdash B$, then $B \in \bar{\Gamma}$. (*Hint*: Look at the proof of lemma 2 in Section 30.2.)

(2) Prove that the clauses (a) through (e) of Section 58.1 are true. (*Hint*: Look at Section 30.3.)

(3) Show that the wffs of system Q can be arranged without repetitions in an enumeration $A_1, A_2, A_3, \ldots$ which is such that every existentially quantified wff $\ulcorner(\exists a)B_a\urcorner$ is immediately followed by a conservative instance B_b, where b is one of the variables 'w_1', 'w_2', $\ldots$ and where the variable of instantiation b occurs in no earlier member of the enumeration.

(4) Let $\bar{\Gamma}$ and $\Gamma_0, \Gamma_1, \Gamma_2, \ldots$ all be as in Section 58.2, and let $\{C_1, \ldots, C_m\}$ be any finite subset of $\bar{\Gamma}$. Prove that, for some r, $\{C_1, \ldots, C_m\}$ is a subclass of Γ_r and of all succeeding classes in the enumeration $\Gamma_0, \Gamma_1, \Gamma_2, \ldots$. (*Hint*: Make use of the fact that one of the members of $\{C_1, \ldots, C_m\}$ occurs after all the others in the enumeration of wffs mentioned in Section 58.2.)

(5) Let Γ be any class of wffs of system Q. Prove that, if $\Gamma \cup \{A\}$ is inconsistent, then $\Gamma \vdash \ulcorner \sim A \urcorner$.

(6)   Replacement of referring singular terms by circled numerals does not always transform a referring singular term into a function designator. For example, such replacement transforms '$5-3$' into '$①-②$', which fails to designate a binary function on the domain of positive integers. State as well as you can the conditions under which such replacement transforms a referring singular term into a function designator on a nonempty domain $\mathfrak{D}$.

(7)   Present a full and careful statement of the syntax of system QIF.

(8)   Present a full and careful statement of the value of a term or wff of system QIF under a minimal interpretation.

(9)   State precisely when superscripts may be dropped from function variables without producing ambiguous abbreviations of wffs of system QIF.

(10)   By appealing to the proof of the Skolem–Gödel theorem given in Chapter 58, prove the Löwenheim theorem and the Löwenheim–Skolem theorem for system Q. (*Hint*: Capitalize on the fact that any maximal, consistent, ω-complete class is satisfiable in the domain of positive integers.)

(11)   Prove the modified Löwenheim–Skolem theorem for system QI; that is, prove that if a class of wffs of system QI is satisfiable, then it is satisfiable in either a finite or a denumerable domain. [*Hint*: Appeal to the proof you supplied in doing Exercise (13) of Chapter 57 and to the result of Exercise (10) above.]

(12)   Prove by mathematical induction on the number of connectives and quantifiers in A that, if A and B differ at most by alphabetic changes of bound variables, then $A \vdash B$ and $B \vdash A$.

61. DECISION PROBLEMS AND INCOMPLETENESS

61.0. Decidability; Church's Thesis

A desire for a thoroughly systematic technique of establishing validity led us to system Q, which, as the consistency and completeness theorems attest, surely satisfies that desire in large measure. But has the desire been completely satisfied? On reflection we find that what we really wanted was an algorithm, an effective or mechanical procedure whose employment requires no ingenuity (but perhaps considerable patience), for recognizing validity. Now, we do possess an algorithm for finding proofs in system Q of valid wffs. Simply searching through an enumeration of the proofs of system Q will eventually turn up a proof of A if A is valid. (It was to dispense with the tedium of such unimaginative searches that we developed the deductive strategies of Section 56.0.) But we do not yet have an algorithm for determining about an arbitrary wff of system Q whether it is valid.

A possible algorithm for validity suggests itself. When confronted with an arbitrary wff A of system Q, put two men (or machines) to work, one searching for a proof of A and the other looking for a false interpretation of A, and then sit back to wait until one or the other announces success. The only difficulty is that, if A is not valid, no announcement may ever come, for we have as yet no assurance that the second man (or machine) will eventually hit upon one of the false interpretations of A. Furthermore, such assurance is simply not to be had. For, as we will shortly see, there is no algorithm for determining about an arbitrary wff of system Q whether it is valid if Church's thesis (see below) is true, and there are excellent reasons to accept Church's thesis.

The existence of an algorithm for determining something should not be confused with either proof or knowledge that a certain procedure is such an algorithm. To appreciate this point, consider the problem of determining the truth value of Goldbach's conjecture.

Writing 'true' on a scrap of paper is an algorithm for determining the truth value of Goldbach's conjecture if the conjecture is true; writing 'false' is an algorithm for determining its truth value if it is false. Goldbach's conjecture is either true or false, so one or the other of these procedures is an algorithm for determining (identifying) the truth value of Goldbach's conjecture. It is not known, however, which of the two procedures is the desired algorithm. Now, when we say that there is no algorithm for determining about an arbitrary wff of system Q whether it is valid, (that is, that there is no decision procedure for validity for wffs of system Q), we are not speaking epistemologically but ontologically. We do not mean that no such algorithm has been discovered or even that no procedure can ever be proved to be such an algorithm. We mean that there is no such algorithm to be discovered.

A formal system is said to be *decidable* if there exists an algorithm for determining about an arbitrary wff of the system whether it is a theorem of the system, that is, for recognizing theoremhood in the system. Systems P and M, for example, are decidable. But rather than talk about decidable systems, we shall talk primarily about decidable sets of natural numbers. This talk about numbers can then be related to formal systems by a special numbering of the syntactical entities of the system called a *Gödel numbering* after Kurt Gödel, who invented the technique. By a *Gödel numbering* of a formal system is meant a one-to-one mapping G of the symbols, formulas, and finite sequences of formulas of the formal system onto a subset Γ of the natural numbers such that

(i)   There is an algorithm which, for any symbol, formula, or finite sequence of formulas, identifies the number mapped with it by G, which is called the *Gödel number of* the object;

(ii)   There is an algorithm which, for any natural number, registers whether it is the Gödel number of anything and, if it is, identifies the object whose Gödel number it is.

[For Gödel numberings of systems Q, QI, and QIF, see Exercises (1)–(3) of Chapter 63.]

A set of natural numbers is said to be *decidable* if there is an algorithm for determining about an arbitrary natural number whether it is a member of the set, that is, for recognizing membership in the set. For example, the set of prime numbers is decidable. (In the case of the set of prime numbers, as in nearly every case in which we know that an algorithm of a certain sort exists, we also happen to know that a certain procedure is such an algorithm. But in the case of determining the truth value of Goldbach's conjecture we know that such an algorithm exists; we even know that one of two simple procedures is such an algorithm, but we do not know which procedure is the desired algorithm.) Similarly, a set of n-tuples of natural numbers is said to be *decidable* if there is an algorithm which determines about an arbitrary n-tuple of natural numbers whether it belongs to the set. Let G be a Gödel numbering of a formal system S, and let Δ_S be the set of the Gödel numbers of the theorems of S. Clearly then, S is decidable if and only if Δ_S is decidable. Unfortunately, the notion of a decidable set of natural numbers or of n-tuples of natural numbers is no more clear than is the notion of an algorithm. If we hope to prove that certain sets of natural numbers or of n-tuples of natural numbers are not decidable, we must first clarify or explicate the notion of a decidable set of numbers or of n-tuples of numbers. To this end Alonzo Church advanced the thesis that *every decidable set of natural numbers or of n-tuples of natural numbers is expressible* (*Church's thesis*).[1] As we will see momentarily, the notion of an *expressible set* (of natural numbers or of n-tuples of natural numbers) is perfectly clear and it is intuitively evident that every expressible set is decidable, so it follows from Church's thesis that the decidable sets are the same as the expressible sets. Therefore, to prove that S is undecidable, it suffices to prove that Δ_S (the set of Gödel numbers of the theorems of S) is not expressible—provided, of course, that we accept Church's thesis. And there are several good reasons to accept it. First, every set known to be decidable that has been investigated for expressibility has been found to be expressible. Second and even more impressively, of the many serious attempts to explicate the notion of decidability, *all* have yielded concepts that have turned out to be equivalent to expressibility in the sense that they all characterize exactly the same sets of natural numbers as decidable.

By *Robinson arithmetic* (hereafter RA) let us understand the postulate system in system QIF which has just seven postulates: the wffs P1–P6 and T14 of Peano arithmetic. If n is a natural

---

[1] In this expository treatment we have permitted ourselves considerable historical license. Church did not literally do what we have reported him as doing, but he did do something tantamount to it.

number, let us write $\bar{n}$ for the numeral of RA that denotes n. Then a set Δ of natural numbers is said to be *expressible* if there is a wff A_{x_1} of RA which has these properties:

(i) A_{x_1} contains no free individual variables other than 'x_1' and 'z_6' (the variable whose value is zero) and no bound occurrences of 'z_6'.

(ii)   For any natural number n, if $n \in \Delta$, then $\vdash A_{\bar{n}}$ (that is, the wff that results on substituting the numeral $\bar{n}$ for 'x_1' in A_{x_1} is a theorem of RA.

(iii)   For any natural number n, if $n \notin \Delta$, then $\vdash \ulcorner {\sim} A_{\bar{n}} \urcorner$.

(The wff A_{x_1} is said *to express* Δ.) RA is obviously consistent, so no wff and its negation will both be theorems of RA. Accordingly it is easy to see that an expressible set Δ of natural numbers is decidable. Given any natural number n, to determine whether $n \in \Delta$ one need only search through the proofs of RA until one comes across either a proof of $A_{\bar{n}}$ (in which case $n \in \Delta$) or a proof of $\ulcorner {\sim} A_{\bar{n}} \urcorner$ (in which case $n \notin \Delta$), where A_{x_1} is a wff that expresses Δ.

Similarly, a set Δ of n-tuples of natural numbers is said to be *expressible* if there is a wff $A_{x_1 \ldots x_n}$ of RA such that

(i) $A_{x_1 \ldots x_n}$ contains no free individual variables other than 'x_1', ..., 'x_n', 'z_6', and no bound occurrences of 'z_6';

(ii)   For any n-tuple $\langle k_1, \ldots, k_n \rangle$ of natural numbers, if $\langle k_1, \ldots, k_n \rangle \in \Delta$, then $\vdash A_{\bar{k}_1 \ldots \bar{k}_n}$;

(iii)   For any n-tuple $\langle k_1, \ldots, k_n \rangle$ of natural numbers, if $\langle k_1, \ldots, k_n \rangle \notin \Delta$, then $\vdash \ulcorner {\sim} A_{\bar{k}_1 \ldots \bar{k}_n} \urcorner$.

(The wff $A_{x_1 \ldots x_n}$ is said *to express* Δ.) Again it is easy to show that all expressible sets of n-tuples of natural numbers are decidable.

61.1. Church's Theorem

Let Δ_T be the set of Gödel numbers of the theorems of system QIF under a given Gödel numbering $\mathcal{G}$. Church has proved that Δ_T is not expressible, a result known as *Church's theorem*. Church's thesis and Church's theorem together entail that system QIF is undecidable, a result we shall call *Church's thesis theorem* to make explicit its dependence on both Church's thesis and Church's theorem. Now it is rather easily shown that systems Q and QI are decidable if and only if system QIF is decidable. Accordingly, the undecidability of systems Q and QI is a corollary of Church's thesis theorem. If we accept Church's thesis, therefore, we must give up hope of ever developing an algorithm for determining about an arbitrary wff of system Q whether it is valid. No such algorithm exists. If it did, system Q would be decidable because the theorems of system Q are the same as the valid wffs. Let us turn, then, to a proof of Church's theorem.

We will prove Church's theorem by showing that the assumption that Δ_T is expressible entails a contradiction. Let Δ_{sub} be the set of triples of natural numbers such that a triple $\langle m,n,s \rangle \in \Delta_{\text{sub}}$ if and only if s is the Gödel number of a wff A_{x_1} and m is the Gödel number of the wff $A_{\bar{n}}$ that results from A_{x_1} by the substitution of the numeral $\bar{n}$ for free occurrences of 'x_1' in A_{x_1}. Now it can be shown, quite laboriously, however, that Δ_{sub} is expressible. Of course, if we assume Church's thesis, we have immediately that Δ_{sub} is expressible, because Δ_{sub} is clearly decidable. So, for the sake of brevity and directness let us assume Church's thesis at this juncture to get the expressibility of Δ_{sub}. Let $S_{x_1 x_2 x_3}$ be a wff of RA that expresses Δ_{sub} and has bound occurrences of no variables other than 'y', 'y_1', 'y_2', ... Then, where $\langle m,n,s \rangle$ is a triple of natural numbers, if $\langle m,n,s \rangle \in \Delta_{\text{sub}}$, then ⊢ $S_{\bar{m}\bar{n}\bar{s}}$ in RA, and if $\langle m,n,s \rangle \notin \Delta_{\text{sub}}$, then ⊢ ⌜$\sim S_{\bar{m}\bar{n}\bar{s}}$⌝ in RA. Hence, because the theorems of RA are all true under its intended interpretation, $S_{\bar{m}\bar{n}\bar{s}}$ is true (false) under the intended (ordinary mathematical) interpretation of RA if and only if s is the Gödel number of a wff A_{x_1} and m is the Gödel number of $A_{\bar{n}}$.

For the sake of indirect proof let us assume that Δ_T is expressible, and let Δ_I be the set of pairs $\langle m,n \rangle$ of natural numbers such that m and n are the respective Gödel numbers of wffs A and B of system QIF such that A implies B. Now it can be shown, somewhat tediously if no appeal is made to Church's thesis, that Δ_I is expressible if Δ_T is expressible. Again, for the sake of brevity and directness we shall derive the desired result from Church's thesis as follows. Δ_T is expressible, so Δ_T is decidable. Let $\langle m,n \rangle$ be any pair of natural numbers and consider whether $\langle m,n \rangle \in \Delta_I$. If either m or n is not a Gödel number of a wff of system QIF, then $\langle m,n \rangle \notin \Delta_I$. So let m and n be Gödel numbers of wffs A and B of system QIF, and let s be the Gödel number of ⌜$A \supset B$⌝. Clearly A implies B (that is, $\langle m,n \rangle \in \Delta_I$) if and only if ⌜$A \supset B$⌝ is a theorem of system QIF, that is, if and only if $s \in \Delta_T$. As Δ_T is decidable, so is Δ_I. And decidable sets are all expressible (Church's thesis), so it follows that there is some wff $I_{x_1x_2}$ of RA which represents Δ_I and which has bound occurrences of no variables except 'y', 'y_1', 'y_2', ... That is, $\vdash I_{\bar{m}\bar{n}}$ if $\langle m,n \rangle \in \Delta_I$, and $\vdash \ulcorner \sim I_{\bar{m}\bar{n}} \urcorner$ if $\langle m,n \rangle \notin \Delta_I$. Hence $I_{\bar{m}\bar{n}}$ is true under the intended (ordinary mathematical interpretation of RA if and only if m and n are Gödel numbers of wffs A and B, respectively, and A implies B. Now let u be the Gödel number of some conjunction of the seven axioms of RA. Then $I_{\bar{u}x_1}$ expresses Δ_R, where Δ_R is the set of theorems of RA, because it follows from the strong completeness theorem for system QIF that a wff is a theorem of RA if and only if it is implied by a conjunction of the axioms of RA. Hence, $\vdash I_{\bar{u}\bar{n}}$ if $n \in \Delta_R$, and $\vdash \ulcorner \sim I_{\bar{u}\bar{n}} \urcorner$ if $n \notin \Delta_R$. And $I_{\bar{u}\bar{n}}$ is true under the intended interpretation of RA if and only if n is the Gödel number of a theorem of RA.

Let $S_{x_2x_1x_1}$ result from $S_{x_1x_2x_3}$ by the simultaneous substitution of 'x_2' for 'x_1', and of 'x_1' for both 'x_2' and 'x_3'. Consider the following wff whose Gödel number is, say, s:

(1) $(\exists x_2)[S_{x_2x_1x_1} \cdot \sim I_{\bar{u}\bar{x}_2}]$ ⠀⠀⠀⠀⠀⠀⠀⠀⠀ Gödel number s

For a number n as value of 'x_1', wff (1) is true under the intended interpretation of RA if and only if n is the Gödel number of a wff A_{x_1} and the wff $A_{\bar{n}}$ is not a theorem of RA. Now consider the following wff:

(2) $(\exists x_2)[S_{x_2\bar{s}\bar{s}} \cdot \sim I_{\bar{u}x_2}]$ ⠀⠀⠀⠀⠀⠀⠀⠀⠀ Gödel number r

Clearly wff (2) is true under the intended (ordinary mathematical) interpretation of RA if and only if the wff that results on substituting the numeral $\bar{s}$ for free occurrences of 'x_1' in wff (1) is not a theorem of RA. But wff (2) is the result of substituting $\bar{s}$ for free 'x_1' in wff (1). Hence (2) is true under the intended interpretation of RA if and only if (2) is not a theorem of RA. So if (2) is true under the intended interpretation of RA, then (2) is not a theorem of RA. But if (2) is false under the intended interpretation of RA, then (2) is also not a theorem of RA, because all the theorems of RA are true under its intended interpretation. But (2) is either true or false under the intended interpretation of RA. Hence (2) is not a theorem of RA. Let r be the Gödel number of (2). As (2) is not a theorem of RA, we have $\vdash \ulcorner \sim I_{\bar{u}\bar{r}} \urcorner$ in RA. And we also have $\vdash S_{\bar{r}\bar{s}\bar{s}}$ in RA. Hence $\vdash \ulcorner S_{\bar{r}\bar{s}\bar{s}} \cdot \sim I_{\bar{u}\bar{r}} \urcorner$ in RA. Whence $\vdash \ulcorner (\exists x_2)[S_{x_2\bar{s}\bar{s}} \cdot \sim I_{\bar{u}x_2}] \urcorner$ in RA by EG. So (2) is a theorem of RA, although we have already shown that (2) is not a theorem of RA. From this contradiction we conclude by indirect proof that our initial assumption was false; that is, we conclude that Δ_T is not expressible (Church's theorem). Rather that would have been our conclusion if we had not assumed Church's thesis several times to establish directly and easily what could have been established only laboriously without it. Strictly speaking, we have proved only that Δ_T is not expressible if Church's thesis is true. But it must be emphasized that *dependence on Church's thesis is unnecessary in the case of Church's theorem but unavoidable in the case of Church's thesis theorem.*

61.2. Gödel Incompleteness Theorem

Are Peano's postulates both consistent and complete with respect to arithmetic truth? That is, under the intended interpretation of PA, is every wff that comes out true a theorem of PA, and is every wff that comes out false a nontheorem of PA? If not, are there other postulate sets that yield a consistent and complete systematization of arithmetical truth? In 1931 Kurt Gödel shocked the mathematical world by proving not only that Peano's postulates fall short of the foregoing ideal but also that, if Church's thesis is true, the ideal is unattainable—*no decidable set of postulates possesses the consistency and completeness described above.* This result is known as the (first) *Gödel incompleteness theorem*, though it would perhaps be better styled the *Gödel incompletability theorem.* (Gödel's second incompleteness theorem has to do with the kinds of procedures needed to prove that a set of postulates such as Peano's postulates is consistent. Compared to the first incompleteness theorem, the import of the second is considerably more obscure.)

To prove the Gödel incompleteness theorem, let us suppose for the sake of indirect proof that Δ is a decidable set of postulates of system QIF which, under the interpretation we gave of PA, is such that if a wff A comes out true, then A is a Δ-theorem, and if A comes out false, A is not a Δ-theorem. Clearly all the truths of RA, but none of the falsehoods of RA, are Δ-theorems. Hence our wff $S_{x_1x_2x_3}$ will have the property that $S_{\bar{m}\bar{n}\bar{s}}$ is a Δ-theorem and is true under the intended interpretation if $\langle m,n,s \rangle \in \Delta_{\text{sub}}$, and $S_{\bar{m}\bar{n}\bar{s}}$ is not a Δ-theorem and is false under the intended interpretation if $\langle m,n,s \rangle \notin \Delta_{\text{sub}}$. Let Δ_P be the set of pairs $\langle m,n \rangle$ of natural numbers such that n is the Gödel number of a wff A and m is the Gödel number of a proof of A from members of Δ as premises. Δ is decidable by assumption, so Δ_P is clearly decidable. Therefore, by Church's thesis, there is a wff $P_{x_1x_2}$ of RA which expresses Δ_P. Thus, in view of the nature of the Δ-system, $P_{\bar{m}\bar{n}}$ is true under the intended (ordinary mathematical) interpretation and is a Δ-theorem if $\langle m,n \rangle \in \Delta_P$, and $P_{\bar{m}\bar{n}}$ is false under the intended interpretation and is not a Δ-theorem if $\langle m,n \rangle \notin \Delta_P$. Consider the following wff:

(1) $(\exists x_2)[S_{x_2x_1x_1} \cdot \sim(\exists x_1)P_{x_1x_2}]$ Gödel number m

Note that for a number n as value of 'x_1', wff (1) comes out true under the intended interpretation and is thus a Δ-theorem if and only if n is the Gödel number of a wff A_{x_1} of system QIF and $A_{\bar{n}}$ is not a Δ-theorem. Let m be the Gödel number of (1) and consider the following wff:

(2) $(\exists x_2)[S_{x_2\bar{m}\bar{m}} \cdot \sim(\exists x_1)P_{x_1x_2}]$

Clearly the value of wff (2) is the same as the value which wff (1) has when m is assigned to 'x_1' as its value. Hence (2) is true under the intended interpretation and is a Δ-theorem if and only if the wff that results on substitution of $\bar{m}$ for 'x_1' in wff (1) is not a Δ-theorem. That is, wff (2) itself is a Δ-theorem if and only if (2) is not a Δ-theorem. But we derived this contradiction from just two assumptions: Church's thesis, and the assumption that Δ was a decidable set of postulates such that all the truths of arithmetic (that is, the wffs of system QIF that come out true under the interpretation associated with PA) and none of the falsehoods of arithmetic are Δ-theorems. Therefore, if Church's thesis is true, so is the Gödel incompleteness theorem.

62. SPECIAL CASES OF THE DECISION PROBLEM

62.0. Special Cases

We have just seen that the decision problem for theoremhood (or validity) in system QIF is unsolvable (Church's thesis theorem) in the sense that there is no decision procedure or algorithm for determining about an arbitrary wff of system QIF whether it is a theorem of system QIF, that is, unsolvable in the sense that the set of valid wffs of system QIF is undecidable. And we remarked that the unsolvability of the decision problems for systems Q and QI follows as a corollary. We will now treat certain special cases of the decision problem for validity. Or, to put the matter differently, we will now investigate the decidability of special classes of valid wffs.

First we will solve the decision problem for validity in the special case of the class Θ of wffs of system Q, where a wff A of system Q belongs to Θ if and only if every quantifier in A is universal and prenex. In other words, we will show that the class Θ is decidable. Now an arbitrary member A of Θ will have the form $\ulcorner(a_1)\ldots(a_n)B\urcorner$, where B is quantifier free, that is, where B contains no quantifiers. We first show that A is valid if and only if B is tautologous. From the semantics of universal quantifiers, it is evident that A is valid if and only if B is valid. Thus if B is tautologous, A is clearly valid. But suppose B is not tautologous. Let $B_1, \ldots, B_k$ be a complete list of the distinct atomic components of B, and let $b_1, \ldots, b_m$ be a complete list of the individual variables that occur in B. B is not tautologous by assumption, so there is an assignment Σ of truth values to $B_1, \ldots, B_k$ such that B would have the value falsehood if each B_i had the truth value assigned it by Σ. Let Σ^* be the following interpretation of B (and hence also of A) whose domain is the set of the variables $b_1, \ldots, b_m$. To each individual variable b_i of B, Σ^* assigns b_i as value. That is, Σ^* assigns an individual variable to itself as its value. If d is a sentential variable, Σ^* assigns to d whatever value Σ assigned to d. And if ϕ is an n-ary predicate variable, an n-tuple $\langle c_1, \ldots, c_n \rangle$ of individuals belongs to the extension assigned to ϕ by Σ^* if and only if $\ulcorner \phi c_1 \ldots c_n \urcorner$ is one of the atomic components of B to which Σ assigns the value truth. From the way Σ^* is constructed, it is evident that B comes out false under Σ^*. Hence A, which is $\ulcorner (a_1) \ldots (a_n) B \urcorner$, also comes out false under Σ^*. Thus A is not valid if B is not tautologous. Therefore, A is valid if and only if B is tautologous. Hence to determine whether an arbitrary member $\ulcorner (a_1) \ldots (a_n) B \urcorner$ of Θ is valid, it suffices to test B for tautologousness by means of truth tables. There is an algorithm for determining the validity of an arbitrary member of Θ, so the decision problem for validity in the special case of Θ is solvable.

A more interesting special case is the class Δ_M of *monadic wffs* of system Q, that is, wffs that contain no occurrences of predicate variables of degree greater than one. That is, the only predicate variables that occur in members of Δ_M are singulary predicate variables. Let A be an arbitrary monadic wff, and let $\phi_1, \ldots, \phi_n$ be a complete list of the distinct predicate variables that occur in A. It can be shown that A is valid if and only if it is valid in the domain $\mathfrak{D}$ of the first 2^n positive integers. (See Exercise [8] of Chapter 63.) As there are only a finite number of ways to assign individuals, truth values, and extensions in the domain $\mathfrak{D}$ to the individual, sentential, and predicate variables of A, one can run through all such interpretations and ascertain the value of A under each. A is valid if and only if it comes out true under every one of them. So in the special case of monadic wffs, there is also a solution to the decision problem for validity (and for theoremhood).

62.1. Syllogisms

Because of their historical interest we shall treat briefly of syllogisms, presenting the familiar Venn-diagrammatic decision procedure for recognizing the correctness of syllogistic arguments. By a *categorical* wff we shall understand a wff that has any of the following four forms, where ϕ and ψ are singulary predicate variables:

$\sim(\exists x)[\phi x \cdot \sim\psi x]$ Universal affirmative (all ϕ are ψ)
$\sim(\exists x)[\phi x \cdot \psi x]$ Universal negative (no ϕ are ψ)

$(\exists x)[\phi x \cdot \psi x]$ Particular affirmative (some ϕ are ψ)

$(\exists x)[\phi x \cdot \sim\psi x]$ Particular negative (some ϕ are not ψ)

In each case, the predicate variables ϕ and ψ are, respectively, called the *grammatical subject* and the *grammatical predicate of* the categorical wff. For example, 'F' is the grammatical subject and 'G' is the grammatical predicate of the universal negative wff '$\sim(\exists x)[Fx \cdot Gx]$'. An argument from two categorical wffs as premises to another categorical wff as conclusion is said to be a *syllogism* if exactly three predicate variables appear in the argument and each of them appears in exactly two of the wffs that form the argument. For example, only the two leftmost arguments below are syllogisms:

$\sim(\exists x)[Fx \cdot \sim Gx]$	$(\exists x)[Gx \cdot Fx]$	$(\exists x)[Gx \cdot Fx]$
$\sim(\exists x)[Gx \cdot \sim Hx]$	$(\exists x)[Hx \cdot Fx]$	$(\exists x)[Hx \cdot Fx]$
$\sim(\exists x)[Fx \cdot \sim Hx]$	$\sim(\exists x)[Gx \cdot Hx]$	$\sim(\exists x)[Fx \cdot Hx]$

The predicate variables of a syllogism are called its *syllogistic terms*. The grammatical subject of the conclusion is called the *minor* syllogistic term, the grammatical predicate of the conclusion is called the *major* syllogistic term, and the remaining predicate variable (which perforce appears in both premises) is called the *middle* syllogistic term *of* the syllogism. The predicate variables in a categorical wff are said to be *distributed* or *undistributed* in accordance with the following table:

	Grammatical subject	Grammatical predicate
Universal affirmative wff	Distributed	Undistributed
Universal negative wff	Distributed	Distributed
Particular affirmative wff	Undistributed	Undistributed
Particular negative wff	Undistributed	Distributed

For example, 'G' is distributed but 'F' is undistributed in the universal affirmative wff '$\sim(\exists x)[Gx \cdot \sim Fx]$'.

This plethora of terminology is quite unnecessary to the presentation of the Venn-diagrammatic decision procedure for determining correctness of syllogisms, but it is needed to state the following set of rules, which also constitute a decision procedure for correctness of syllogisms. We present these rules because, traditionally, syllogistic decision procedures have often been couched as sets of rules similar to those given here. The correct syllogisms are precisely those which violate none of these five rules:

(i)   The middle syllogistic term must be distributed once and only once.

(ii) The major syllogistic term must be distributed twice or not at all.

(iii) The minor syllogistic term must be distributed twice or not at all.

(iv) If the conclusion is negative, then one and only one premiss must be negative.

(v)   If any premiss is negative, the conclusion must be negative.

For example, of the two syllogisms exhibited above (the third argument is not a syllogism) the first is correct because it violates none of the five rules; the second is not correct because it violates at least one rule: rules (i), (ii), (iii), and (iv). That these rules constitute a decision procedure or algorithm for correctness of syllogisms is of course hardly evident, but they may be shown to do so by means of Venn diagrams.

A Venn diagram is nothing but a duly marked and labeled diagram consisting of three circles that overlap like these:

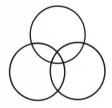

We pictorially represent the content of a categorical wff as follows. Each circle represents the extension of the predicate variable associated with it. *Shading* indicates *emptiness* of the set corresponding to the shaded region. A bar indicates the nonemptiness of at least one of the regions in which the bar lies. For example, the content of the universal affirmative wff '$\sim(\exists x)[Gx \cdot \sim Hx]$', which means 'All G are H', is represented in the Venn diagram

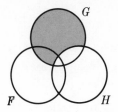

And the content of the particular negative wff '$(\exists x)[Fx \cdot \sim Gx]$' is represented in the Venn diagram

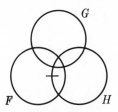

To test a syllogism for correctness, one need merely represent in a single Venn diagram the content of each premiss and then inspect to see whether the truth of the conclusion is vouchsafed by the diagram. [See Exercise (9) of Chapter 63.] If it is, then the syllogism is correct; if not, not. For example:

$\sim(\exists x)[Gx \cdot \sim Fx]$	All G are F
$(\exists x)[Gx \cdot Hx]$	Some G are H
$(\exists x)[Fx \cdot Hx]$	Some F are H

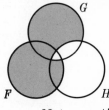

Correct!

$\sim(\exists x)[Fx \cdot \sim Gx]$	All F are G
$\sim(\exists x)[Gx \cdot \sim Hx]$	All G are H
$(\exists x)[Fx \cdot Hx]$	Some F are H

Not correct!

A syllogism is correct if and only if its associated conditional is valid and that conditional is a monadic wff, so the decision procedure for validity of monadic wffs mentioned in Section 62.0 could itself be adapted as a decision procedure for correctness of syllogisms.

62.2.   Reduction of Decision Problems;
Prenex Normal Forms

The decision problem for validity in the case of a class Γ of wffs is said to be *reducible to* the decision problem for validity in the case of a class Δ of wffs if there is an algorithm which, when applied to any member A of Γ, yields a member B of Δ such that A is valid if and only if B is valid. The algorithm is said to be a *reduction of* the decision problem for validity for Γ *to* that for Δ. Some reductions of decision problems are quite trivial and uninteresting. For example, mapping every wff onto '$p \vee \sim p$' is a reduction of the decision problem for validity in the case of the class of valid wffs of system Q to the decision problem for validity in the case of the class $\{'p \vee \sim p'\}$, and mapping a wff A onto $\ulcorner \sim \sim A \urcorner$ reduces the decision problem for validity for wffs of system Q to that for the class of wffs that begin with at least two tildes. In this section we present an important reduction of the decision problem which reduces the decision problem for validity for wffs of system Q to that for wffs in prenex normal form.

A wff is said to be *in prenex normal form* if all occurrences of quantifiers in it are prenex and nonvacuous. And A is a *prenex normal form of* a wff B if A is in prenex normal form and A is equivalent to B. We now describe an algorithm which, when applied to any wff of system Q, yields a prenex normal form of it. This algorithm, therefore, is clearly a reduction of the decision problem for validity for wffs of system Q to that for wffs in prenex normal form. It consists in successively transforming a given wff into a series of wffs each of which is equivalent to its predecessor until a wff in prenex normal form is eventually reached. The algorithm consists of the following eight steps:

Step One.   Given a wff C, replace each well-formed part of the form $\ulcorner A \supset B \urcorner$ or $\ulcorner A \equiv B \urcorner$ by $\ulcorner \sim A \vee B \urcorner$ or $\ulcorner A \cdot B \vee \sim A \cdot \sim B \urcorner$, respectively. Delete all vacuous quantifiers.

Step Two. Given a wff C, let $\ulcorner(a)A\urcorner$ or $\ulcorner(\exists a)A\urcorner$ be the first occurrence of a quantified well-formed part of C such that there are occurrences of the variable a in C which do not lie within this occurrence of $\ulcorner(a)A\urcorner$ or $\ulcorner(\exists a)A\urcorner$. Then throughout this occurrence of $\ulcorner(a)A\urcorner$ or $(\exists a)A\urcorner$ substitute b for a, where b is the first individual variable in lexicographical order after all the individual variables of C. Repeat this step until no longer applicable.

Step Three. Given a wff C, replace the first well-formed part of the form $\ulcorner\sim(a)A\urcorner$ or $\ulcorner\sim(\exists a)A\urcorner$ by $\ulcorner(\exists a)\sim A\urcorner$ or $\ulcorner(a)\sim A\urcorner$, respectively. Repeat this step until no longer applicable.

Step Four. Given a wff C, replace the first well-formed part of the form $\ulcorner(a)A \vee B\urcorner$ or $\ulcorner(\exists a)A \vee B\urcorner$ by $\ulcorner(a)[A \vee B]\urcorner$ or $\ulcorner(\exists a)[A \vee B]\urcorner$, respectively. (Note that, as a result of step two, the variable a will not occur in B.) Repeat until no longer applicable.

Step Five. Given a wff C, replace the first well-formed part of the form $\ulcorner A \vee (b)B\urcorner$ or $\ulcorner A \vee (\exists b)B\urcorner$ by $\ulcorner(b)[A \vee B]\urcorner$ or $\ulcorner(\exists b)[A \vee B]\urcorner$, respectively. Repeat until no longer applicable.

Step Six. Given a wff C, replace the first well-formed part of the form $\ulcorner(a)A \cdot B\urcorner$ or $\ulcorner(\exists a)A \cdot B\urcorner$ by $\ulcorner(a)[A \cdot B]\urcorner$ or $\ulcorner(\exists a)[A \cdot B]\urcorner$, respectively. Repeat until no longer applicable.

Step Seven. Given a wff C, replace the first well-formed part of the form $\ulcorner A \cdot (b)B\urcorner$ or $\ulcorner A \cdot (\exists b)B\urcorner$ by $\ulcorner(b)[A \cdot B]\urcorner$ or $\ulcorner(\exists b)[A \cdot B]\urcorner$, respectively. Repeat until no longer applicable.

Step Eight. Stop if a wff in prenex normal form has been produced; otherwise start in again at step three.

The use of this algorithm to obtain a prenex normal form of a given wff is illustrated by the following sequence of wffs which are the successive transforms of the starting wff:

$(z)[(x)(Fx \supset (\exists y)Gyx) \cdot \sim(\exists x)(y)Gxy]$	Starting wff
$(x)(\sim Fx \vee (\exists y)Gyx) \cdot \sim(\exists x)(y)Gxy$	Step one
$(z)(\sim Fz \vee (\exists y)Gyz) \cdot \sim(\exists x)(y)Gxy$ $\left.\vphantom{\begin{matrix}a\\b\end{matrix}}\right\}$	Step two
$(z)(\sim Fz \vee (\exists w_1)Gw_1z) \cdot \sim(\exists x)(y)Gxy$	
$(z)(\sim Fz \vee (\exists w_1)Gw_1z) \cdot (x)\sim(y)Gxy$ $\left.\vphantom{\begin{matrix}a\\b\end{matrix}}\right\}$	Step three
$(z)(\sim Fz \vee (\exists w_1)Gw_1z) \cdot (x)(\exists y)\sim Gxy$	
$(z)(\exists w_1)(\sim Fz \vee Gw_1z) \cdot (x)(\exists y)\sim Gxy$	Step five
$(z)[(\exists w_1)(\sim Fz \vee Gw_1z) \cdot (x)(\exists y)\sim Gxy]$ $\left.\vphantom{\begin{matrix}a\\b\end{matrix}}\right\}$	Step six
$(z)(\exists w_1)[(\sim Fz \vee Gw_1z) \cdot (x)(\exists y)\sim Gxy]$	
$(z)(\exists w_1)(x)[(\sim Fz \vee Gw_1z) \cdot (\exists y)\sim Gxy]$ $\left.\vphantom{\begin{matrix}a\\b\end{matrix}}\right\}$	Step seven
$(z)(\exists w_1)(x)(\exists y)[(\sim Fz \vee Gw_1z) \cdot \sim Gxy]$	

The last wff in the sequence above is a prenex normal form of the starting wff. It is left to the reader to show that the algorithm just presented does what we claimed—generate a prenex normal form of any starting wff. [See Exercise (12) of Chapter 63.]

63.   EXERCISES

(1)   Supply an effective enumeration, without repetition, of the symbols of system QIF. (*Hint*: Study the diagram below.)

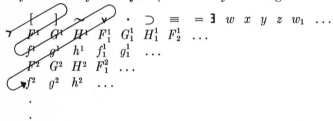

(2)   Let ε be an effective enumeration, without repetition, of the symbols of system QIF. Let 2^k be the Gödel number of the kth symbol of ε. If $\ulcorner b_1 b_2 \ldots b_n \urcorner$ is a formula (finite sequence of symbols) of system QIF and m_i is the Gödel number of b_i, let $r_1^{m_1} \times r_2^{m_2} \times \ldots \times r_n^{m_n}$ be the Gödel number of the sequence $\ulcorner b_1 b_2 \ldots b_n \urcorner$, where r_i is the ith prime after 2. (For example, r_3 is 7.) Similarly, if $A_1, A_2, \ldots, A_n$ is a finite sequence of formulas of system QIF and s_i is the Gödel number of A_i, let $r_1^{s_1} \times r_2^{s_2} \times \ldots \times r_n^{s_n}$ be the Gödel number of the sequence $A_1, A_2, \ldots, A_n$. Show that the above mapping is a Gödel numbering of system QIF. What is the Gödel number of '$[x = x]$'? Let $m = 3^2 \times 11^3 \times 7^1$. What is m the Gödel number of, if anything? Of what, if anything, is 16 the Gödel number? On what properties of prime factorization do these results depend?

(3)   Construct a Gödel numbering of system QIF that makes no especial use of prime factorization properties. Construct Gödel numberings of systems Q and QI.

(4) Does there exist a set Δ of wffs of system QIF, which may be either decidable or undecidable, such that all the truths of arithmetic but none of the falsehoods are Δ-theorems? (*Hint*: Consider the set of all the truths of arithmetic.)

(5) Let Δ be a finite set of wffs of system QIF. Show that the decision problem for validity is solvable in the special case of the class Δ. Is every finite set of wffs decidable?

(6) Why does it follow that, if Δ is expressible, then there is a wff A of RA which expresses Δ and which contains bound occurrences of no variables other than 'y', 'y_1', 'y_2', ...?. Where in the proof given of Church's theorem did we appeal to this fact? (*Hint*: Capitalize on the fact that wffs which differ only by alphabetic changes of bound variables are equivalent.)

[7] Let A be a closed monadic wff. Prove that there is a closed monadic wff B which is equivalent to A and which is devoid of nested quantifiers.

⟨8⟩ Let A be any monadic wff of system Q. Prove that A is valid if and only if A is valid in the domain of the first 2^n positive integers, where n is the number of distinct predicate variables that occur in A. (*Hint*: Make use of the result of Exercise [7].)

(9) The description of the Venn-diagrammatic decision procedure for correctness of syllogisms, as presented in Section 62.1, left much to the reader's intelligence. Formulate purely mechanical rules for diagramming categorical premisses and for verifying whether the content of a Venn diagram "vouchsafes the truth of the conclusion" of a syllogism.

(10) Verify that the five rules given in Section 62.1 constitute a decision procedure for correctness of syllogisms.

(11) The premiss in which the major (minor) syllogistic term appears is called the *major* (*minor*) *premiss* of the syllogism. Syllogisms are divided into so-called *figures* according to the grammatical position that the middle syllogistic term occupies in the major and minor premisses thus:

	1st Figure	*2nd Figure*	*3rd Figure*	*4th Figure*
Major premiss	Subject	Predicate	Subject	Predicate
Minor premiss	Predicate	Predicate	Subject	Subject

For example, the first figure is the set of all syllogisms in which the middle syllogistic term is the grammatical subject of the major premiss and the grammatical predicate of the minor premiss. Syllogisms are also divided into so-called *moods* according to the types of categorical wffs they contain. Letting A, E, I, and O stand for universal affirmative, universal negative, particular affirmative, and particular negative, respectively, we can represent the mood of a syllogism by an ordered triple of letters that signifies what type categorical wff is the major premiss, the minor premiss, and the conclusion, respectively. For example, the mood $\langle I,E,O \rangle$ is the set of all syllogisms whose major premiss is a particular affirmative wff, whose minor premiss is a universal negative wff, and whose conclusion is a particular negative wff. Identify the correct syllogisms by figure and mood.

(12)   Prove that the eight-step algorithm described in Section 62.2 will transform any starting wff into an equivalent wff in prenex normal form. (*Hint*: First show that the wffs successively generated by the algorithm are equivalent to one another. Then show that the algorithm always terminates by exploiting the fact that, after step two, the effect of each transformation is to replace a quantifier occurrence by one buried beneath one fewer occurrences of sentential connectives.)

(13)   Is the decision problem for validity (or provability in system Q) solvable in the special case of wffs of system Q in prenex normal form?

Appendixes

Appendix A.
SET THEORY

Introduction to Set Theory

The reader unfamiliar with set theory may find the following remarks helpful in his effort to understand the occasional set-theoretical remarks of this book. By a *set* or *class* is meant a collection of things, called the *members of* the class, which are said *to belong to* the set or class. (The expressions 'set' and 'class' are used herein as synonyms.) The symbol '$\in$' is used to designate membership. Thus the expression 'Socrates $\in$ the set of human beings' means that Socrates is a member of, that is, belongs to, the set of human beings. A set is often specified by indicating a property possessed exclusively by its members. For example, we could specify the set of even numbers as the set of numbers that possess the property of being divisible by two. If the indicated property is possessed by nothing whatsoever, for example, the property of being an orange crow, the corresponding set has no members and is said to be *null* or *empty*. Thus the set of orange crows is empty, as is also the set of centaurs.

Sets are considered *identical* if they have the same membership. For example, the set of orange crows is identical with the set of centaurs, and the set of Cadillac automobiles is identical with the set of cars of the most expensive line manufactured by General Motors, and presumably the set of creatures that have hearts is the same as the set of creatures that have kidneys.

Let Γ and Δ be sets. By the *union of Γ and Δ* is meant the set to which something belongs if and only if it is a member of Γ or of Δ or of both. For example, the set of positive integers is the union of the set of even numbers and the set of odd numbers. The symbol '$\cup$' is used to express the union of sets. Thus $\Gamma \cup \Delta$ is a set, the union of Γ and Δ. By the *intersection of Γ and Δ* is meant the set to which something belongs if and only if it is a member of both Γ and Δ. For example, the set of even primes (which has only one member, the number two) is the intersection of the set of prime numbers and the set of even numbers, and the set with no numbers (the *null set* or the *empty set*) is the intersection of the set of odd numbers and the set of even numbers. The symbol '∩' is used to express intersection. Thus Γ ∩ Δ is a set, the intersection of Γ and Δ.

Again let Γ and Δ be sets. Γ is said to be a *subset of* Δ if every member of Γ is also a member of Δ. For example, the set of primes is a subset of the set of integers, and the set of women is a subclass of the set of human beings. (The expressions 'subset' and 'subclass' are synonymous.) The symbol '⊆' is used to mean 'is a subset of.' Thus ⌜Γ ⊆ Δ⌝ means ⌜Γ is a subset of Δ⌝. Notice that every set is trivially a subset of itself. Γ is said to be a *proper subset* of Δ if Γ is a subset of Δ and, in addition, there is at least one thing which is a member of Δ but which is not a member of Γ. For example, the set of primes is a proper subset of the set of integers, but the set of creatures with hearts is apparently not a proper subset of the set of creatures with kidneys. The expressions 'is included in' and 'is a subset of' are synonymous. Thus ⌜Γ ⊆ Δ⌝ also means ⌜Γ is included in Δ⌝; for this reason the symbol '⊆' is often called the sign for *class inclusion*. Care must be taken not to confuse the class-inclusion sign '⊆' with the set-membership sign '∈'. Let '𝒫' and '𝓔' denote, respectively, the set of positive integers and the set of even positive integers. Then '5 ∈ 𝒫' is true, but '5 ⊆ 𝒫' is false. On the other hand, '𝓔 ⊆ 𝒫' is true, whereas '𝓔 ∈ 𝒫' is false.

One way (already mentioned) to specify a class is to indicate a property possessed exclusively by all its members. Another way is simply to list its membership. (Obviously this can be done only for finite classes.) The customary way to list membership is to put the names of the members between braces. For example, '{Socrates,Plato,Aristotle}' denotes the set whose members are Socrates, Plato, and Aristotle, and '{1,3,5,7,9}' denotes the set of the first five odd integers. The order in which its members happen to be listed is irrelevant to the composition of a set. Thus {Socrates,Plato,Aristotle} and {Aristotle,Socrates,Plato} are the same set. A set of objects must be sharply distinguished from an *ordered set* of those objects. For example, the set {Socrates,Plato, Aristotle} is something quite different from the ordered set ⟨Socrates,Plato,Aristotle⟩, which in turn is not identical with the ordered set ⟨Plato,Socrates,Aristotle⟩. Like sets, an ordered set has members, namely the things ordered; unlike sets, an ordered set also involves a particular ordering of its members, any of which may even occupy more than one place in the ordering. Ordered sets are *identical* if they have not only the same membership but, in addition, the members are arranged in exactly the same order. All these ordered sets, for example, are distinct from one another ⟨Socrates,Plato,Socrates⟩, ⟨Socrates,Plato,Aristotle⟩, and ⟨Aristotle,Plato,Socrates⟩. An ordered set with n order places or positions is called an *ordered n-tuple*. For example, ⟨Socrates,Plato, Socrates⟩ and ⟨Socrates,Plato,Aristotle⟩ are ordered 3-tuples or, more idiomatically, ordered triples. (Clearly an ordered n-tuple will have at least one and at most n members.) Ordered 2-tuples are also called *ordered pairs*. It proves very convenient to identify ordered 1-tuples with the corresponding sets of one member, called *singletons* or *unit sets*. Thus we shall regard the ordered 1-tuple ⟨Socrates⟩ to be the same thing as the unit set {Socrates}.

Exercises

(1) Explain how the *angle brackets* '⟨' and '⟩' are used to form a name of an ordered set.

(2) Prove that Γ is a proper subset of Δ if and only if it is true that $\Gamma \subseteq \Delta$ and it is false that $\Delta \subseteq \Gamma$.

(3) Prove that if $\Gamma \subseteq \Delta$ and $\Delta \subseteq \Gamma$, then $\Gamma = \Delta$.

(4) Prove that every class includes (that is, has as a subset) at least one class. Prove that the null set is the only set that does not include a proper subset of itself.

(5) Which of the following are true?

(a) $\{5,7\} \subseteq \mathcal{P}$ (g) $\mathcal{P} \subseteq \mathcal{E}$

(b) $(\mathcal{E} \cup \mathcal{P}) \subseteq \mathcal{P}$ (h) $\{\ \} \subseteq \{3,10\}$

(c) $(\mathcal{E} \cap \mathcal{P}) \subseteq \mathcal{P}$ (i) $\mathcal{P} \subseteq (\mathcal{E} \cup \mathcal{P})$

(d) $(\mathcal{E} \cup \mathcal{P}) = \mathcal{P}$ (j) $3 \in (\mathcal{E} \cap \mathcal{P})$

(e) $\langle 3,2,1 \rangle = \langle 1,2,3 \rangle$ (k) $\{3,3,3\} = \{3\}$

(f) $\langle 3,2,1 \rangle = \langle 3,2,1,1 \rangle$ (l) $\langle 5 \rangle = \{5\}$

(6) Sometimes the two ways of specifying a class are run together, as when the expression '$\{1,2,3,\ldots\}$' is used to designate the set of positive integers. Discuss.

(7) Prove that an ordered n-tuple has at least one and at most n members.

Appendix B.
SEMANTIC TABLEAUX

Semantic Tableaux for Truth-Functional Logic

In Section 14.3 we sketched a short-cut method for establishing the validity of wffs of LSP. The essence of the method consists in reasoning from the structure of a wff to a value assignment that falsifies it. (Hereafter we shall refer to a falsifying value assignment of a wff as a *countermodel* of it.) If the method leads to a countermodel, the wff is not valid; if the method *cannot* lead to a countermodel, the wff is valid. In this appendix we present the method of semantic tableaux, usually credited to E. W. Beth, which is a more rigorous and systematic version of the short-cut method of Section 14.3. The tableau method (hereafter TM) provides a simple, highly economical algorithm for deciding validity in LSP. Moreover, as we will soon see, the applicability of TM is by no means limited to the logic of truth functions.

A (semantic) tableau is simply a two-columned configuration of occurrences of wffs. (The *left-hand column* of a tableau represents *truth*, and the *right-hand column* of a tableau represents *falsehood*.) A tableau is said to be *closed* if the same wff occurs in both of its columns. A tableau that is not closed is said to be *open*. For example, tableau (1) is closed but tableau (2) is open.

(1)

	$\sim(p \cdot q) \vee (p \vee q)$ ✓
	$\sim(p \cdot q)$ ✓
	$p \vee q$ ✓
$p \cdot q$	✓
	p ✓
	q ✓
p	✓
q	✓

(2)

	$\sim q \vee (p \vee \sim q)$ ✓
	$\sim q$ ✓
	$p \vee \sim q$ ✓
q	✓
	p ✓

(The significance of the check marks will be explained presently.) Let Δ be the set of sentential variables that occur in any wff appearing anywhere in a tableau. Then the tableau is said *to determine the following value assignment* Σ to members of Δ. Let $b \in \Delta$: If b

occurs standing alone, that is, not as a part of a larger wff, in the left-hand column of the tableau, then Σ assigns truth to b; otherwise, Σ assigns falsehood to b. For example, tableau (1) determines the assignment of truth to both 'p' and 'q', and tableau (2) determines the assignment of falsehood to 'p' and truth to 'q'. Notice that the value assignment determined by the closed tableau (1) is a model of the initial wff ' $\sim(p \cdot q) \vee (p \vee q)$ ' of tableau (1), whereas the value assignment determined by the open tableau (2) is a countermodel of the initial wff of tableau (2).

A set of tableaux is said to be *closed* if every member of the set is closed. A set of tableaux is said to be *open* if it is not closed. For example, the set $\{(1),(2)\}$ is open, but the set $\{(1)\}$ is closed. We will see that TM usually leads to a set of several tableaux rather than to (a set of) just one tableau.

To decide by TM whether a wff B of LSP is valid, one enters an occurrence of B as the initial wff in the right-hand column of an empty tableau. Then one applies the tableau-construction rules (given below) to see whether or not a closed set of tableaux results. The basic idea behind the construction process is to determine whether the supposition of falsehood (entering B in the right-hand column) leads to a contradiction (closed set of tableaux), the rules of tableau construction being rules that trace out the consequences of the initial supposition. If the supposition of falsehood eventuates in a contradiction, B is valid; if it does not lead to a contradiction (that is, if the construction process never eventuates in a closed set of tableaux), B is not valid.

TM boasts seven rules of tableau construction, two for each kind of molecular wffs of LSP (negations, alternations, conjunctions) and one for atomic wffs. The first rule is called *negation right* (hereafter NR) and applies to an occurrence of a negation $\ulcorner \sim A \urcorner$ in the right-hand column of a tableau. NR prescribes that an occurrence of A be entered in the left-hand column of the tableau. For example, when applied to the second formula in tableau (3), NR yields tableau (4).

(3)

$\sim(p \cdot q) \vee r$	$\checkmark$
$\sim(p \cdot q)$	
r	

(4)

$\sim(p \cdot q) \vee r$	$\checkmark$
$\sim(p \cdot q)$	$\checkmark$
r	
$p \cdot q$	

(When occurrences of formulas are introduced into a tableau, they

are entered on successively lower lines to facilitate determination
of the order of their introduction into the tableau. Also, whenever
a tableau-construction rule has been applied to an occurrence of a
wff in a tableau, a check mark, '$\checkmark$', is entered at its right to indicate
that the given formula occurrence has been *dispatched*. When TM
calls for a tableau-construction rule to be applied within a given
tableau, the rule relevant to the earliest undispatched occurrence
of a wff in the tableau is applied to that occurrence.) The idea
behind NR is quite simple: If $\ulcorner \sim A \urcorner$ is false, then A is true.

For the sake of economy, if NR or any other tableau-construction
rule prescribes that an occurrence of a wff A be entered in a certain
column of a tableau, we shall not make the entry if there already is
an occurrence of A in that column. For example, application of
NR to the third wff in tableau (5) yields tableau (6).

(5)

$$p \ \left| \begin{array}{ll} & \checkmark \\ \sim p \vee q & \checkmark \\ \sim p & \\ q & \end{array} \right.$$

(6)

$$p \ \left| \begin{array}{ll} & \checkmark \\ \sim p \vee q & \checkmark \\ \sim p & \checkmark \\ q & \end{array} \right.$$

That is, the sole effect of the application of NR to the aforementioned occurrence of '$\sim p$' is to place a "dispatched" check mark
alongside that occurrence of '$\sim p$', because the left-hand column
already contains an occurrence of 'p'.

The other negation rule is called *negation left* (hereafter NL) and
applies to an occurrence of a negation $\ulcorner \sim A \urcorner$ in the left-hand column of a tableau. NL prescribes that an occurrence of A be entered
in the right-hand column of the tableau. For example, applied to
the second wff in tableau (7), NL yields tableau (8).

(7)

$$\sim (p \vee \sim p) \ \left| \begin{array}{ll} \sim\sim(p \vee \sim p) & \checkmark \\ & \end{array} \right.$$

(8)

$$\sim (p \vee \sim p) \ \left| \begin{array}{ll} \sim\sim(p \vee \sim p) & \checkmark \\ & \checkmark \\ p \vee \sim p & \end{array} \right.$$

The idea behind NL is that if $\ulcorner \sim A \urcorner$ is true, then A is false.

The first alternation rule is called *alternation right* (hereafter AR)
and applies to an occurrence of an alternation $\ulcorner A \vee B \urcorner$ in the
right-hand column of a tableau. AR prescribes that an occurrence
of A and an occurrence of B be entered on distinct lines in the

right-hand column of the tableau. For example, when applied to the third wff of tableau (8), AR yields the following:

$$\sim(p \lor \sim p) \quad \left|
\begin{array}{ll}
\sim\sim(p \lor \sim p) & \checkmark \\
 & \checkmark \\
p \lor \sim p & \checkmark \\
p & \\
\sim p &
\end{array}
\right.$$

And when applied to the third wff of tableau (9), AR yields tableau (10).

(9)

$$\left|
\begin{array}{ll}
p \lor (q \lor p) & \checkmark \\
p & \checkmark \\
q \lor p &
\end{array}
\right.$$

(10)

$$\left|
\begin{array}{ll}
p \lor (q \lor p) & \checkmark \\
p & \checkmark \\
q \lor p & \checkmark \\
q &
\end{array}
\right.$$

The idea behind AR is also very simple: If $\ulcorner A \lor B \urcorner$ is false, then both A and B are false.

The second alternation rule is called *alternation left* (hereafter AL) and applies to an occurrence of an alternation $\ulcorner A \lor B \urcorner$ in the left-hand column of a tableau. The idea behind AL is that if $\ulcorner A \lor B \urcorner$ is true, then *either* A is true *or* B is true. Unlike the three rules already formulated, AL calls for "splitting" a tableau into two tableaux. When applied to an occurrence of $\ulcorner A \lor B \urcorner$ in the left-hand column of a tableau, AL prescribes that the tableau be split into two tableaux, one having an occurrence of A in the left-hand column and the other having an occurrence of B in the left-hand column. For example, when applied to the second wff in the tableau

$$\sim p \lor (p \lor r) \quad \left|
\begin{array}{ll}
\sim[\sim p \lor (p \lor r)] & \checkmark
\end{array}
\right.$$

AL yields tableaux (11) and (12).

(11)

$$\sim p \lor (p \lor r) \left|
\begin{array}{ll}
\sim[\sim p \lor (p \lor r)] & \checkmark \\
 & \checkmark \\
\sim p &
\end{array}
\right.$$

(12)

$$\sim p \lor (p \lor r) \left|
\begin{array}{ll}
\sim[\sim p \lor (p \lor r)] & \checkmark \\
 & \checkmark \\
p \lor r &
\end{array}
\right.$$

Both to save time and space and to simplify proofs of metatheorems about TM, we shall split a tableau in the following treelike manner, rather than replicate it as was done above:

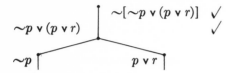

Each complete path running downward from the topmost node constitutes a tableau. The left-hand and right-hand paths of the above tree diagram, for example, correspond to tableaux (11) and (12), respectively. For ordering purposes (see below), we shall think of the left-hand path (tableau) as introduced earlier than the right-hand path (tableau).

We leave it to the reader to state the pair of tableau-construction rules for conjunction: *conjunction right* (KR) and *conjunction left* (KL). We caution the reader that KR will prescribe splitting the given tableau in much the same manner that AL prescribes splitting.

The seventh tableau-construction rule applies to occurrences of atomic wffs of LSP (sentential variables) standing alone in either column of a tableau. It prescribes only that a check mark be placed alongside the occurrence of the given atomic wff.

Let us call each application of a rule in a tableau-construction process a *stage* of the construction process. The seven tableau-construction rules are to be applied in the following order. If a rule is to be applied within a given tableau at a given stage of a construction process, one picks out the earliest undispatched formula occurrence in the tableau and applies to it the relevant tableau-construction rule. (For example, if the earliest undispatched formula occurrence is an alternation in the left-hand column, one applies AL to it.) If the given tableau contains no undispatched formula occurrences, one moves on to the next later tableau, if any. If the construction process has produced several tableaux (through splitting), one makes only one application of a rule within a given tableau before moving on to the next later tableau. (By convention, we take the first tableau to be the next tableau "after" the last tableau.) The construction process continues until all occurrences of formulas in all tableaux have been dispatched.

To use TM to decide the validity of an arbitrary wff A of LSP, one merely enters an occurrence of A in the right-hand column of an empty tableau and then initiates the construction process of applying the seven tableau-construction rules. It can be shown that the construction process will terminate, that is, that one will eventually reach a stage when every formula occurrence in every tableau has been dispatched. Let us call the set of tableaux which have been produced at that stage the *terminal set of tableaux*. If the terminal set of tableaux is closed, A is valid; if the terminal set of tableaux is open, A is not valid. Moreover, if the terminal set Ω of tableaux is open, each open member of Ω determines a value assignment that is a countermodel of A. For example, because it is open, the terminal set (13) shows that '$\sim[\sim p \vee (p \vee r)]$' is not valid.

(13)

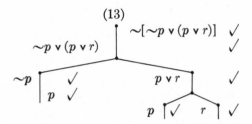

Furthermore, as each tableau of the set (13) is open, each determines a countermodel of the initial wff. For example, the second tableau determines the countermodel which assigns truth to 'p' and falsehood to 'r'. Since it is closed, the terminal set (14) of tableaux shows that the wff '$\sim(\sim p \vee q) \vee \sim(p \cdot \sim q)$' is valid.

(14)

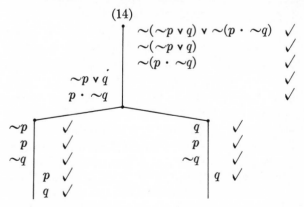

When distinct tableaux are run together as a tree, one must exercise some care in dispatching a wff that occurs above a branching. Our treelike way of combining distinct tableaux makes it imperative that any entry prescribed by a rule applied to a wff occurring *above a branching* be made *in every path below* the given formula occurrence. For example, when KL was applied to the fifth formula in the process of constructing (14), there was already a branching beneath that formula occurrence. Accordingly, an occurrence of 'p' and an occurrence of '$\sim q$' were put in the left-hand column of each path beneath the occurrence of '$p \cdot \sim q$' to which KL was applied. The making of such multiple entries is merely the tree counterpart of successively applying the same rule to occurrences of the same wff in the several distinct tableaux that are run together as a tree.

Exercises

(1)   Formulate carefully the tableau-construction rules KR and KL.

(2)   Prove that the tableau-construction process terminates when applied to an otherwise empty tableau that contains an occurrence of a wff of LSP in one of its columns.

(3)   Prove that the tableau-construction process terminates when applied to a tableau whose columns contain a finite number of occurrences of wffs of LSP.

[4]   Let Ω be the terminal set of tableaux that results when the tableau-construction process is applied to an otherwise empty tableau that has an occurrence of a wff A of LSP in the right-hand column. Prove that A is valid if Ω is closed. (*Hint*: show that, at each construction stage, the openness of the set of tableaux resulting at that stage is a necessary condition of the falsifiability of A.) Prove that A is not valid if Ω is open. (*Hint*: Let Ω' be the terminal set of tableaux that results when the tableau-construction process is applied to a tableau $\mathfrak{I}$ containing a finite number of occurrences of wffs of LSP. Prove, by mathematical induction on the maximum number of occurrences of connectives in any wff occurring in $\mathfrak{I}$, that each open member of Ω' determines a model of every wff that

occurs in its left-hand column and a countermodel of every wff that occurs in its right-hand column.)

(5) Formulate tableau-construction rules for conditionals (CR and CL) and biconditionals (BR and BL). (*Hint*: CL, BR, and BL will all prescribe splitting.)

(6) Let $A_1, \ldots, A_n, B$ be wffs of LSP. Put occurrences of $A_1, \ldots, A_n$ in the left-hand column, and an occurrence of B in the right-hand column, of an empty tableau and then apply the tableau-construction rules. In Exercise (3) you proved that the construction process terminates. Now prove that $A_1, \ldots, A_n$ jointly imply B if and only if the terminal set of tableaux is closed.

Semantic Tableaux for Quantificational Logic

One can obtain a tableau method for establishing the validity of the valid wffs of LSQ by adding to TM several tableau-construction rules for universally and existentially quantified wffs. For the sake of simplicity, however, we shall here develop a tableau method that is adequate only to closed wffs of LSQ that are devoid of vacuous quantifiers. That is, the method suffices to establish the validity of any closed wff of LSQ that happens to be valid and that does not contain vacuous quantifiers. [We shall assume that the reader has completed Exercise (5) above and has therefore formulated the truth-functional tableau-construction rules CR, CL, BR, and BL.]

Our first tableau-construction rule for quantified wffs is called *universal left* (UL) and applies to an occurrence of a universally quantified wff $\ulcorner(a)A_a\urcorner$ in the left-hand column of a tableau. If the tableau contains at least one open wff, that is, a wff with free individual variables, UL prescribes that, for every individual variable b that occurs free in any wff in the tableau, an occurrence of the instance A_b of $\ulcorner(a)A_a\urcorner$ be entered in the left-hand column of the tableau.[1] But if the tableau contains no open wffs, UL prescribes that an occurrence of the instance A_c of $\ulcorner(a)A_a\urcorner$ be entered in the left-hand column of the tableau, where c is the first individual variable in lexicographical order after all the individual

---

[1] In this extension of TM we continue the economical practice of not making an entry in a column, if the entry would merely be a duplication of a wff already appearing in the column.

variables that occur in wffs of the tableau. For example, repeated application of UL in tableau (15) yields tableau (16).

(15)	(16)	
$(w)(x)(y)Fwxy$	$(w)(x)(y)Fwxy$	✓
	$(x)(y)Fzxy$	✓
	$(y)Fzzy$	✓
	$Fzzz$	✓

Let Δ be the set of variables (individual, sentential, and predicate) that occur free in the wffs of a tableau $\mathfrak{I}$. The tableau $\mathfrak{I}$ shall be considered *to determine the following interpretation* Σ of the wffs it contains. The domain of Σ is the set Δ_v of all individual variables in Δ, unless Δ_v is empty; if Δ_v is empty, the domain of Σ is the unit set of the number zero. (If Δ_v is empty, any nonempty set could have been chosen as the domain of Σ.) To an individual variable b in Δ, Σ assigns b itself as its value. To an n-ary predicate variable ϕ in Δ, Σ assigns as the extension of ϕ the set of all n-tuples $\langle b_1, \ldots, b_n \rangle$ of individual variables such that $\ulcorner \phi b_1 \ldots b_n \urcorner$ occurs standing alone (that is, not as a proper part of a larger wff) in the left-hand column of $\mathfrak{I}$. And to a sentential variable c in Δ, Σ assigns truth to c if c occurs standing alone in the left-hand column of $\mathfrak{I}$; otherwise, Σ assigns falsehood to c. For example, tableau (16) determines the interpretation in the domain whose sole member is the variable 'z', which assigns 'z' as value of 'z', and which assigns $\{\langle 'z', 'z', 'z' \rangle\}$ as the extension or value of 'F'. Notice that each wff in the left-hand column of (16) comes out true under the foregoing interpretation. Reflecting on the interpretation determined by a tableau, we see that the idea behind UL is that what is true of everything is individually true of each member of the UD. [See Exercise (1)].

The next tableau-construction rule is called *universal right* (UR) and applies to an occurrence of a universally quantified wff $\ulcorner (a)A_a \urcorner$ in the right-hand column of a tableau. UR prescribes that an occurrence of the instance A_c of $\ulcorner (a)A_a \urcorner$ be entered in the right-hand column of the tableau, where c is the first individual variable in lexicographical order after all the individual variables that occur in wffs of the tableau. *In addition*, UR prescribes that one delete any check mark ("dispatched" mark) modifying a universally quantified wff in the left-hand column or an existentially quantified wff in the right-hand column of the tableau. For example, applied to the third wff in tableau (17), UR yields tableau (18).

$$(17)$$

$(x) \sim(y)Gxy$	$\checkmark$
$\sim(y)Gzy$	$\checkmark$
	$(y)Gzy$

$$(18)$$

$(x) \sim(y)Gxy$	
$\sim(y)Gzy$	$\checkmark$
	$(y)Gzy$ $\checkmark$
	Gzw_1

Notice that the tableau-construction process does not terminate when applied to tableau (17). For the sake of illustration, we exhibit the result of the first several stages of applying the tableau-construction process to (17).

$$(19)$$

$(x) \sim(y)Gxy$		$\checkmark$
$\sim(y)Gzy$		$\checkmark$
	$(y)Gzy$	$\checkmark$
	Gzw_1	$\checkmark$
$\sim(y)Gw_1y$		$\checkmark$
	$(y)Gw_1y$	$\checkmark$
	Gw_1x_1	$\checkmark$
$\sim(y)Gx_1y$		$\checkmark$
	$(y)Gx_1y$	

As with TM, we regard the construction process as *terminated* when every wff occurrence in every tableau of the set of tableaux has been dispatched. For the sake of simplicity, let us also regard the tableau-construction process as *terminated* at any stage that results in a closed set of tableaux. [Notice that the tableau-construction process will not terminate when applied to tableau (17), not even in this enlarged sense of "terminate".] The rationale behind UR is that what is not true of everything is false of at least one member of the UD.

As $\ulcorner(\exists a)A_a\urcorner$ is equivalent to $\ulcorner\sim(a)\sim A_a\urcorner$, we could handle existentially quantified wffs by means of a rule prescribing that an occurrence of $\ulcorner\sim(a)\sim A_a\urcorner$ be entered in a tableau column that contains an occurrence of $\ulcorner(\exists a)A_a\urcorner$. But instead, for the sake of symmetry, we shall adopt rules for existentially quantified wffs, rules that are analogous to UL and UR. The first rule is analogous to UL; it is called *existential right* (ER) and applies to an occurrence of an existentially quantified wff $\ulcorner(\exists a)A_a\urcorner$ in the right-hand column of a tableau. ER prescribes that, for every individual variable b that occurs free in any wff of the tableau, an occurrence of A_b be entered in the right-hand column of the tableau. If no individual variable occurs free in any wff in the tableau, ER prescribes that an occurrence of A_c be entered in the right-hand column of the tableau, where c is the first individual variable in lexicographical order after all the individual variables that occur in wffs of the tableau.

The second rule is analogous to UR; it is called *existential left* (EL) and applies to an occurrence of an existentially quantified wff $\ulcorner(\exists a)A_a\urcorner$ in the left-hand column of a tableau. EL prescribes that an occurrence of the instance A_c of $\ulcorner(\exists a)A_a\urcorner$ be entered in the left-hand column of the tableau, where c is the first individual variable in lexicographical order after all the individual variables that occur in wffs of the tableau. *In addition*, EL prescribes that one delete any check mark ("dispatched" sign) modifying a universally quantified wff in the left-hand column or an existentially quantified wff in the right-hand column of the tableau.

Our tableau method for establishing the validity of valid *closed* wffs of LSQ is now complete. To apply it to a closed wff C of LSQ, put an occurrence of C in the right-hand column of an empty tableau and then initiate the tableau-construction process. It can be proved that if the tableau-construction process *ever* terminates in a closed set of tableaux, then C is valid; if it *never* terminates in a closed set of tableaux, then C is not valid. Here are a few examples:

$$(20)$$

	$(\exists x)(y)Hxy \supset (x)(\exists y)Hxy$	$\checkmark$
$(\exists x)(y)Hxy$		$\checkmark$
	$(x)(\exists y)Hxy$	$\checkmark$
$(y)Hzy$		$\checkmark$
	$(\exists y)Hw_1y$	$\checkmark$
Hzz		$\checkmark$
Hzw_1		$\checkmark$
	Hw_1z	$\checkmark$
	Hw_1w_1	$\checkmark$

When applied to '$(\exists x)(y)Hxy \supset (x)(\exists y)Hxy$' the tableau method terminated in the open set (20) of tableaux, so the wff '$(\exists x)(y)Hxy \supset (x)(\exists y)Hxy$' is not valid. [The reader may verify that the interpre-

tation determined by the open tableau (20) is a countermodel of
its initial wff.]

(21)

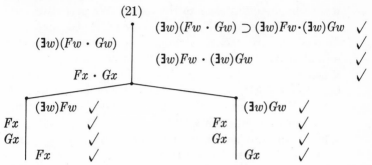

$$(\exists w)(Fw \cdot Gw) \supset (\exists w)Fw \cdot (\exists w)Gw \quad \checkmark$$

$$(\exists w)(Fw \cdot Gw) \quad \checkmark$$

$$(\exists w)Fw \cdot (\exists w)Gw \quad \checkmark$$

$$Fx \cdot Gx \quad \checkmark$$

$$(\exists w)Fw \quad \checkmark \qquad\qquad (\exists w)Gw \quad \checkmark$$

$$Fx \qquad\qquad\qquad\qquad Fx \quad \checkmark$$

$$Gx \qquad\qquad\qquad\qquad Gx \quad \checkmark$$

$$Fx \quad \checkmark \qquad\qquad\qquad Gx \quad \checkmark$$

Since it terminates in a closed set of tableaux, tableau-construction
(21) shows that the initial wff '$(\exists w)(Fw \cdot Gw) \supset (\exists w)Fw \cdot (\exists w)Gw$'
is valid.

It is a corollary of Church's thesis theorem that the set of valid
closed wffs of LSQ is undecidable. Nevertheless, it might *seem* that
the tableau method described above provides an algorithm for
deciding whether a closed wff of LSQ is valid. After all, need not
one only apply the method to a closed wff until the construction
process terminates (if the terminal set of tableaux is closed, the
wff is valid; if not, not) or until it becomes evident that the construction process will never terminate (in which case the wff is not
valid)? Sometimes it does indeed become evident that the construction process will never terminate, as in the case of (17). But it
follows from Church's thesis theorem that there is no algorithm for
determining whether or not an arbitrary tableau-construction
process will ever terminate. There may be mechanical routines for
deciding in many cases whether the construction process will
terminate, but, if we accept Church's thesis, we must acknowledge
that there is no general mechanical routine for deciding whether
tableau-construction processes for closed wffs of LSQ will ever
terminate or not. Applied to closed wffs of LSQ, the tableau
method is a useful and powerful method of establishing validity,
but it inevitably falls short of being an algorithm for deciding
validity.

Exercises

(1) In our formulation of the tableau-construction rule UL, we
did not explicitly state our intention that, with respect to

the instance A_b of $\ulcorner (a)A_a \urcorner$, b is to be the variable of instantiation, but took it for granted that the notation 'A_b' would make our intention clear to the reader. We permitted ourselves the same latitude in formulating UR, EL, and ER. To preclude any misunderstanding, provide unexceptionable formulations of all four of these construction rules.

(2) When applied within a tableau containing only closed wffs, both UL and ER call for introducing into the tableau a wff with a free variable. Explain the rationale for introducing a free variable into such a tableau.

(3) What is the rationale behind the deletion of check marks prescribed by both UR and EL?

(4) What is the general rationale behind EL and ER?

(5) Show by a counterexample that the tableau-construction process developed in the immediately preceding section is not generally applicable to open wffs of LSQ. [*Hint*: Try to apply the method to '$Fy \cdot (x)(\exists y)Gxy \supset (\exists y)Gzy$'.]

(6) Formulate tableau-construction rules that apply indifferently to open and closed wffs of LSQ, whether or not they contain vacuous quantifiers.

(7) Use the tableau method to show the validity of those closed wffs of LSQ that were shown to be valid by deductions in Chapters 54 and 56.

(8) To appreciate the directness of the tableau method, try to show by a deduction within system Q that the wff

$$(y)[(x)[Gxy \equiv Fx \cdot \sim (\exists z)(Gxz \cdot Gzx)] \supset \sim Fy]$$

is valid. Then apply the tableau method to show that this wff is valid.

(9) Let $A_1, \ldots, A_n$ be closed wffs of LSQ that jointly imply a closed wff B. Explain how one can use the tableau method to establish that $A_1, \ldots, A_n$ jointly imply B.

(10) An open wff of LSQ is valid if and only if any of its universal closures is valid. Explain, therefore, how one can use the tableau method to establish indirectly the validity of valid open wffs.

(11) Show that the undecidability of the class of valid closed wffs of LSQ follows from Church's thesis theorem that the class of valid wffs of LSQ is undecidable.

[12]   Let the tableau method be applied to a closed wff C of LSQ. Prove that, if the construction process terminates, then C is valid or not according as the terminal set of tableaux is closed or not. Show also that, if the construction terminates in an open set Ω of tableaux, each open member of Ω determines a countermodel of C.

Appendix C.
ALTERNATIVE PROOF OF
THE COMPLETENESS
OF SYSTEM P

The powerful methods of Leon Henkin, employing maximal consistent classes, were used in Sections 30.2 and 30.3 to prove the completeness of system P. (Henkin developed these methods to prove the completeness of quantificational systems such as system Q, and they were used to that purpose in Chapter 58.) In this appendix we apply the methods of László Kalmár to give a quite different proof of the completeness of system P. We shall prove two lemmas that jointly yield the completeness theorem for system P as a corollary.

Lemma 1.   Let B be a wff of system P and let $a_1, \ldots, a_n$ be distinct sentential variables. Let $\varepsilon_1, \varepsilon_2, \ldots, \varepsilon_{2^n}$ be a complete list of the distinct sequences of wffs of the form $A_1^*, \ldots, A_n^*$, where each A_i^* $(1 \leq i \leq n)$ is either a_i or $\ulcorner \sim a_i \urcorner$. Then, if $\varepsilon_1 \vdash B$, $\varepsilon_2 \vdash B, \ldots, \varepsilon_{2^n} \vdash B$, then $\vdash B$.

We prove lemma 1 by weak mathematical induction on the number of variables in the list $a_1, \ldots, a_n$. Suppose there is only one variable in the list, that is, suppose $n = 1$; then the lemma claims that, if $a_1 \vdash B$ and $\ulcorner \sim a_1 \urcorner \vdash B$, then $\vdash B$. That this claim is true is evident from the result of Exercise (1) below. Thus the induction basis has been established. Let us assume as our hypothesis of induction that the lemma holds when there are k variables in the list, and consider a list $a_1, \ldots, a_k, a_{k+1}$ of $k + 1$ distinct variables. Suppose that, for any sequence of the form $A_1^*, \ldots, A_k^*, A_{k+1}^*$, where each A_i^* $(1 \leq i \leq k + 1)$ is either a_i or $\ulcorner \sim a_i \urcorner$, we have $A_1^*, \ldots, A_k^*, A_{k+1}^* \vdash B$. Then, for *any* such sequence $A_1^*, \ldots, A_k^*$ we have that $A_1^*, \ldots, A_k^*, a_{k+1} \vdash B$ and $A_1^*, \ldots, A_k^*, \ulcorner \sim a_{k+1} \urcorner \vdash B$. Whence, by the result of Exercise (1) below, we have that $A_1^*, \ldots, A_k^* \vdash B$. Hence, by the hypothesis of induction, $\vdash B$. Thus we have established the induction step. By weak mathematical induction, therefore, we conclude that lemma 1 is true.

> Lemma 2.   Let $a_1, \ldots, a_n$ be a list of distinct variables that includes every variable which occurs in a wff B of system P, and let Σ be an interpretation of B that assigns a value to each variable in the list $a_1, \ldots, a_n$. Let $A_i (1 \leq i \leq n)$ be a_i or $\ulcorner \sim a_i \urcorner$ according as Σ assigns t or f to a_i. Then either $A_1, \ldots, A_n \vdash B$ or $A_1, \ldots, A_n \vdash \ulcorner \sim B \urcorner$ according as the value of B under Σ is t or f, respectively.

We prove lemma 1 by strong mathematical induction on the number of occurrences of connectives in B. If there are zero occurrences of connectives in B, then $B = a_1$ and the claim of the lemma is obviously true, because $a_1 \vdash a_1$ and $\ulcorner \sim a_1 \urcorner \vdash \ulcorner \sim a_1 \urcorner$. Thus the induction basis has been established. Let us assume as hypothesis of induction that the lemma holds for wffs B with k or fewer occurrences of connectives. Let $a_1, \ldots, a_n$ be a complete list of the distinct variables that occur in a wff B with $k + 1$ occurrences of connectives, and let Σ be an interpretation of B. B will have one of the two forms, $\ulcorner \sim C \urcorner$ or $\ulcorner D \supset E \urcorner$. Suppose B is $\ulcorner \sim C \urcorner$. If B comes out true under Σ, then C comes out false under Σ. By the hypothesis of induction, therefore, $A_1, \ldots, A_n \vdash \ulcorner \sim C \urcorner$. But B is $\ulcorner \sim C \urcorner$. Hence $A_1, \ldots, A_n \vdash B$. But if B comes out false under Σ, then C comes out true under Σ, and, by the hypothesis of induction, $A_1, \ldots, A_n \vdash C$. And, $\ulcorner \sim B \urcorner$ is $\ulcorner \sim \sim C \urcorner$, so it follows that $A_1, \ldots, A_n \vdash B$ by T2 of Section 30.1. Therefore, whether B comes out true or false under Σ, either $A_1, \ldots, A_n \vdash B$ or $A_1, \ldots, A_n \vdash \ulcorner \sim B \urcorner$ according as B comes out true or false under Σ. Hence, if B is $\ulcorner \sim C \urcorner$, lemma 2 holds for B. Suppose, however, that B is $\ulcorner D \supset E \urcorner$. If B comes out false under Σ, then D and E are, respectively, true and false under Σ. So, by the hypothesis of induction, $A_1, \ldots, A_n \vdash D$ and $A_1, \ldots, A_n \vdash \ulcorner \sim E \urcorner$. Hence, by the result of Exercise (3) below, $A_1, \ldots, A_n \vdash \ulcorner \sim [D \supset E] \urcorner$. But B is $\ulcorner D \supset E \urcorner$. Hence $A_1, \ldots, A_n \vdash \ulcorner \sim B \urcorner$. If B comes out true under Σ, then there are two subcases to consider according as D is false under Σ or E is true under Σ. Consider the first subcase when D is false under Σ. Then, by the hypothesis of induction, $A_1, \ldots, A_n \vdash \ulcorner \sim D \urcorner$. Whence $A_1, \ldots, A_n \vdash \ulcorner D \supset E \urcorner$ by the result of Exercise (4) below. But B is $\ulcorner D \supset E \urcorner$. Hence $A_1, \ldots, A_n \vdash B$. Now consider the second subcase when E is true under Σ. Then, by the hypothesis of induction, $A_1, \ldots, A_n \vdash E$. Whence $A_1, \ldots, A_n \vdash$ $\ulcorner D \supset E \urcorner$ by the result of Exercise (4) below. But B is $\ulcorner D \supset E \urcorner$. Hence $A_1, \ldots, A_n \vdash B$. We have shown that, if the wff B with $k + 1$ occurrences of connectives is $\ulcorner D \supset E \urcorner$, then $A_1, \ldots, A_n \vdash B$ or $A_1, \ldots, A_n \vdash \ulcorner \sim B \urcorner$ according as B comes out true or false under Σ. Together with the analogous result for the case when B is $\ulcorner \sim C \urcorner$, this establishes the induction step. By strong mathematical induction, therefore, we conclude that lemma 2 is true.

To derive the completeness theorem for system P from lemmas 1 and 2, we let $a_1, \ldots, a_n$ be a complete list of the distinct variables in a *valid* wff B of system P and let $A_1, \ldots, A_n$ be any sequence of wffs such that, for each i $(1 \leq i \leq n)$, A_i is either a_i or $\ulcorner \sim a_i \urcorner$. Let Σ be the interpretation of B that assigns to each a_i $(1 \leq i \leq n)$ truth or falsehood according as A_i is a_i or $\ulcorner \sim a_i \urcorner$. As B is valid, B comes out true under Σ. Hence, by lemma 2, $A_1, \ldots, A_n \vdash B$. But $A_1, \ldots, A_n$ was an arbitrary sequence of wffs such that, for each i $(1 \leq i \leq n)$, A_i is a_i or $\ulcorner \sim a_i \urcorner$. Therefore, there is a proof of B from any such sequence of hypotheses. By lemma 1, therefore, $\vdash B$. Hence, by L1 of Section 30.0, B is a theorem of system P. That is, we have shown that, if B is a valid wff of system P, then B is a theorem of system P (completeness theorem for system P).

Exercises

(1) Prove that, if $A_1, \ldots, A_{n-1}, A_n \vdash B$ and $A_1, \ldots, A_{n-1}, \ulcorner \sim A_n \urcorner \vdash B$, then $A_1, \ldots, A_{n-1} \vdash B$. (*Hint*: Use the deduction theorem to show that '$(p \supset q) \supset [(\sim p \supset q) \supset q]$' is a theorem of system P.)

(2) Explain how the following diagram illustrates the strategy behind the proof of lemma 1 given in this appendix.

$$
\begin{array}{l}
\left.\begin{array}{l} p,q,r \vdash B \\ p,q,\sim r \vdash B \end{array}\right\} \; \left.\begin{array}{l} p,q \vdash B \\ \\ p,\sim q \vdash B \end{array}\right\} \; \left.\begin{array}{l} p \vdash B \\ \\ \\ \\ \end{array}\right\} \\
\left.\begin{array}{l} p,\sim q,r \vdash B \\ p,\sim q,\sim r \vdash B \end{array}\right\} \\
\left.\begin{array}{l} \sim p,q,r \vdash B \\ \sim p,q,\sim r \vdash B \end{array}\right\} \; \left.\begin{array}{l} \sim p,q \vdash B \\ \\ \sim p,\sim q \vdash B \end{array}\right\} \; \sim p \vdash B \\
\left.\begin{array}{l} \sim p,\sim q,r \vdash B \\ \sim p,\sim q,\sim r \vdash B \end{array}\right\}
\end{array} \Biggr\} \vdash B
$$

(3) Prove that, if $A_1, \ldots, A_n \vdash B$ and $A_1, \ldots, A_n \vdash \ulcorner \sim C \urcorner$, then $A_1, \ldots, A_n \vdash \ulcorner \sim [B \supset C] \urcorner$. (*Hint*: Show that '$p \supset [\sim q \supset \sim(p \supset q)]$' is a theorem of system P by first showing that 'p', '$\sim q$', '$p \supset q$' $\vdash$ 'q' and 'p', '$\sim q$', '$p \supset q$' $\vdash$ '$\sim q$' and then applying L4 of Section 30.2.)

(4) Prove that, if $A_1, \ldots, A_n \vdash \ulcorner \sim B \urcorner$, then $A_1, \ldots, A_n \vdash \ulcorner B \supset C \urcorner$ for any wff C. Prove also that, if $A_1, \ldots, A_n \vdash C$, then $A_1, \ldots, A_n \vdash \ulcorner B \supset C \urcorner$ for any wff B.

Appendix D.
ALTERNATIVE PROOF OF THE COMPACTNESS THEOREM FOR SYSTEM P

In Section 30.4 we derived the compactness theorem for system P as a corollary of the lemma that every consistent class of wffs of system P is satisfiable. (In virtue of the relationship between LSP and system P, the compactness theorem for LSP follows immediately from the compactness theorem for system P.) Unlike the deduction theorem or the completeness theorem, the compactness theorem for system P makes no reference or allusion to the axioms and rules of inference of system P, but only to its grammar and semantics. It should be possible, therefore, to give a proof of the compactness theorem which, unlike the proof given in Section 30.4, depends on no theorem that makes reference or allusion to the axioms and rules of inference of system P. In this section we present such a proof, one due in all essentials to W. V. O. Quine.

Clearly, if a class Γ of wffs (of system P) is satisfiable, every finite subclass of Γ is satisfiable. It is proof of the converse that poses a challenge. Let us begin our proof of the converse by supposing that every finite subclass of a class Γ of wffs (of system P) is satisfiable, but that Γ is not itself satisfiable. Let us regard an interpretation Σ as a set of ordered pairs $\langle a, \alpha \rangle$, where a is a variable of system P and α is a truth value, such that no two members of Σ have the same first element. (The intuitive idea is that Σ assigns α to a, and that an interpretation may assign only one value to a variable.) An interpretation Σ' shall be said to be an *extension of* an interpretation Σ if Σ is a subset of Σ'. (Intuitively, Σ' is an extension of Σ if and only if Σ' makes every value assignment made by Σ.) And let us say that an interpretation Σ *condemns* a class Δ of wffs of system P if no extension of Σ is a model of Δ. (Note that we do *not* require that Σ be an interpretation of Δ, that is, that Σ assign a value to every variable that occurs in any wff of Δ.) Let $b_1, b_2, b_3, \ldots$ be the lexicographical ordering of the variables of system P, and consider the following enumeration $\mathcal{E}$ of interpretations, where $\mathcal{E}$ is $\Sigma_0, \Sigma_1, \Sigma_2, \ldots$.

Σ_0 = the empty set

$\Sigma_{i+1} = \Sigma_i \cup \{\langle b_{i+1}, t \rangle\}$, if $\Sigma_i \cup \{\langle b_{i+1}, t \rangle\}$ does not condemn any finite subclass of Γ; otherwise,

$\Sigma_{i+1} = \Sigma_i \cup \{\langle b_{i+1}, f \rangle\}$

We claim that no interpretation in the enumeration $\mathcal{E}$ condemns any finite subclass of Γ, and we prove our claim by weak mathematical induction on the place of an interpretation in the enumeration $\mathcal{E}$. To establish the basis of the induction, we observe that Σ_0 condemns no finite subset of Γ, because Σ_0 is the empty set and every finite subset of Γ is satisfiable. As hypothesis of induction, let us assume that Σ_i condemns no finite subset of Γ, and let us try to show that the hypothesis of induction entails that Σ_{i+1} also condemns no finite subclass of Γ. If $\Sigma_{i+1} = \Sigma_i \cup \{\langle b_{i+1}, t \rangle\}$, then from the way $\mathcal{E}$ is formed we know that Σ_{i+1} condemns no finite subset of Γ. Suppose, however, that $\Sigma_{i+1} = \Sigma_i \cup \{\langle b_{i+1}, f \rangle\}$. If $\Sigma_i \cup \{\langle b_{i+1}, f \rangle\}$ condemns no finite subclass of Γ, then nothing remains to be proved. So let us also suppose that $\Sigma_i \cup \{\langle b_{i+1}, f \rangle\}$ condemns some finite subclass Γ_f of Γ. We know from the way $\mathcal{E}$ is formed that $\Sigma_i \cup \{\langle b_{i+1}, t \rangle\}$ also condemns some finite subclass Γ_t of Γ; otherwise, Σ_{i+1} would not be $\Sigma_i \cup \{\langle b_{i+1}, f \rangle\}$. It follows that $\Gamma_f \cup \Gamma_t$, a finite subclass of Γ, is condemned by Σ_i, contrary to our assumption that Σ_i condemns no finite subclass of Γ. Hence, if Σ_i condemns no finite subclass of Γ, then Σ_{i+1} also condemns no finite subclass of Γ. By weak mathematical induction, therefore, we infer that no member of $\mathcal{E}$ condemns any finite subclass of Γ.

Let $\overline{\Sigma}$ be the union of all the members of $\mathcal{E}$. Since $\overline{\Sigma}$ assigns exactly one value to every variable of system P, $\overline{\Sigma}$ is obviously an interpretation of Γ. But $\overline{\Sigma}$ is not a model of Γ, because by assumption Γ is not satisfiable. Let A be a member of Γ that comes out false under $\overline{\Sigma}$; clearly there is at least one such wff. Let b_k be the lexicographically latest variable which occurs in A. Obviously, then, because Σ_k and $\overline{\Sigma}$ make the same assignments to the variables of A, A comes out false under Σ_k. But then Σ_k condemns the class $\{A\}$ which is a finite subclass of Γ. But Σ_k is a member of $\mathcal{E}$, and we have already shown that no member of $\mathcal{E}$ condemns any finite subclass of Γ. From this contradiction we conclude by indirect proof that, if every finite subclass of Γ is satisfiable, then Γ is satisfiable. This terminates our proof of the compactness theorem for system P.

Exercises

(1)   Derive the compactness theorem for LSP as a corollary of the compactness theorem for system P. That is, prove that a class of wffs of LSP is satisfiable if and only if every finite subclass of it is satisfiable.

(2)   Quine refers to the compactness theorem as the "theorem of infinite conjunction". Explain why Quine's appellation is both appropriate and suggestive.

(3)   Show that, if $\Sigma \cup \{\langle b,t \rangle\}$ condemns Γ_t and $\Sigma \cup \{\langle b,f \rangle\}$ condemns Γ_f, then Σ condemns $\Gamma_t \cup \Gamma_f$.

(4)   Show that, if a wff A comes out false under an interpretation Σ, then Σ condemns the class $\{A\}$.

(5)   What emendations, if any, are required to convert Quine's proof of the compactness theorem for system P (the proof given above) into a proof of the compactness theorem for LSP?

Appendix E.
ALTERNATIVE PROOF
OF THE COMPLETENESS
OF SYSTEM Q

The completeness theorem for system Q is an easy corollary of the following two lemmas.[1]

Lemma 1.   If A is a wff of system Q and if A^* is the prenex normal form of A generated by the algorithm of Section 62.2, then ⊢ $\ulcorner A \equiv A^* \urcorner$; that is, $\ulcorner A \equiv A^* \urcorner$ is a theorem of system Q.

Lemma 2.   If A is a closed wff of system Q in prenex normal form, then either A is satisfiable or ⊢ $\ulcorner \sim A \urcorner$.

Before attending to their proof, let us derive the completeness theorem for system Q from these two lemmas. Let A be any valid wff of system Q and let $a_1, \ldots, a_n$ be a list of individual variables among which is found every individual variable that occurs free in A. Then $\ulcorner (a_1) \ldots (a_n) A \urcorner$ is valid. Let $\bar{A}$ be the prenex normal form of $\ulcorner \sim (a_1) \ldots (a_n) A \urcorner$ generated by the algorithm of Section 62.2. As $\ulcorner (a_1) \ldots (a_n) A \urcorner$ is valid, $\bar{A}$ is not satisfiable. Furthermore, $\bar{A}$ is closed. [See Exercise (1) below.] Therefore, by lemma 2, ⊢ $\ulcorner \sim \bar{A} \urcorner$. But ⊢ $\ulcorner \sim (a_1) \ldots (a_n) A \equiv \bar{A} \urcorner$ by lemma 1. Therefore, ⊢ $\ulcorner (a_1) \ldots (a_n) A \urcorner$. But $\ulcorner (a_1) \ldots (a_n) A \urcorner$ ⊢ A. Therefore, ⊢ A. This terminates our proof that, if A is valid, then A is a theorem of system Q (completeness theorem for system Q), subject to supplying proofs of the two lemmas above.

Proof of lemma 1 is left to the reader. We begin our proof of lemma 2 by letting A be a closed wff of system Q in prenex normal form. If A is quantifier-free, then A is either satisfiable or ⊢ $\ulcorner \sim A \urcorner$ by the result of Exercise (3). So suppose A is not quantifier free. Then $A = \ulcorner (Q_1) \ldots (Q_n) M \urcorner$, where each $\ulcorner (Q_i) \urcorner (1 \leq i \leq n)$ is either an existential or a universal quantifier and where M is a quantifier-free wff. We construct a (possibly infinite) sequence Ω of lines as

---

[1] The proof given in this appendix is an adaptation of the proof of completeness to be found in the appendix of W. V. O. Quine, *Methods of Logic*, Holt, Rinehart and Winston, Inc., New York, rev. ed., 1963.

follows. The first line of Ω consists of A set down by RP. Subsequent lines of Ω are set down by EI or UG in the following way. We imagine that Ω is the left-hand column of a semantic tableau in which we are to apply only the two rules EL and UL, and that A (set down by RP) is the initial wff of the tableau. If the application of EL to an existentially quantified line $\ulcorner(\exists a)B_a\urcorner$ prescribes that an occurrence of B_b be entered in the left-hand column of the tableau, we use EI on line $\ulcorner(\exists a)B_a\urcorner$ to set B_b down as the next line of Ω. And if the application of UL to a universally quantified line $\ulcorner(a)B_a\urcorner$ prescribes that an occurrence of each of the wffs B_{b_1}, B_{b_2}, $\ldots$, B_{b_j} be entered in the left-hand column of the tableau, we repeatedly use UI on line $\ulcorner(a)B_a\urcorner$ to set down B_{b_1}, B_{b_2}, $\ldots$, B_{b_j} as the next lines of Ω. We continue the construction of the sequence until neither EL nor UL any longer applies; if such a point is never reached, Ω will contain infinitely many lines. The construction of a sequence like Ω is illustrated below.

$*_1(1)$	$(y)(\exists w)(x)[Fyw \equiv \sim Gxw]$	RP		$\checkmark$
$*_1(2)$	$(\exists w)(x)[Fzw \equiv \sim Gxw]$	UI(1)	UL(1)	$\checkmark$
$*_1(3)$	$(x)[Fzw_1 \equiv \sim Gxw_1]$	EI(2) $\boxed{w_1}$	EL(2)	
$*_1(4)$	$(\exists w)(x)[Fw_1w \equiv \sim Gxw]$	UI(1)	UL(1)	$\checkmark$
$*_1(5)$	$Fzw_1 \equiv \sim Gzw_1$	UI(3)	UL(3)	
$*_1(6)$	$Fzw_1 \equiv \sim Gw_1w_1$	UI(3)	UL(3)	
$*_1(7)$	$(x)[Fw_1x_1 \equiv \sim Gxx_1]$	EI(4) $\boxed{x_1}$	EL(4)	
$*_1(8)$	$(\exists w)(x)[Fx_1w \equiv \sim Gxw]$	UI(1)	UL(1)	$\checkmark$
$*_1(9)$	$Fzw_1 \equiv \sim Gx_1w_1$	UI(3)	UL(3)	
$*_1(10)$	$Fw_1x_1 \equiv \sim Gzx_1$	UI(7)	UL(7)	
$*_1(11)$	$Fw_1x_1 \equiv \sim Gw_1x_1$	UI(7)	UL(7)	
$*_1(12)$	$Fw_1x_1 \equiv \sim Gx_1x_1$	UI(7)	UL(7)	
$*_1(13)$	$(x)[Fx_1y_1 \equiv \sim Gxy_1]$	EI(8) $\boxed{y_1}$	EL(8)	
$*_1(14)$	$(\exists w)(x)[Fy_1w \equiv \sim Gxw]$	UI(1)	UL(1)	

$\cdot$ $\cdot$ $\cdot$ $\cdot$

$\cdot$ $\cdot$ $\cdot$ $\cdot$

$\cdot$ $\cdot$ $\cdot$ $\cdot$

(This construction will never terminate.)

It can be proved that the following four statements about Ω are true.

(a)   For every positive integer k, the first k lines of Ω constitute a finishable deduction. (The ordering requirement C2 of Section 54.4 will be satisfied by listing the variables flagged in the first k lines of Ω in the inverse order of their introduction into Ω.)

(b) Let Δ be the set of individual variables that occur free in lines of Ω. (The initial line of Ω is a prenex normal wff that is not quantifier-free, so Δ is nonempty.) Moreover, for each $b \in \Delta$ and for each universally quantified line $\ulcorner(a)B_a\urcorner$ of Ω, the instance B_b of $\ulcorner(a)B_a\urcorner$, with b as the variable of instantiation, will occur as a line of Ω.

(c) For each existentially quantified line $\ulcorner(\exists a)B_a\urcorner$ of Ω, a conservative instance B_b of $\ulcorner(\exists a)B_a\urcorner$ will occur as a line of Ω, where the variable of instantiation b is a member of Δ.

(d) The set of quantifier-free lines of Ω is nonempty.

Let Γ be the set of quantifier-free lines of Ω. Let $\mathcal{E}$ be an enumeration A_1, A_2, ... of all the distinct atomic wffs that occur in members of Γ. ($\mathcal{E}$ may be an infinite sequence.) Let Γ^* be the set of sentential wffs that result by the simultaneous substitution of $\ulcorner p_i\urcorner$ for A_i, for every i ($i = 1, 2, 3, \ldots$), in each member of Γ. First, we will show that, if Γ^* is not satisfiable, then $\vdash \ulcorner{\sim}A\urcorner$ in system Q. [Remember, A is the first wff of Ω; $A = \ulcorner(Q_1)\ldots(Q_n)M\urcorner$.] Suppose, then, that Γ^* is not satisfiable. By the compactness theorem, then, some finite nonempty subset Γ_0^* of Γ^* is not satisfiable. [See Exercise (5) below.] Let Γ_0 be the set of wffs that result by the simultaneous substitution of A_i for $\ulcorner p_i\urcorner$, for every i ($i = 1, 2, 3, \ldots$), in each member of Γ^*. Clearly Γ_0 is a finite nonempty subset of Γ. Let $B_1, \ldots, B_k$ be a complete list of the members of Γ_0. Then the conjunction $\ulcorner B_1 \cdot \ldots \cdot B_k\urcorner$ is truth-functionally contradictory. [See Exercise (10) of Chapter 47.] Because each B_i ($1 \leq i \leq k$) will occur as a line of Ω exactly once, one of them, say B_j, will occur after all the others as some line (m) of Ω. Then the following deduction is a proof of $\ulcorner{\sim}A\urcorner$; that is, it is a finished deduction having $\ulcorner{\sim}(Q_1)\ldots(Q_n)M\urcorner$ as unstarred last line.

$$
\begin{array}{lll}
{*}_1(1) & A & \text{RP} \\
{*}_1(2) & \ldots & \ldots \\
\quad\cdot & & \\
\quad\cdot & & \qquad\qquad \text{First } m \text{ lines of } \Omega \\
\quad\cdot & & \\
{*}_1(m) & B_j & \ldots \\
{*}_1(m+1) & B_1 \cdot \ldots \cdot B_k & \text{TF (numerals referring to each } B_i) \\
(m+2) & A \supset B_1 \cdot \ldots \cdot B_k & \text{Cd}{*}_1(m+1) \\
(m+3) & {\sim}A & \text{TF}(m+2)
\end{array}
$$

Hence, if Γ^* is not satisfiable, then $\vdash \ulcorner \sim A \urcorner$. But suppose Γ^* is satisfiable. Let Σ^* be a value assignment to the set of variables $\ulcorner p_i \urcorner$ ($i = 1, 2, 3, \ldots$) such that Σ^* is a model of Γ^*. For each $A_i \in \mathcal{E}$, let $\Sigma^*(A_i)$ be the truth value which Σ^* assigns to $\ulcorner p_i \urcorner$. We now use this function Σ^* on the members of $\mathcal{E}$ to characterize an interpretation Σ that is a model of every line of Ω. The domain of Σ is the set Δ, that is, the set of individual variables that occur free in lines of Ω. To an individual variable b that occurs free in any line of Ω, Σ assigns b as the value of itself. To a sentential variable b that occurs in any line of Ω, Σ assigns $\Sigma^*(b)$ as its value. To a k-ary predicate variable ϕ that occurs in any line of Ω, Σ assigns as its extension the set of all k-tuples $\langle a_1, \ldots, a_k \rangle$ of individuals (members of Δ) such that $\Sigma^*(\phi a_1 \ldots a_k) = t$. That Σ is a model of each line of Ω can be proved by weak mathematical induction on the number of quantifier occurrences in a line L of Ω. If L contains zero occurrences of quantifiers, it is obvious that L comes out true under Σ. (As Σ^* is a model of Γ^*, clearly Σ is a model of Γ.) This establishes the induction basis. Let us assume, as our hypothesis of induction, that Σ is a model of every line of Ω that contains r occurrences of quantifiers, and let L be any line of Ω that has $r + 1$ occurrences of quantifiers. Then L will be either $\ulcorner (\exists a) B_a \urcorner$ or $\ulcorner (a) B_a \urcorner$, where B_a is a wff with r quantifier occurrences. Suppose L is $\ulcorner (\exists a) B_a \urcorner$. Then, by statement (c) about Ω, a conservative instance B_b of $\ulcorner (\exists a) B_a \urcorner$, with b as the variable of instantiation, occurs as a line of Ω. B_b contains r quantifier occurrences, so it falls under the hypothesis of induction. Hence Σ is a model of B_b. Let Σ_1 be the minimal interpretation of $\ulcorner (\exists a) B_a \urcorner$ determined by Σ, and let Σ_2 be like Σ_1 except that Σ_2 assigns b to a. Clearly, the value of B_a under Σ_2 is the same as the value of B_b under Σ. Hence Σ_2 is a model of B_a. By the semantics of the existential quantifier, therefore, $\ulcorner (\exists a) B_a \urcorner$ comes out true under Σ_1. Hence Σ is a model of $\ulcorner (\exists a) B_a \urcorner$. But suppose L is $\ulcorner (a) B_a \urcorner$. Let Σ_3 be the minimal interpretation of $\ulcorner (a) B_a \urcorner$ determined by Σ, and let b be an arbitrary member of the domain of Σ (that is, $b \in \Delta$). Let Σ_4 be like Σ_3 except that Σ_4 assigns b to a. Then Σ_4 is a minimal interpretation of B_a that determines Σ_3. But by statement (b) about Ω, the conservative instance B_b of $\ulcorner (a) A_a \urcorner$, with b as the variable of instantiation, occurs as a line of Ω. B_b has r quantifier occurrences, so B_b falls under the hypothesis of induction and thus comes out true under Σ. Hence B_a comes out true under Σ_4. But Σ_4 was an arbitrary minimal interpretation of B_a that determines Σ_3. Hence, by the semantics of the universal quantifier, $\ulcorner(a)B_a\urcorner$ comes out true under Σ_3. Therefore, Σ is a model of $\ulcorner(a)B_a\urcorner$. This completes the induction step. By weak mathematical induction, then, we conclude that Σ is a model of each line of Ω. And, because A, $A = \ulcorner(Q_1)\ldots(Q_n)M\urcorner$, is the first line of Ω, Σ is a model of A. We have shown, therefore, that A is satisfiable if Γ^* is satisfiable, and that $\vdash \ulcorner\sim A\urcorner$ if Γ^* is not satisfiable. But Γ^* is either satisfiable or not. Therefore, either A is satisfiable or $\vdash \ulcorner\sim A\urcorner$. This terminates our proof of lemma 2.

Exercises

(1) Let A^* be the prenex normal form of A generated by the algorithm of Section 62.2. Prove that, if A is closed, then A^* is also closed.

[2] Prove lemma 1 of this appendix.

(3) Prove that, if A is a quantifier-free wff of system Q, then either A is satisfiable or $\vdash \ulcorner\sim A\urcorner$.

(4) Prove that the four statements (a)–(d) made in this appendix are all true of Ω. (*Hint*: Remember that any line of Ω is preceded by only finitely many other lines.)

(5) Let LSP$^+$ be the language schema that results on adding '$\supset$' and '$\equiv$', together with appropriate formation and semantical rules, to LSP. Prove the compactness theorem for LSP$^+$. (*Hint*: See Appendix D.) Is the empty set satisfiable?

(6) Exhibit the first twenty lines of the sequence Ω that has the following as its first line:

$*_1(1)$ $(\exists x)(y)(\exists z)(w)\sim Hwxywz$ RP

(7) Derive the Löwenheim theorem for system Q as a corollary of the proof of completeness given in this appendix. [*Hint:* Remember that A is satisfiable if and only if $\ulcorner(\exists a_1)\ldots(\exists a_n)A\urcorner$ is satisfiable.]

Appendix F.
ALTERNATIVE APPROACHES TO THE SEMANTICS OF QUANTIFIERS

The approach taken in Section 46.4 to explain the meaning of quantified wffs of LSQ is only one of several viable alternatives. In this appendix we present two other approaches, only one of which closely resembles that of Section 46.4.

We present the similar approach first. To have a label for it, let us call it alternative ℬ, and let us refer to the semantics of Section 46.4 as alternative 𝒜. Alternative ℬ defines an *interpretation* as a nonempty domain (UD) together with an assignment of appropriate values to *every* variable of LSQ, that is, to each individual, sentential, and predicate variable of LSQ. (By *appropriate* value assignments we mean, of course, that individuals, that is, members of the UD, are assigned to the individual variables, sets of n-tuples of individuals are assigned to n-ary predicate variables, and truth values are assigned to sentential variables.) Let b be a variable of LSQ. Then interpretations I_1 and I_2 shall be said to be *b-variants of one another* if I_1 and I_2 are alike except perhaps with respect to the values they assign to b. The basic semantical concept of approach ℬ is the *value of a wff under an interpretation*. The value of a wff A under an interpretation I may be defined inductively thus:

(i)   [Like clause (i) of Section 46.4 with 'I' substituted for 'Σ'.]

(ii)   [Like clause (ii) of Section 46.4 with 'I' substituted for 'Σ'.]

(iii)   [Like clause (iii) of Section 46.4 with 'I' substituted for 'Σ' and with the parenthetical sentence deleted.]

(iv)   If A is $\ulcorner B \cdot C \urcorner$, then the value of A is truth under I if both B and C come out true under I; otherwise, A comes out false under I.

(v)–(vii)   The clauses for '$\mathbf{v}$', '$\supset$', and '$\equiv$' are analogous to (iv).

(viii)   If A is $\ulcorner(\exists b)B\urcorner$, the value of A under I is truth if B comes out true under at least one b-variant of I; otherwise A comes out false under I.

(xi)   If A is $\ulcorner(b)B\urcorner$, the value of A under I is truth if B comes out true under every b-variant of I; otherwise A comes out false under I.

There is much that is attractive about alternative ℬ. It is in some respects simpler than 𝒶. Moreover, the adoption of alternative ℬ would have facilitated proof of some of the semantical meta-theorems proved in the text. Nevertheless, we favored approach 𝒶, primarily because it pays more overt respect to the important distinction between free and bound occurrences of individual varia-bles, free occurrences functioning as dummy singular terms, bound occurrences functioning as pronouns. The reader who prefers ap-proach ℬ can, without much difficulty or effort, adapt our presenta-tion of symbolic logic to that alternative.

The second alternative to our own approach is the classical approach of Alfred Tarski, who has the honor of being the first logician to formulate the semantics of quantifiers in a clear and adequate way. Although more complicated than alternatives 𝒶 or ℬ, the Tarskian approach merits attention as a somewhat dif-ferent route to the same destination.

Tarski understands an *interpretation of* a wff A of LSQ to consist in a nonempty domain (UD) together with an appropriate value assignment to at least each sentential and predicate variable that occurs in A; the only restriction on an interpretation of a wff is that no values are assigned to any individual variables.[1] Consider an interpretation I of a wff A, and let 𝔇 be the domain of I. Let Ω be the set of all denumerable sequences of elements of 𝔇; that is, Ω is the set of all denumerable sequences of individuals. Let ε be the particular one-to-one mapping of the positive integers onto the individual variables of LSQ which maps each integer k with the kth individual variable in the lexicographical ordering of the in-dividual variables. Let $\mathcal{S}$ be an arbitrary member of Ω, and let b be an arbitrary individual variable. By $\mathcal{S}(b)$ we shall understand the mth element of $\mathcal{S}$, where m is the number mapped with b by ε. Now we can give an inductive definition of the basic semantical

---

[1] Again, as when we discussed the work of Church and Gödel, we allow ourselves some historical license.

concept of Tarski's approach: what it means to say that sequence
S *satisfies* wff A *relative to* interpretation I:

(i)   If A is a sentential variable, sequence S *satisfies A relative to I* if and only if I assigns truth to A.

(ii) If A is an atomic wff $\ulcorner\phi a_1\ldots a_n\urcorner$, then sequence S *satisfies A relative to I* if and only if $\langle S(a_1),\ldots, S(a_n)\rangle$ belongs to the extension that I assigns to ϕ.

(iii) If A is $\ulcorner\sim B\urcorner$, then sequence S *satisfies A relative to I* if and only if S does not satisfy B relative to I. (Note that I will also be an interpretation of B.)

(iv) If A is $\ulcorner B \cdot C\urcorner$, then S *satisfies A relative to I* if and only if S satisfies both B and C relative to I.

(v)–(vii) [Clauses for 'v', '$\supset$', and '$\equiv$' are analogous to (iv).]

(viii) If A is $\ulcorner(\exists b)B\urcorner$, then S *satisfies A relative to I* if and only if there is at least one sequence S' in Ω such that
   (a) For every individual variable c which is distinct from b, $S'(c) = S(c)$;
   (b) S' satisfies B relative to I.

(ix) If A is $\ulcorner(b)B\urcorner$, then S *satisfies A relative to I* if and only if B is satisfied relative to I by every sequence S' of Ω which is such that, for every individual variable c distinct from b, $S'(c) = S(c)$.

Let I be an interpretation of A, and let Ω be the set of all denumerable sequences of individuals of the domain of I. Tarski stipulates that A shall be said to be *true under I* if every sequence in Ω satisfies A relative to I; if no sequence in Ω satisfies A relative to I, then A shall be said to be *false under I*.

Notice that, on Tarski's approach, some wffs of LSQ will not have a truth value under interpretation. For example, 'Fy' comes out neither true nor false under the interpretation in the domain of positive integers that assigns the set of primes to 'F' as its extension. Other consequences of Tarski's approach are elicited by the exercises below.

Exercises

(1) Show that, on Tarski's semantical approach, $\ulcorner\sim A\urcorner$ comes out true (false) under an interpretation I of $\ulcorner\sim A\urcorner$ if and only if A comes out false (true) under I.

(2)   Let I be a Tarskian interpretation of $\ulcorner A \cdot B \urcorner$. Show that, on Tarski's semantics, $\ulcorner A \cdot B \urcorner$ comes out true under I if and only if both A and B come out true under I. Show that $\ulcorner A \cdot B \urcorner$ may come out false under I even though neither A nor B has a truth value under I.

(3)   Let I be a Tarskian interpretation of $\ulcorner A \supset B \urcorner$. Show that each of the following are true of Tarski's approach:

(a)   If A is false under I, then $\ulcorner A \supset B \urcorner$ is true under I.

(b)   If B is true under I, then $\ulcorner A \supset B \urcorner$ is true under I.

(c)   If A and B are, respectively, true and false under I, then $\ulcorner A \supset B \urcorner$ comes out false under I.

(d)   If both A and $\ulcorner A \supset B \urcorner$ are true under I, then B is also true under I.

(e)   If $\ulcorner A \supset B \urcorner$ and B are, respectively, true and false under I, then A comes out false under I.

(4)   Let I be a Tarskian interpretation of a wff A of LSQ. Show that, on Tarski's semantical approach, each of the following claims is true:

(a) A does not come out both true and false under I.

(b)   If A is tautologous, then A comes out true under I.

(c)   If A is truth-functionally contradictory (that is, a substitution instance of an invalid wff of LSP), then A comes out false under I.

(d)   If A comes out true under I, then $\ulcorner (a_1) \ldots (a_n) A \urcorner$ comes out true under I, where $a_1, \ldots, a_n$ are arbitrary individual variables.

(e)   Let $b_1, \ldots, b_n$ be a complete list of the free individual variables of A, and let S_1 and S_2 be denumerable sequences of individuals of the domain of I such that, for each b_i $(1 \leq i \leq n)$, $S_1(b_i) = S_2(b_i)$. Show that either both S_1 and S_2 satisfy A relative to I or neither S_1 nor S_2 satisfies A relative to I. (*Hint*: Use strong mathematical induction on the number of occurrences of connectives and quantifiers in A.)

(f)   If A is a closed wff, then A has a truth value under I. [*Hint*: Clause (f) is a simple corollary of clause (e).]

[5]   Approaches α and $\mathfrak{B}$, as well as the Tarskian approach, all construe a *valid* wff to be a wff that comes out true under every

interpretation of it. Prove that each of these three approaches characterizes the same class of wffs of LSQ as the class of wffs that are valid on that approach.

(6)   Explain how approach ℬ is able to dispense with the notion of a minimal interpretation.

[7]   Let A be a closed wff of LSQ, and let I_a, I_b, and I_t be, respectively, an ℂ-interpretation of A, a ℬ-interpretation of A, and a Tarskian interpretation of A. Show that, if I_a, I_b, and I_t all have the same UD and all make the same value assignments to the sentential and predicate variables of A, then A comes out with the same value under each of these three interpretations on the semantical theory appropriate to that interpretation.

Appendix G.
QUANTIFICATION THEORY
WITH MODALITY

Kripke's 1959 Semantics; LSQ-M

The treatment of modality in Part Three was limited to systems of sentential logic supplemented by modal operators. The present appendix deals with the logic of systems that result when modal operators are added to quantification theory. As a mature discipline, quantification theory with modality is quite young. Although the discipline had already somewhat come of age by 1946 when Rudolf Carnap published his paper "Modalities and Quantification,"[1] the semantical contributions of Saul Kripke's 1959 paper "A Completeness Theorem in Modal Logic"[2] stimulated a decade of intense and fruitful research which even now continues unabated. Although no single semantical viewpoint dominates contemporary research, the various semantical theories resemble each other closely enough to make for easy transition from one to another. The semantical theory presented in the first section of the present appendix comes from Kripke's 1959 paper.

The modal systems about to be introduced have a common syntax, namely the vocabulary of LSQ supplemented by the modal operator '□', and the formation rules of LSQ supplemented by the following rule: *If A is a wff,* ⌜□A⌝ *is also a wff.* We shall refer to this common syntactical schema as "LSQ-M".

The first semantics that we will give for LSQ-M is Kripke's 1959 semantics. Before presenting a careful statement of this semantics, we shall first give an intuitive, informal account of the meaning of a wff under an interpretation. Let 𝔇 be any nonempty set. We are to think of 𝔇 as the domain of individuals that exist in some possible world W; the world W may be, but need not be, the actual or real world. We make the fundamental assumption that *whatever exists in any possible world exists in every possible world;* that is, we

---

[1] *Journal of Symbolic Logic,* vol. 11 (1946), pp. 33–64.
[2] *Ibid.,* vol. 24 (1959), pp. 1–14.

assume that, for any possible world W', $\mathfrak{D}$ is the set of individuals which exist in W'. Of course, the same object may have quite different properties, or stand in quite different relations, in two distinct possible worlds. For example, although Brutus assassinates Caesar in the actual world, Caesar may die of old age in some world in which Brutus remains loyal to him. Accordingly, a full account of the reference of an n-ary predicate ϕ must indicate not only what n-tuples of individuals belong to the extension of ϕ in W, but, for each possible world W', what n-tuples of individuals belong to the extension of ϕ in W'. We also assume that *necessity is tantamount to truth in all possible worlds;* that is, we regard $\ulcorner \Box A \urcorner$ as true in W if and only if A is true in every possible world. Consequently, the truth value of A in W depends on the truth value of A in each possible world.

The foregoing informal account of Kripke's 1959 semantics should enable the reader to grasp quickly and easily the more careful and systematic account to be given now. For the sake of simplicity, we shall follow semantical alternative $\mathfrak{B}$ of Appendix F when presenting Kripke's semantics.

In unadorned quantification theory we dealt with interpretations on a domain of individuals $\mathfrak{D}$. Now we deal with interpretations on a *system of worlds* $\langle \Omega, \mathfrak{D} \rangle$, where Ω and $\mathfrak{D}$ are any nonempty sets. Intuitively, we may think of Ω as the set of possible worlds and, pursuant to our assumption that whatever exists in any possible world exists in every possible world, we may think of $\mathfrak{D}$ as the domain of individuals for each of the possible worlds. By *an interpretation* Σ *on a system of worlds* $\langle \Omega, \mathfrak{D} \rangle$, we shall mean a function on all the ordered pairs $\langle V, W \rangle$, where V is a variable of LSQ-M and W is a member of Ω, such that:

(a)   If V is a sentential variable, $\Sigma(V,W)$ is a truth value.

(b)   If V is an n-ary predicate variable, $\Sigma(V,W)$ is a set of n-tuples of members of $\mathfrak{D}$. (The gist of this clause is that Σ assigns to a predicate variable an extension in each possible world.)

(c)   If V is an individual variable, $\Sigma(V,W)$ is a member of $\mathfrak{D}$, and, for any members W_1 and W_2 of Ω, $\Sigma(V,W_1) = \Sigma(V,W_2)$. (The gist of the second clause is that Σ assigns the same value to an individual variable in each possible world.)

We now state an inductive definition of the *value of a wff A in a world W under an interpretation* Σ *on a system of worlds* $\langle \Omega, \mathfrak{D} \rangle$, *where* $W \in \Omega$:

(i)   If A is a sentential variable, then the value of A in W under Σ on $\langle\Omega,\mathfrak{D}\rangle$ is $\Sigma(A,W)$.

(ii)   If A is an atomic wff $\ulcorner\phi a_1\ldots a_n\urcorner$, then the value of A in W under Σ on $\langle\Omega,\mathfrak{D}\rangle$ is truth if the n-tuple $\langle\Sigma(a_1,W), \ldots, \Sigma(a_n,W)\rangle$ belongs to the set $\Sigma(\phi,W)$ of n-tuples of individuals; otherwise, the value of A in W under Σ on $\langle\Omega,\mathfrak{D}\rangle$ is falsehood.

(iii)   If A is $\ulcorner\sim B\urcorner$, then the value of A in W under Σ on $\langle\Omega,\mathfrak{D}\rangle$ is opposite to the value of B in W under Σ on $\langle\Omega,\mathfrak{D}\rangle$.

(iv)   If A is $\ulcorner B \cdot C\urcorner$, then the value of A in W under Σ on $\langle\Omega,\mathfrak{D}\rangle$ is truth if both B and C have the value truth in W under Σ on $\langle\Omega,\mathfrak{D}\rangle$; otherwise, the value of A in W under Σ on $\langle\Omega,\mathfrak{D}\rangle$ is falsehood.

(v)–(vii)   The clauses for '$\vee$', '$\supset$', and '$\equiv$' are similar to (iv).

(viii)   If A is $\ulcorner\Box B\urcorner$, then the value of A in W under Σ on $\langle\Omega,\mathfrak{D}\rangle$ is truth if, for every $W' \in \Omega$, the value of B in W' under Σ on $\langle\Omega,\mathfrak{D}\rangle$ is truth; otherwise, the value of A in W under Σ on $\langle\Omega,\mathfrak{D}\rangle$ is falsehood.

(ix)   If A is $\ulcorner(b)B\urcorner$, then the value of A in W under Σ on $\langle\Omega,\mathfrak{D}\rangle$ is truth if, for every interpretation Σ' on $\langle\Omega,\mathfrak{D}\rangle$ which is a b-variant of Σ, the value of B in W under Σ' on $\langle\Omega,\mathfrak{D}\rangle$ is truth; otherwise, the value of A in W under Σ on $\langle\Omega,\mathfrak{D}\rangle$ is falsehood. (Two interpretations on $\langle\Omega,\mathfrak{D}\rangle$ are *b-variants of one another* if they differ at most in the assignments they make to b.)

(x)   If A is $\ulcorner(\exists b)B\urcorner$, then the value of A in W under Σ on $\langle\Omega,\mathfrak{D}\rangle$ is truth if, for at least one interpretation Σ' on $\langle\Omega,\dot{\mathfrak{D}}\rangle$ which is a b-variant of Σ, the value of B in W under Σ' on $\langle\Omega,\mathfrak{D}\rangle$ is truth; otherwise, the value of A in W under Σ on $\langle\Omega,\mathfrak{D}\rangle$ is falsehood.

Relative to Kripke's 1959 semantics explained above, the concepts of satisfiability and validity may be defined as follows. A wff of LSQ-M shall be said to be *satisfiable in* a system of worlds $\langle\Omega,\mathfrak{D}\rangle$ if it comes out true in some member of Ω (that is, in some world that belongs to Ω) under some interpretation on $\langle\Omega,\mathfrak{D}\rangle$. And a wff of LSQ-M shall be said to be *satisfiable* if it is satisfiable in at least one system of worlds. Similarly, a wff of LSQ-M shall be said to be *valid in* a system of worlds $\langle\Omega,\mathfrak{D}\rangle$ if it comes out true in every member of Ω (that is, in every world that belongs to Ω) under every interpretation on $\langle \Omega, \mathfrak{D} \rangle$. And a wff of LSQ-M shall be called *valid* if it is valid in every system of worlds.

Let us now investigate some of the consequences of the foregoing definitions. Notice that for any wff A, A is valid if and only if $\ulcorner \Box A \urcorner$ is valid. Similarly, where '$\Diamond$' is understood to abbreviate '$\sim\Box\sim$', a wff A is satisfiable if and only if $\ulcorner \Diamond A \urcorner$ is satisfiable. Furthermore, $\ulcorner (a)A \urcorner$ is valid if and only if $\ulcorner \Box A \urcorner$ is valid, and $\ulcorner (\exists a)A \urcorner$ is satisfiable if and only if $\ulcorner \Diamond A \urcorner$ is satisfiable. As to particular wffs, all instances of any of the five following schemata are readily seen to be valid: '$\Box A \supset A$', '$\Box(A \supset B) \supset [\Box A \supset \Box B]$', '$\Box A \supset \Box\Box A$', '$A \supset \Box\Diamond A$', and '$\sim\Box A \supset \Box\sim\Box A$'. Also, the so-called *Barcan formula* '$(x)\Box Fx \supset \Box(x)Fx$' and the *converse Barcan formula* '$\Box(x)Fx \supset (x)\Box Fx$' turn out to be valid wffs of LSQ-M relative to Kripke's 1959 semantics.

Now, as in the case of P-languages and Q-languages, validity is intended to be a necessary and sufficient condition of the logical truth of fully interpreted wffs of LSQ-M, that is, of wffs that have been invested with sense. But many philosophers and logicians would deny that the Barcan and converse Barcan formulas become logical truths when invested with sense. For example, having repudiated the assumption that whatever exists in any possible world exists in every possible world, some logicians and philosophers would insist that the statement 'If it is necessarily the case that everything exists, then everything necessarily exists' is false. That is, they would maintain that the converse Barcan formula becomes a false sentence when 'F' is taken to mean '① exists'. Accordingly, these logicians and philosophers would not accept Kripke's 1959 semantics as an adequate analysis of the meaning of necessity. Wider semantical theories that do not confer validity on the Barcan and converse Barcan formulas will be introduced shortly. For the present, however, we will continue to employ Kripke's 1959 semantical analysis.

System Q-M; Natural Deduction System of Quantification Theory with Modality

By adding two simple rules to the seven deduction rules of system Q we obtain a natural deduction system, to be called "system Q-M," which is both consistent and complete with respect to validity (as validity is defined for wffs of LSQ-M relative to Kripke's 1959 semantics). The first of the two additional rules is called the *Aristotelian rule* (AR). The rule AR states that *a wff A may be set down as the nth line of a deduction if* ⌜□*A*⌝ *occurs as an earlier line* (*k*) *of the deduction, provided*

(i) *at the left of* (*n*) *one puts an occurrence of every star which occurs at the left of* (*k*), *and*
(ii) *at the right of* (*n*) *one writes* ⌜AR(*k*)⌝.

The following deductions illustrate the use of AR.

*₁(1)	□*p*	RP
*₁(2)	*p*	AR(1)
(3)	□*p* ⊃ *p*	Cd*₁(2)

*₁(1)	(*x*)□*Fx*	RP
*₁(2)	□*Fx*	UI(1)
*₁(3)	*Fx*	AR(2)
*₁(4)	(*x*)*Fx*	UG(3) |⌐
(5)	(*x*)□*Fx* ⊃ (*x*)*Fx*	Cd*₁(4)

Intuitively speaking, we may describe AR as a rule that authorizes the passage from necessity to actuality, that is, as a rule that authorizes the inference from ⌜□*A*⌝ to *A*. Like the five rules RP, TF, UI, EG, and Cd, the rule AR also preserves soundness in a deduction.

To formulate conveniently the second additional deduction rule, we need to extend the notion of a fully modalized wff (see Section 40.4) to wffs of LSQ-M. An occurrence of a variable in a wff *A* is said to be *modalized in A* if that occurrence of the variable is part of the scope of an occurrence of '□' in *A*. And a wff *B* is said to be *fully modalized* if every free occurrence of a variable (whether sentential, individual or predicate) in *B* is modalized in *B*. For example, the Barcan formula '(*x*)□*Fx* ⊃ □(*x*)*Fx*' is fully modalized, but '□(*x*)*Fx* ⊃ (*x*)*Fx*' is not fully modalized, because the second occurrence of '*F*' is free but not modalized in that wff. (Relative to Kripke's 1959 semantics, one can show by strong mathematical induction on the number of occurrences of connectives and quantifiers in a wff *A* that, if *A* is fully modalized, then *A* is equivalent to ⌜□*A*⌝.)

The second additional deduction rule is called the *rule of necessi-*

tation (RN).[3] The rule RN states that *a wff* $\ulcorner \Box A \urcorner$ *may be set down as the nth line of a deduction if* A *occurs as an earlier line* (k) *of the deduction, provided*

(i)   *all the premisses of* (k), *if any, are fully modalized,*

(ii) *no variable that has been flagged in the deduction occurs free in* (k) *or in any premiss of* (k),

(iii) *at the left of* (n) *one puts an occurrence of every star that appears at the left of* (k), *and*

(iv) *at the right of* (n) *one writes* $\ulcorner RN(k) \urcorner$.

The following deductions illustrate the use of RN.

$*_1(1)$	$\Box(p \supset q)$	RP
$*_2(2)$	$\Box p$	RP
$*_1(3)$	$p \supset q$	AR(1)
$*_2(4)$	p	AR(2)
$*_1*_2(5)$	q	TF(3)(4)
$*_1*_2(6)$	$\Box q$	RN(5)
$*_1(7)$	$\Box p \supset \Box q$	Cd$*_2$(6)
(8)	$\Box(p \supset q) \supset [\Box p \supset \Box q]$	Cd$*_1$(7)

$*_1(1)$	$(x)\Box Fx$	RP
$*_1(2)$	$\Box Fy$	UI(1)
$*_1(3)$	Fy	AR(2)
$*_1(4)$	$(x)Fx$	UG(3)
$*_1(5)$	$\Box(x)Fx$	RN(4)
(6)	$(x)\Box Fx \supset \Box(x)Fx$	Cd$*_1$(5)

The rule RN may be described as a rule that authorizes, under certain conditions, the inference from actuality to necessity; the conditions are chosen in such a way that RN preserves soundness in a deduction. (See below.)

The notion of a *finished deduction* is the same for system Q-M as for system Q. Similarly, a *proof* is again taken to be a finished deduction with unstarred last line, and a *theorem* is understood to be the last line of a proof. Now, relative to Kripke's 1959 semantics, one can show that system Q-M is both consistent and complete with respect to validity. That is, every theorem of system Q-M is valid (consistency theorem for system Q-M), and

[3] I am indebted to my colleague Herbert E. Hendry for the formulation of the rule RN given here.

every valid wff of system Q-M is a theorem of system Q-M (completeness theorem for system Q-M). In this appendix, however, we will sketch a proof only of the consistency theorem for system Q-M. We will assume the following lemma: The last line of any finished deduction in which the rule RN is *not* employed is sound in that deduction. [See Exercise (6) at the end of this appendix.]

To prove that the last line of any proof in system Q-M is valid, we proceed by strong mathematical induction on the number of uses of the rule RN in the proof. If RN has been used zero times in the proof, then we know from the lemma stated in the preceding paragraph that the last line of the proof is valid. This establishes the induction basis. Let us assume as hypothesis of induction that the last line of every proof in which n or fewer uses have been made of RN is valid, and let Ω, where Ω is the sequence of lines L_1, L_2, ..., L_r, be a proof in which $n + 1$ uses have been made of RN. Let L_m be the latest line of Ω that was set down in accordance with RN. Now L_m is some wff $\ulcorner \Box A \urcorner$. From the statement of the rule RN, we know that L_m is derived from some earlier line L_k, $L_k = A$, which either is unstarred or else has premisses all of which are fully modalized. We consider first the case of unstarred L_k. Note that, because L_k is unstarred, it follows from proviso (ii) of RN that the first k lines of Ω form a proof with n or fewer uses of RN. Hence, by the hypothesis of induction, A is valid. But then $\ulcorner \Box A \urcorner$ is also valid. Let a_1, ..., a_j be a complete list of the distinct free individual variables (if any) of $\ulcorner \Box A \urcorner$. $\ulcorner \Box A \urcorner$ is valid, so $\ulcorner (a_1) \ldots (a_j) \Box A \urcorner$ is also valid. We convert the deduction Ω into a deduction Ω^* by putting the following sequence of lines in front of Ω, at the same time modifying old line (m) of Ω so as to be derived *not* from old line (k) by RN but from new line $(j + 1)$ by TF and making any required changes in premiss indicators and numerals throughout Ω:

$*_1(1)$	$(a_1) \ldots (a_j) \Box A$	RP
$*_1(2)$	$(a_2) \ldots (a_j) \Box A$	UI(1)
.		
.		
.		
$*_1(j)$	$(a_j) \Box A$	UI($j - 1$)
$*_1(j + 1)$	$\Box A$	UI(j)

Note that Ω^* will be a finished deduction (obviously no flagged variable will occur free in the last line or in any premiss of the last line) and that the last line of Ω^* is the same wff as the last line of Ω. So, if the last line of Ω^* is unstarred, we know from the hypothesis of induction that it is valid, because only n uses are made of RN in Ω^*. If the last line of Ω^* is starred, line (1) will be its sole premiss. In this event we add one more line $(r + j + 2)$:

$$(r + j + 2) \quad (a_1)\ldots(a_j)\,\square A \supset B \qquad\qquad \text{Cd*}_1(r + j + 1)$$

where B is the last line of Ω^* and of Ω. The resulting sequence is a proof of $(r + j + 2)$ in which n uses are made of RN. So we know from the hypothesis of induction that $\ulcorner(a_1)\ldots(a_j)\,\square A \supset B\urcorner$ is valid. And since $\ulcorner(a_1)\ldots(a_j)\,\square A\urcorner$ is also valid, we know that B is valid, too. So, whether or not the last line of Ω^* (namely B) is starred, it is valid. But B is also the last line of Ω. We have shown, therefore, that in the first case considered, namely when line L_k of Ω is unstarred, the last line of Ω is valid.

We now consider in rough outline the case when L_k is starred, leaving details to the reader. Let L_k be the following line:

$$*_{i_1}\ldots*_{i_s}(k) \quad A \qquad\qquad\qquad\qquad \ldots$$

By adding steps of Cd and TF to the first k lines of Ω, one can obtain a proof of the conditional $\ulcorner(i_1)\cdot\ldots\cdot(i_s) \supset A\urcorner$ in which n or fewer uses of RN are made. By the hypothesis of induction, then, this conditional is valid. But then $\ulcorner(i_1)\cdot\ldots\cdot(i_s) \supset \square A\urcorner$ is also valid, because the conjunction $\ulcorner(i_1)\cdot\ldots\cdot(i_s)\urcorner$ is fully modalized. [See Exercise (7).] Let $b_1, \ldots, b_h$ be a complete list of the distinct individual variables that occur free in the aforementioned conditional. As the conditional is valid, so is $\ulcorner(b_1)\ldots(b_h)[(i_1)\cdot\ldots\cdot(i_s) \supset \square A]\urcorner$. From this point on, the reader should proceed as in the first case treated above. Namely, he should construct a new deduction Ω^* by putting the following sequence of lines in front of Ω, at the same time modifying old line (m) of Ω so as to be derived *not* from old line (k) by RN but from new line $(h + 1)$ *and* old lines (i_1), $\ldots, (i_s)$ by TF and making any required changes in premiss indicators and numerals throughout Ω:

$$*_1(1) \quad (b_1)\ldots(b_h)[(i_1)\cdot\ldots\cdot(i_s) \supset \square A] \qquad\qquad \text{RP}$$
$$*_1(2) \quad (b_2)\ldots(b_h)[(i_1)\cdot\ldots\cdot(i_s) \supset \square A] \qquad\qquad \text{UI(1)}$$
$$\cdot$$
$$\cdot$$
$$\cdot$$
$$*_1(h) \quad (b_h)[(i_1)\cdot\ldots\cdot(i_s) \supset \square A] \qquad\qquad\qquad \text{UI}(h - 1)$$
$$*_1(h + 1) \quad (i_1)\cdot\ldots\cdot(i_s) \supset \square A \qquad\qquad\qquad\quad \text{UI}(h)$$

The remainder of the argument parallels exactly the reasoning used in the first case above.

This completes the sketch of our proof of the consistency theorem for system Q-M.

Alternative Semantics for Quantification Theory with Modality (KA)

Dropping from Kripke's 1959 semantics the assumption that what exists in any possible world exists in every possible world yields a semantics for LSQ-M which some philosophers and logicians find more palatable than Kripke's 1959 semantics. We shall refer to this alternative semantics as alternative "KA". The basic idea behind KA, then, is that the domains of different possible worlds may be different. To say in a world W that everything has some property is to say that every object which exists in W has that property. Accordingly, with respect to a given possible world W, one can quantify over only the individuals which exist in W, that is, over only the elements of the domain of W. Although one can quantify over only the individuals which exist in W, predicates may be true in W of individuals which do not exist in W but exist in other possible worlds. For example, the predicate '①️ is conceived of as a winged horse' is true in this world of Pegasus, although Pegasus does not exist in this world but exists only in certain possible worlds.

The foregoing ideas assume the following semantical form. In alternative KA, one takes a *system of worlds* to be any ordered triple $\langle \Omega, \mathfrak{D}, f \rangle$, where Ω is a nonempty set (intuitively, the set of possible worlds), $\mathfrak{D}$ is a nonempty set (the set of things that exist in at least one possible world), and f is a function from members of Ω (from possible worlds) to nonempty subsets of $\mathfrak{D}$ (to domains of individuals) such that $\mathfrak{D}$ is the union of all the sets $f(W)$, $W \in \Omega$. Intuitively, $f(W)$ is the set of things that exist in W. The notion of an *interpretation on a system of worlds* can be taken over into KA unchanged from Kripke's 1959 semantics. Replacing clauses (ix) and (x) of the corresponding definition for Kripke's 1959 semantics by clauses (ix)* and (x)* below, one obtains for semantics KA an inductive definition of the *value of a wff A in a world W under an interpretation Σ on a system of worlds* $\langle \Omega, \mathfrak{D}, f \rangle$, *where* $W \in \Omega$:

(ix)*   If A is $\ulcorner (b)B \urcorner$, then the value of A in W under Σ on $\langle \Omega, \mathfrak{D}, f \rangle$ is truth if, for every interpretation Σ' on $\langle \Omega, \mathfrak{D}, f \rangle$ which is a

b-variant of Σ and which assigns a member of $f(W)$ to b, the value of B in W under Σ' on $\langle \Omega, \mathfrak{D}, f \rangle$ is truth; otherwise, the value of A in W under Σ on $\langle \Omega, \mathfrak{D}, f \rangle$ is falsehood.

(x)* If A is $\ulcorner(\mathbf{\exists} b)B\urcorner$, then the value of A in W under Σ on $\langle \Omega, \mathfrak{D}, f \rangle$ is truth if, for at least one interpretation Σ' on $\langle \Omega, \mathfrak{D}, f \rangle$ which is a b-variant of Σ and which assigns a member of $f(W)$ to b, the value of B in W under Σ' on $\langle \Omega, \mathfrak{D}, f \rangle$ is truth; otherwise the value of A in W under Σ on $\langle \Omega, \mathfrak{D}, f \rangle$ is falsehood.

Some wffs of LSQ-M which are valid relative to Kripke's 1959 semantics turn out not to be valid relative to alternative semantics KA. For example, neither the Barcan formula nor the converse Barcan formula is valid relative to KA. The reader may verify that the Barcan formula comes out false in W_1 under the interpretation Σ on the system of worlds $\langle \Omega, \mathfrak{D}, f \rangle$, where

$$\Omega = \{W_1, W_2\} \qquad \mathfrak{D} = \{1,2\}$$
$$f(W_1) = \{1\} \qquad f(W_2) = \{1,2\}$$
$$\Sigma('F', W_1) = \{1\} \qquad \Sigma('F', W_2) = \{1\}$$

On the other hand, every wff of LSQ-M that is valid relative to semantics KA is also valid relative to Kripke's 1959 semantics. Examples of wffs of LSQ-M that are valid relative to semantics KA include all instances of the schemata '$\Box A \supset A$', '$\Box(A \supset B) \supset [\Box A \supset \Box B]$', '$\Box A \supset \Box \Box A$', '$A \supset \Box \Diamond A$', and '$\sim \Box A \supset \Box \sim \Box A$'. In contrast to the Barcan formula and its converse, the wff '$\Box(x)\Box Fx \supset \Box(x)Fx$' is valid relative to semantics KA.

Alternative Semantics for Quantification Theory with Modality (KB)

Heretofore we have construed necessity as truth in all possible worlds. An alternative concept of necessity arises when we allow certain possible worlds to be absolutely irrelevant to the truth value of statements in a possible world W. From this viewpoint, necessity in W amounts to truth in all possible worlds which are relevant to W, *not* to truth in all possible worlds without exception. This concept of necessity presupposes, of course, a specification of which possible worlds are relevant to which. In this section we will formulate another alternative to Kripke's 1959 semantics, an alternative that we shall call semantics "KB". Like Kripke's

1959 semantics, KB retains the assumption that what exists in any possible world exists in every possible world, but, unlike the 1959 semantics, KB construes necessity in a possible world as truth in all possible worlds relevant to it.

In semantics KB, a *system of worlds* is any ordered triple $\langle \Omega, \mathfrak{D}, R \rangle$, where Ω is a nonempty set (intuitively, the set of possible worlds), $\mathfrak{D}$ is a nonempty set (the set of individuals that exist in any, and therefore in every, possible world), and R is a reflexive relation on Ω. ('RW_1W_2' means 'W_2 is relevant to W_1'.) By stipulating that R be reflexive, we ensure that each possible world is relevant to itself. The notion of an *interpretation* for KB is the same as for Kripke's 1959 semantics. And to get for KB an inductive definition of the *value of a wff A in a world W under an interpretation Σ on a system of worlds $\langle \Omega, \mathfrak{D}, R \rangle$, where $W \in \Omega$*, we need to make only the following modification to clause (viii) of the corresponding definition for Kripke's 1959 semantics:

(viii)*   If A is $\ulcorner \Box B \urcorner$, then the value of A in W under Σ on $\langle \Omega, \mathfrak{D}, R \rangle$ is truth if, for every possible world W' that is relevant to W (that is, for every $W' \in \Omega$ such that RWW'), the value of B in W' under Σ on $\langle \Omega, \mathfrak{D}, R \rangle$ is truth; otherwise the value of A in W under Σ on $\langle \Omega, \mathfrak{D}, R \rangle$ is falsehood.

If R is a transitive relation on Ω, then $\langle \Omega, \mathfrak{D}, R \rangle$ is said to be an S4 *system of worlds*. Similarly, if R is both a transitive and a symmetrical relation on Ω, then $\langle \Omega, \mathfrak{D}, R \rangle$ is said to be an S5 *system of worlds*. By an S4-*formula* of LSQ-M we shall mean a wff of LSQ-M that is valid (relative to semantics KB) in every S4 system of worlds, that is, a wff that comes out true (relative to KB) in every world W under every interpretation on every S4 system of worlds to which W belongs. Similarly, by an S5-*formula* of LSQ-M we shall mean a wff of LSQ-M that is valid (relative to semantics KB) in every S5 system of worlds, that is, a wff that comes out true (relative to KB) in every world W under every interpretation on every S5 system of worlds to which W belongs. Now it can be shown that the S5-formulas are the same as the wffs of LSQ-M which are valid relative to Kripke's 1959 semantics. Moreover, a sentential formula of LSQ-M (that is, a wff containing only sentential variables, sentence connectives, and grouping indicators) is an S5-formula if and only if it is valid in the sense of Section 34.1 (that is, if and only if it has the value truth on every row of every table in a plenary set of truth tables). Furthermore, it can be proved that a sentential formula of LSQ-M is an S4-formula if and only if it is a theorem of the system S4 described in Exercise [11] of Chapter 41. (The only truth-functional connectives of the system S4 just mentioned are the tilde and horseshoe, so obviously we must understand the remaining truth-functional connectives of LSQ-M to have been introduced by definition in order to make our last claim true.)

Let us call "system M" the system determined by the primitive basis that results when axiom 6 is dropped from the primitive basis of the system S5 presented in Section 40.0. And by an M-*formula* let us understand any sentential wff of LSQ-M that is valid in every system of worlds $\langle \Omega, \mathfrak{D}, R \rangle$ relative to semantics KB. It can be proved that a sentential wff of LSQ-M is an M-formula if and only if it is a theorem of system M.

Combining the characteristic features of semantics KA and semantics KB yields still another semantics for LSQ-M, which we shall call semantics "KAB". In semantics KAB we not only drop the assumption that what exists in any possible world exists in every possible world, but we also construe necessity in a possible world as truth in all possible worlds relevant to it. Accordingly, in KAB we understand a *system of worlds* to be any ordered quadruple $\langle \Omega, \mathfrak{D}, R, f \rangle$, where Ω is a nonempty set (intuitively, the set of possible worlds), $\mathfrak{D}$ is a nonempty set (the set of individuals that exist in at least one possible world), R is a reflexive relation on Ω ('RW_1W_2' means 'W_2 is relevant to W_1'), and f is a function from members of Ω to nonempty subsets of $\mathfrak{D}$ such that $\mathfrak{D}$ is the union of all the sets $f(W)$, $W \in \Omega$. Intuitively, $f(W)$ is the set of individuals that exist in W. To get an inductive definition for semantics KAB of the *value of a wff A in a world W under an interpretation* Σ *on a system of worlds* $\langle \Omega, \mathfrak{D}, R, f \rangle$, one need merely replace clauses (viii), (ix), and (x) of the corresponding definition for Kripke's 1959 semantics by clauses (viii)*, (ix)*, and (x)* formulated above.

Let us call a system of worlds $\langle \Omega, \mathfrak{D}, R, f \rangle$ an S5* *system of worlds* if R is both transitive and symmetrical on Ω. And by an S5*-*formula* of LSQ-M let us understand a wff of LSQ-M that is valid in every S5* system of worlds (relative to semantics KAB). Although every S5*-formula is also an S5-formula, some S5-formulas are not S5*-formulas.

The semantical alternatives described in this appendix represent only a small sample of the practically unlimited variety of semantical theories of LSQ-M which are alternatives to Kripke's 1959 semantics. For example, one might develop a semantics in which the domains of different possible worlds are mutually disjoint, or a semantics in which the relevance relation among possible worlds is not necessarily reflexive, or a semantics which allows that some possible worlds have empty domains, and so on. Familiarity with this appendix should enable the reader to grasp easily presentations of such alternatives, and even to construct alternatives tailored to his own philosophical tastes.

Exercises

(1) Prove relative to Kripke's 1959 semantics that all instances of the following schemata are valid: '$\Box A \supset A$', '$\Box(A \supset B) \supset [\Box A \supset \Box B]$', '$\Box A \supset \Box \Box A$', '$A \supset \Box \Diamond A$', and '$\sim\Box A \supset \Box \sim \Box A$'. Prove also that $\ulcorner\Box A\urcorner$ is valid if and only if $\ulcorner(a)A\urcorner$ is valid, and that $\ulcorner\Box A\urcorner$ is valid if and only if A is valid.

(2) For wffs of LSQ-M that do not contain any occurrences of the box '$\Box$', does Kripke's 1959 semantics differ in any significant way from the semantics of Section 46.4?

(3) Prove relative to Kripke's 1959 semantics that each of the six rules RP, TF, UI, EG, Cd, and AR preserves soundness in deductions of system Q-M.

(4) Prove relative to Kripke's 1959 semantics that if A is fully modalized, then A is equivalent to $\ulcorner\Box A\urcorner$.

(5) Prove that relative to Kripke's 1959 semantics the rule RN preserves soundness in a deduction.

(6) Relative to Kripke's 1959 semantics, prove that the last line of any finished deduction of system Q-M in which RN is *not* used is sound in that deduction. (*Hint:* First show that every line of a deduction in which only the six rules RP, TF, UI, EG, Cd, and AR are used is sound in that deduction. Then proceed as in the last part of Section 54.5.)

(7) Prove that the definition of a *fully modalized wff* given below is equivalent to the one given in the second section of this appendix in the sense that exactly the same wffs of LSQ-M turn out to be fully modalized whichever definition is adopted.

(i)   If A is a wff, then $\ulcorner \Box A \urcorner$ is fully modalized.

(ii) If B and C are fully modalized and b is an individual variable, then $\ulcorner \sim B \urcorner$, $\ulcorner B \cdot C \urcorner$, $\ulcorner B \vee C \urcorner$, $\ulcorner B \supset C \urcorner$, $\ulcorner B \equiv C \urcorner$, $\ulcorner (\exists b)B \urcorner$, and $\ulcorner (b)B \urcorner$ are all fully modalized.

(iii) A wff is fully modalized if and only if its being so follows from the above rules.

(8) Prove, by constructing proofs of them in system Q-M, that the following wffs of LSQ-M are valid relative to Kripke's 1959 semantics: '$\Box(x)Fx \supset (x)\Box Fx$', '$p \supset \Diamond p$', '$p \supset \Box \Diamond p$', '$\sim \Diamond p \supset \Box[p \supset (x)Fx]$', and '$\Box(x)(Fx \supset Gx) \supset [(x)\Box Fx \supset \Box(x)Gx]$'. Are '$(\exists x)Fx \equiv \Diamond Fx$' and '$(x)Fx \equiv \Box Fx$' also theorems of system Q-M?

(9) Relative to Kripke's 1959 semantics, prove that if $\ulcorner A \supset B \urcorner$ is valid and A is fully modalized, then $\ulcorner A \supset \Box B \urcorner$ is valid. [*Hint*: Use the result of Exercise (4).]

(10) Fill in the details of the proof of the consistency theorem for system Q-M (relative to Kripke's 1959 semantics) that was outlined in the present appendix.

(11) Show that the converse Barcan formula is not valid relative to alternative semantics KA. Prove that every wff of LSQ-M that is valid relative to semantics KA is also valid relative to Kripke's 1959 semantics. (*Hint*: If for every $W \in \Omega$, $f(W) = \mathfrak{D}$, a system of worlds $\langle \Omega, \mathfrak{D}, f \rangle$ essentially collapses into a system of worlds $\langle \Omega, \mathfrak{D} \rangle$.)

(12) Prove that '$\Box(x)\Box Fx \supset \Box(x)Fx$' is valid relative to semantics KA. Show that its converse '$\Box(x)Fx \supset \Box(x)\Box Fx$' is not valid relative to semantics KA.

(13) Prove that every wff of LSQ which is valid relative to the customary semantics given in Part Four is also valid relative to semantics KA.

(14) Prove that a wff of LSQ-M is valid relative to Kripke's 1959 semantics if and only if it is an S5-formula. Prove that a sentential formula of LSQ-M is an S5-formula if and only if it comes out true on every row of every table in a plenary set of truth tables for it (see Section 34.1). Is every S4-formula also an S5-formula? Are M-formulas also S4-formulas?

(15) Exhibit an S5-formula that is not also an S5*-formula. Prove that every S5*-formula is also an S5-formula. Are

the S5*-formulas the same wffs as the wffs of LSQ-M that are valid relative to semantics KA?

(16) By an S4* *system of worlds* let us understand a system of worlds $\langle \Omega, \mathfrak{D}, R, f \rangle$ such that R is transitive. And by an S4*-*formula* let us understand a wff of LSQ that is valid in every S4* system of worlds (relative to semantics KAB). Exhibit an S4*-formula that is neither an S4-formula nor an S5*-formula.

{17} In nonmodal logic one can explain identity by means of Leibniz's famous principle of the identity of indiscernibles as follows: Two things are identical if and only if every property of either is also a property of the other. Can a similar Leibnizian account of identity be given for identity across possible worlds? If not, what sense does it make to say, for example, that Caesar is identical with a certain individual in another possible world? To what degree does the application of quantification theory with modality to the logical analysis of ordinary language modal discourse depend on having satisfactory answers to the foregoing questions?

(18) Prove that '$\Box(p \vee \Box \sim p) \supset \Box(\sim p \vee \Box p)$' is an S5-formula but is not an S4-formula.

(19) When it was said that one obtained one or another of the modal semantics alternative to Kripke's 1959 semantics by substituting specified clauses for certain clauses in the truth definition of the 1959 semantics, it was taken for granted that all the clauses must be modified so as to make reference to the appropriate kind of systems of worlds. State in full the truth definitions of semantics KA, KB, and KAB, that is, the definitions of the value of a wff in a world W under an interpretation on a system of worlds to which W belongs.

Appendix H.
TENSE LOGIC

In Section 50.2 we remarked that predicates can be construed as tensed or as tenseless. For example, the extension of the predicate '① is a Cretan', when that predicate is taken as tenseless, is the set of all persons who are now, have been, or will be Cretans. But if taken as tensed, the predicate '① is a Cretan' has the set of all Cretans who are now living as its present extension. Notice that the extension of a tensed predicate is relative to time and may differ from one moment to another. For example, Epimenides belonged to the extension of '① is a Cretan' in the sixth century B.C., but he obviously does not belong to the extension which that predicate has now. Clearly, therefore, the reference of a tensed predicate is fully specified only when its extension at every moment is indicated. A tenseless predicate may be thought of as a degenerate case of a tensed predicate, namely as a tensed predicate whose extension is the same at all moments.

For want of devices for tensing, we are obliged to de-tense English predicates before we can stipulate their synonymy with predicate variables of Q-languages, that is, before we can invest the predicate variables of a Q-language with sense. In the case of the predicate '① is a Cretan', de-tensing does not generate over-much artificiality, since a person who belongs to its extension at any time belongs to its extension at every moment of his existence. But with respect to predicates like '① lived about 2500 years ago', de-tensing generates considerable artificiality. To say now (January 2, 1970) that Epimenides lived about 2500 years ago, we might use the (conceived as) tenseless predicate '① lives about 2500 years before January 2, 1970' to invest the predicate variable 'H' with sense. Then, with 'z' denoting Epimenides, the expression 'Hz' would mean 'Epimenides lives about 2500 years before January 2, 1970', a tenseless statement whose synonymy with the tensed statement 'Epimenides lived about 2500 years ago' is surely problematic. Nevertheless, 'Hz' is true if and only if the tensed statement 'Epimenides lived about 2500 years ago' is true on January 2, 1970. Accordingly, 'Hz' can accomplish some portion, however minute, of the semantical work that the latter tensed statement can do. It seems evident, however, that the sense of tensed English statements can be fully captured in a formalized language only if that formalized language does more justice to the tense of predicates and of statements than Q-languages are able to do. In particular, it would seem that in the semantics of such a formalized language the extension of a predicate would be relative to time, that is, that for each moment M, the predicate would be assigned an extension at M.

Just as the extension of a tensed predicate is relative to time, so the truth value of a tensed statement exhibits temporal relativity. That is, tensed statements are not true or false *simpliciter*, but *true at a moment* or *false at a moment*. For example, the tensed statement 'Caesar crossed the Rubicon' is true at the present time but was false when Caesar was an infant. A tenseless statement may be regarded as a degenerate tensed statement, namely as a tensed statement whose truth value is the same at all moments.

The application of tensed predicates to referring singular terms produces tensed statements. For example, application of '① lived about 2500 years ago' to 'Epimenides' yields the tensed sentence 'Epimenides lived about 2500 years ago' which is true today but was false when Paul wrote his epistle to Titus. Similarly, when quantifiers are used to convert a tensed predicate into a sentence, the result is a tensed statement. For example, '$(\exists x)(x$ lived about 2500 years ago)' is true today but was false when life first evolved in our universe. But it is not necessary that a sentence contain tensed predicates in order to be a nondegenerate tensed statement. For example, in a language in which quantifiers are taken to express present existence, as opposed to membership in the universe of discourse (see Section 50.2), and in which 'H' is synonymous with the (taken as) de-tensed predicate '① lives about 2500 years before January 2, 1970', the wff '$(\exists y)Hy$' would be a tensed statement which is now false since no creature that was alive 2500 years ago now exists, but which was true during the lifetime of Epimenides when such creatures abounded.

Tensing capitalizes on the temporal relativity of the truth value of a statement. One applies a past-tense operator '**P**' to a statement A to form a tensed statement $\ulcorner \mathbf{P}A \urcorner$ which is true at a moment M if and only if A is true at some moment earlier than M. Thus a natural reading of $\ulcorner \mathbf{P}A \urcorner$ is $\ulcorner$It has been the case that $A \urcorner$. Similarly, by prefixing a future-tense operator '**F**' to a statement A, one gets a tensed statement $\ulcorner \mathbf{F}A \urcorner$ which is true at a moment M if and only if A is true at some moment later than M. A natural reading of $\ulcorner \mathbf{F}A \urcorner$ is $\ulcorner$ It will be the case that $A \urcorner$. With a little ingenuity we can express every conceivable tense by means of these two tense operators and truth-functional sentence connectives. For example, using the tensed predicates '① attacks England' and '① invades Russia', we might state that Hitler had already attacked England when he invaded Russia as follows:

P[Hitler attacks Russia $\cdot$ **P**(Hitler invades England)]

Or, letting 'p' and 'q' abbreviate the present-tense statements 'Americans land on Mars' and 'Russians land on Venus' respectively, we might assert that Americans will already have landed on Mars when the Russians land on Venus as follows:

F$(q \cdot \mathbf{P}p \cdot \sim\mathbf{P}q)$

The semantical interplay between quantifiers and tensed predicates merits further comment. Let ϕ be a tensed predicate, i.e. a predicate whose extension is relative to time. Then $\ulcorner(\mathbf{\exists}b)\phi b \urcorner$ is a tensed statement which is *true at* a moment M if and only if at least one member of the universe of discourse belongs to the extension which ϕ has at M. Note that in order for $\ulcorner(\mathbf{\exists}b)\phi b \urcorner$ to be true at M it is not necessary that there exist at M some member of the universe of discourse that belongs to the extension which ϕ has at M. All that is required is that some member of the universe of discourse belong to the extension which ϕ has at M, whether or not it exists at M is immaterial. For example, if the universe of discourse is the set of all human beings who have lived, are now living, or will live, then '$(\mathbf{\exists}x)(x$ is dead)' is true at the present moment since some human beings who no longer exist belong to the present extension of '① is dead'. (We assume for the sake of example that human beings exist only when they are alive.) Similarly, $\ulcorner(b)\phi b \urcorner$ is a tensed statement which is true at a moment M if and only if every member of the universe of discourse belongs to the extension which ϕ has at M. Thus, in our example, '$(x)(x$ is living)' is false at the present moment since some members of the universe of discourse (e.g. Epimenides) do not belong to the extension which '① is living' now has. With tensed predicates at hand, it is only natural to introduce quantifiers which do not merely express membership in the universe of discourse as do the familiar $\ulcorner(\exists b)\urcorner$ and $\ulcorner(b)\urcorner$, but which also express present existence. We shall write these *temporal quantifiers* as $\ulcorner\langle\exists b\rangle\urcorner$ and $\ulcorner\langle b\rangle\urcorner$ to distinguish them sharply from the familiar a-temporal quantifiers. Where ϕ is a tensed predicate, the expression $\ulcorner\langle\exists b\rangle\phi b\urcorner$ is a tensed statement which is true at a moment M if and only if at least one member of the universe of discourse which exists at M belongs to the extension which ϕ has at M. In our example, '$\langle\exists x\rangle(x$ is dead)' is false at the present moment since no human being now existing is dead (we stipulated that a corpse is not a human being), but '$\langle\exists x\rangle(x$ is living)' is true at the present moment and at every moment at which human beings live. Similarly, the expression $\ulcorner\langle b\rangle\phi b\urcorner$ is a tensed statement which is true at a moment M if and only if every member of the universe of discourse which exists at M belongs to the extension which ϕ has at M. In our example, '$\langle x\rangle(x$ is living)' is true not only at the present moment but at every moment, whereas '$\langle x\rangle(x$ is an American citizen)' is presently false, has always been false, and will probably always be false. Clearly, $\ulcorner(b)\phi b\urcorner$ implies $\ulcorner\langle b\rangle\phi b\urcorner$, and $\ulcorner\langle\exists b\rangle\phi b\urcorner$ implies $\ulcorner(\exists b)\phi b\urcorner$. The reader should show by means of counterexamples that the converse implications do not obtain, that is, that $\ulcorner\langle b\rangle\phi b\urcorner$ does not imply $\ulcorner(b)\phi b\urcorner$ and that $\ulcorner(\exists b)\phi b\urcorner$ does not imply $\ulcorner\langle\exists b\rangle\phi b\urcorner$.

Now it might appear that the familiar a-temporal quantifiers $\ulcorner(\exists b)\urcorner$ and $\ulcorner(b)\urcorner$ could be defined thus:

$$(\exists b)\phi b =_{\text{Df}} \langle\exists b\rangle\phi b \vee \mathbf{P}\langle\exists b\rangle\phi b \vee \mathbf{F}\langle\exists b\rangle\phi b$$
$$(b)\phi b =_{\text{Df}} \langle b\rangle\phi b \cdot {\sim}\mathbf{P}{\sim}\langle b\rangle\phi b \cdot {\sim}\mathbf{F}{\sim}\langle b\rangle\phi b$$

This appearance is illusory, however. From the foregoing definitions it would not follow that $\ulcorner(\exists b)\phi b\urcorner$ is true at a moment M if and only if some individual (member of the universe of discourse) belongs to the extension which ϕ has at M, but it would rather follow that $\ulcorner(\exists b)\phi b\urcorner$ is true at M if and only if some individual at some moment of its existence belongs to the extension which ϕ has at that moment. Similarly, the foregoing definitions do not entail that $\ulcorner(b)\phi b\urcorner$ is true at M if and only if every individual belongs to the extension which ϕ has at M; rather, they entail that $\ulcorner(b)\phi b\urcorner$ is true at M if and only if every individual at every moment of its existence belongs to the extension which ϕ has at that moment.

One word of caution. Note that '$\mathbf{P}\langle\exists x\rangle Fx$' does not mean 'It has been the case that there is now an F', but means rather 'It has been the case that there was then an F' or more simply 'There has been an F'. Although by itself '$\langle\exists x\rangle Fx$' expresses the present existence of an F, the past-tense operator in '$\mathbf{P}\langle\exists x\rangle Fx$' purports to transport one conceptually to an earlier time which is to be conceived of as the present relative to which '$\langle\exists x\rangle Fx$' asserts existence. The reader will avoid confusion if he relies more on semantical rules and less on informal readings. In the case at hand, the semantical rules make it clear that '$\mathbf{P}\langle\exists x\rangle Fx$' is true at moment M if and only if '$\langle\exists x\rangle Fx$' is true at some moment earlier than M, that is, if and only if at some moment earlier than M there exists an individual who belongs to the extension which 'F' has at that moment.

Logical systems which incorporate tense operators such as '$\mathbf{P}$' and '$\mathbf{F}$' are known as *tense logics*. Obviously it would be pointless to incorporate tense operators into a system the semantics of which made the truth values of wffs independent of time. And, if one is going to deal overtly with tenses at all, it is only natural to insist that the extensions of predicates also be made relative to time. Tensed predicates, in turn, would be somewhat inappropriate in a quantificational system all the quantifiers of which express a-temporal existence, that is, merely express membership in the universe of discourse. In the remainder of this appendix we shall present the semantics of a system of quantificational tense logic obtained by adding the tense operators '$\mathbf{P}$' and '$\mathbf{F}$' and temporal quantifiers to LSQ. This system, which we shall call "LSQ-T", is due in all essentials to the logician Nino Cocchiarella. In LSQ-T both the truth values of wffs and the extensions of predicate variables are relative to time; in addition, LSQ-T boasts temporal quantifiers which express present existence as well as the familiar a-temporal quantifiers. The semantics of LSQ-T turns out to be quite similar to semantics KAB of LSQ-M (see Appendix G).

The vocabulary of LSQ-T consists of the vocabulary of LSQ supplemented by the tense operators '$\mathbf{P}$' and '$\mathbf{F}$' and the angle brackets '$\langle$' and '$\rangle$'. We leave it to the reader to formulate the formation rules of LSQ-T [see Exercise (4)].

In formulating the semantics of LSQ-T ,we make one assumption about time order, namely that the moments of time are serially ordered by the "earlier than" relation [see Exercise (5)]. Relative to LSQ-M, interpretations are given on a system of worlds; relative to LSQ-T, interpretations are given on an historical system.

By an *historical system* is meant any ordered quadruple $\langle \Omega, \mathfrak{D}, R, f \rangle$ such that Ω is a nonempty set (intuitively, Ω is the set of moments of time), $\mathfrak{D}$ is a nonempty set (intuitively, $\mathfrak{D}$ is the set of things which exist at some moment or other), R is a serial-order relation on Ω (intuitively, R is the "earlier than" relation among moments), f is a function from members of Ω to nonempty subsets of $\mathfrak{D}$ (intuitively, where M is a moment of Ω, $f(M)$ is the set of things which exist at moment M), and $\mathfrak{D}$ is the union of all the sets $f(M)$, $M \in \Omega$. By an *interpretation* Σ *on an historical system* $\langle \Omega, \mathfrak{D}, R, f \rangle$ is meant a function Σ on the ordered pairs $\langle V, M \rangle$, where V is a (sentential, individual, or predicate) variable of LSQ-T and M is a member of Ω, such that:

(i) If V is a sentential variable, then $\Sigma(V,M)$ is a truth value. (Intuitively, $\Sigma(V,M)$ is the truth value of the sentence V at moment M.)

(ii) If V is an *n*-ary predicate variable, then $\Sigma(V,M)$ is a set of *n*-tuples of members of $\mathfrak{D}$. (Intuitively, $\Sigma(V,M)$ is the extension of the predicate V at moment M.)

(iii) If V is an individual variable, then $\Sigma(V,M)$ is a member of $\mathfrak{D}$ and, for every member M' of Ω, $\Sigma(V,M) = \Sigma(V,M')$. (Intuitively, $\Sigma(V,M)$ is the individual denoted by V at every moment of time.)

Note that an interpretation may assign to a predicate variable different extensions at different moments. Thus the semantics of LSQ-T does full justice to the temporal relativity of the extension of a tensed predicate. Tensed predicates like '① is sleeping' which may be true of an individual at some times and false at others are rendered easily and naturally into LSQ-T.

We now formulate an inductive definition of the *value of a wff A at a moment M under an interpretation* Σ *on an historical system* $\langle \Omega, \mathfrak{D}, R, f \rangle$, *where* $M \in \Omega$:

(i) If A is a sentential variable, then the value of A at M under Σ on $\langle \Omega, \mathfrak{D}, R, f \rangle$ is $\Sigma(A,M)$.

(ii) If A is an atomic wff $\ulcorner \phi a_1 \ldots a_n \urcorner$, then the value of A at M under Σ on $\langle \Omega, \mathfrak{D}, R, f \rangle$ is truth if the *n*-tuple $\langle \Sigma(a_1,M), \ldots, \Sigma(a_n,M) \rangle$ belongs to the set $\Sigma(\phi,M)$; otherwise, the value of A at M under Σ on $\langle \Omega, \mathfrak{D}, R, f \rangle$ is falsehood.

(iii) If A is $\ulcorner \sim B \urcorner$, then the value of A at M under Σ on

$\langle\Omega,\mathfrak{D},R,f\rangle$ is opposite to the value of B at M under Σ on $\langle\Omega,\mathfrak{D},R,f\rangle$.

(iv) If A is $\ulcorner B \cdot C \urcorner$, then the value of A at M under Σ on $\langle\Omega,\mathfrak{D},R,f\rangle$ is truth if both B and C have the value truth at M under Σ on $\langle\Omega,\mathfrak{D},R,f\rangle$; otherwise, the value of A at M under Σ on $\langle\Omega,\mathfrak{D},R,f\rangle$ is falsehood.

(v)–(vii) The clauses for '∨', '⊃', and '≡' are similar to (iv).

(viii) If A is $\ulcorner \mathbf{P}B \urcorner$, then the value of A at M under Σ on $\langle\Omega,\mathfrak{D},R,f\rangle$ is truth if there is a member M' of Ω such that $RM'M$ and such that the value of B at M' under Σ on $\langle\Omega,\mathfrak{D},R,f\rangle$ is truth; otherwise, the value of A at M under Σ on $\langle\Omega,\mathfrak{D},R,f\rangle$ is falsehood.

(ix) If A is $\ulcorner \mathbf{F}B \urcorner$, then the value of A at M under Σ on $\langle\Omega,\mathfrak{D},R,f\rangle$ is truth if there is a member M' of Ω such that RMM' and such that the value of B at M' under Σ on $\langle\Omega,\mathfrak{D},R,f\rangle$ is truth; otherwise, the value of A at M under Σ on $\langle\Omega,\mathfrak{D},R,f\rangle$ is falsehood.

(x) If A is $\ulcorner (b)B \urcorner$, then the value of A at M under Σ on $\langle\Omega,\mathfrak{D},R,f\rangle$ is truth if, for every interpretation Σ' on $\langle\Omega,\mathfrak{D},R,f\rangle$ which is a b-variant of Σ, the value of B at M under Σ' on $\langle\Omega,\mathfrak{D},R,f\rangle$ is truth; otherwise, the value of A at M under Σ on $\langle\Omega,\mathfrak{D},R,f\rangle$ is falsehood.

(xi) If A is $\ulcorner (\exists b)B \urcorner$, then the value of A at M under Σ on $\langle\Omega,\mathfrak{D},R,f\rangle$ is truth if, for at least one interpretation Σ' on $\langle\Omega,\mathfrak{D},R,f\rangle$ which is a b-variant of Σ, the value of B at M under Σ' on $\langle\Omega,\mathfrak{D},R,f\rangle$ is truth; otherwise, the value of A at M under Σ on $\langle\Omega,\mathfrak{D},R,f\rangle$ is falsehood.

(xii) If A is $\ulcorner \langle b\rangle B \urcorner$, then the value of A at M under Σ on $\langle\Omega,\mathfrak{D},R,f\rangle$ is truth if, for every interpretation Σ' on $\langle\Omega,\mathfrak{D},R,f\rangle$ which is a b-variant of Σ and which assigns a member of $f(M)$ to b, the value of B at M under Σ' on $\langle\Omega,\mathfrak{D},R,f\rangle$ is truth; otherwise, the value of A at M under Σ on $\langle\Omega,\mathfrak{D},R,f\rangle$ is falsehood.

(xiii) If A is $\ulcorner \langle \exists b\rangle B \urcorner$, then the value of A at M under Σ on $\langle\Omega,\mathfrak{D},R,f\rangle$ is truth if, for at least one interpretation Σ' on $\langle\Omega,\mathfrak{D},R,f\rangle$ which is a b-variant of Σ and which assigns a member of $f(M)$ to b, the value of B at M under Σ' on $\langle\Omega,\mathfrak{D},R,f\rangle$ is truth; otherwise, the value of A at M under Σ on $\langle\Omega,\mathfrak{D},R,f\rangle$ is falsehood.

Finally, a wff of LSQ-T is said to be *valid in* an historical system $\langle\Omega,\mathfrak{D},R,f\rangle$ if it comes out true at every moment of Ω under every interpretation on $\langle\Omega,\mathfrak{D},R,f\rangle$. A wff of LSQ-T is said to be *valid* if it is valid in every historical system. Cocchiarella has constructed logistic systems of LSQ-T which are both consistent and complete with respect to validity. The interested reader may consult Cocchiarella's doctoral dissertation.[1] The following are examples of valid wffs of LSQ-T:

$\langle\exists x\rangle Fx \supset (\exists x)Fx$ $(\exists x)\mathbf{P}Fx \equiv \mathbf{P}(\exists x)Fx$

$(x)Fx \supset \langle x\rangle Fx$ $\mathbf{P}(x)Fx \supset (x)\mathbf{P}Fx$

$\mathbf{PP}p \supset \mathbf{P}p$ $(\exists x)\mathbf{F}Fx \equiv \mathbf{F}(\exists x)Fx$

$\mathbf{FF}p \supset \mathbf{F}p$ $\mathbf{F}(x)Fx \supset (x)\mathbf{F}Fx$

$\mathbf{PF}p \supset \mathbf{PFPF}p$ $\mathbf{F}(p \vee \sim p) \supset (\sim\mathbf{F}\sim p \supset \mathbf{F}p)$

$\mathbf{P}(p \vee q) \equiv \mathbf{P}p \vee \mathbf{P}q$ $\mathbf{P}(p \vee \sim p) \supset (\sim\mathbf{P}\sim p \supset \mathbf{P}p)$

$\mathbf{F}(p \vee q) \equiv \mathbf{F}p \vee \mathbf{F}q$ $\mathbf{F}(p \vee \sim p) \supset (p \supset \mathbf{FP}p)$

     $\mathbf{P}(p \vee \sim p) \supset (p \supset \mathbf{PF}p)$

Some wffs of LSQ-T seem to be valid on a first reading but under closer analysis can be seen to be nonvalid. Some examples are:

$\mathbf{P}p \supset \mathbf{PP}p$ $(x)\mathbf{P}Fx \supset \mathbf{P}(x)Fx$

$\mathbf{F}p \supset \mathbf{FF}p$ $(x)\mathbf{F}Fx \supset \mathbf{F}(x)Fx$

$p \supset \mathbf{FP}p$ $\mathbf{P}\langle\exists x\rangle Fx \supset \langle\exists x\rangle\mathbf{P}Fx$

$p \supset \mathbf{PF}p$ $\langle\exists x\rangle\mathbf{P}Fx \supset \mathbf{P}\langle\exists x\rangle Fx$

$\sim\mathbf{F}\sim p \supset \mathbf{F}p$ $(\exists x)Fx \equiv \langle\exists x\rangle Fx \vee \mathbf{P}\langle\exists x\rangle Fx \vee \mathbf{F}\langle\exists x\rangle Fx$

$\sim\mathbf{P}\sim p \supset \mathbf{P}p$ $(x)Fx \equiv \langle x\rangle Fx\cdot\sim\mathbf{P}\sim\langle x\rangle Fx\cdot\sim\mathbf{F}\sim\langle x\rangle Fx$

Exercises

{1} On what grounds might one argue that an utterance made on January 2, 1970 of the statement 'Epimenides lived about 2500 years ago' is not synonymous with an utterance of the statement 'Epimenides lived about 2500 years before January 2, 1970' made at the same time?

{2} Would someone who held that all predicates are tenseless and that quantifiers do not express present existence but

---

[1] Nino Cocchiarella, *Tense Logic: A Study of Temporal Reference* (doctoral thesis, UCLA, 1966). Actually, Cocchiarella's semantics differs slightly from ours. Cocchiarella demands neither that $f(M)$ be nonempty nor that $\mathfrak{D}$ be the union of all the sets $f(M)$, $M \in \Omega$.

only membership in the universe of discourse be committed to denying that the truth value of a statement is relative to time?

(3)   Where 'p' and 'q' respectively abbreviate the present-tense statements 'Americans land on Mars' and 'Russians land on Venus', why is '$\mathbf{F}(q \cdot \mathbf{P}p)$' an inadequate rendering of the statement 'Americans will have landed on Mars when Russians land on Venus'? Produce a translation of 'Russians landed on Venus before Americans landed on Mars'.

(4)   Formulate the formation rules of LSQ-T. (*Hint*: Treat '$\mathbf{P}$' and '$\mathbf{F}$' as singulary sentence connectives.)

(5)   A set Ω of two or more members is said to be *serially ordered by* a relation R if the following three conditions obtain:

   (a)   If α and β are distinct members of Ω, then either $R\alpha\beta$ or $R\beta\alpha$;

   (b) R is irreflexive on Ω, that is, for no member α of Ω is it the case that $R\alpha\alpha$; and

   (c) R is transitive on Ω.

(In the context of tense logic, we shall say that a set Ω that has exactly one member α is *serially ordered by* a relation R if it is not the case that $R\alpha\alpha$.) Cite several familiar illustrations of serial-order relations on sets.

[6]   Prove that the familiar a-temporal quantifiers $\ulcorner (b) \urcorner$ and $\ulcorner (\exists b) \urcorner$ cannot be defined in the system that results when these quantifiers are dropped from the system LSQ-T.

(7)   Establish the validity of all the wffs of LSQ-T that are listed as valid at the end of this appendix. Prove that every valid wff of LSQ is also a valid wff of LSQ-T. If A is a valid wff of LSQ-T, are $\ulcorner \mathbf{P}A \urcorner$ and $\ulcorner \mathbf{F}A \urcorner$ also valid wffs of LSQ-T? Prove that A is a valid wff of LSQ-T if and only if $\ulcorner A \cdot {\sim}\mathbf{P}{\sim}A \cdot {\sim}\mathbf{F}{\sim}A \urcorner$ is a valid wff of LSQ-T. Find a counter-model of each wff of LSQ-T that is listed as nonvalid at the end of this appendix.

{8}   Compare and contrast semantics KAB for LSQ-M (see Appendix G) with the semantics for LSQ-T given in the present appendix. By varying certain semantical assumptions about possible worlds and about the existence of individuals, one generates alternative modal semantics for LSQ-M. What assumptions about time and existence of individuals might one vary in order to generate alternative tense semantics for LSQ-T?

[9] Let S be the system that results from LSQ-T when the definition of an interpretation Σ on an historical system $\langle \Omega, \mathfrak{D}, R, f \rangle$ is modified thus: (ii) If V is an n-ary predicate variable, then $\Sigma(V, M)$ is a set of n-tuples of members of $\mathfrak{D}$ and, for every member M' of Ω, $\Sigma(V, M') = \Sigma(V, M)$. In other words, S is the system which results when the predicate variables of LSQ-T have been de-tensed. Are the following wffs valid in S?

$$(b)A \equiv \langle b \rangle A \cdot \sim\mathbf{P}\sim\langle b \rangle A \cdot \sim\mathbf{F}\sim\langle b \rangle A$$
$$(\exists b)A \equiv \langle \exists b \rangle A \vee \mathbf{P}\langle \exists b \rangle A \vee \mathbf{F}\langle \exists b \rangle A$$

Can the familiar quantifiers $\ulcorner (b) \urcorner$ and $\ulcorner (\exists b) \urcorner$ be defined in S in terms of the temporal quantifiers $\ulcorner \langle b \rangle \urcorner$ and $\ulcorner \langle \exists b \rangle \urcorner$, sentence connectives, and tense operators? Conversely, can $\ulcorner \langle b \rangle \urcorner$ and $\ulcorner \langle \exists b \rangle \urcorner$ be defined in terms of $\ulcorner (b) \urcorner$, $\ulcorner (\exists b) \urcorner$, sentence connectives, and tense operators?

⟨10⟩ Develop a decision procedure for validity of sentential wffs of LSQ-T, that is, wffs that contain no variables other than sentential variables.

(11) Let LSQ-TN be the system that results when the present-tense operator 'N' is added to LSQ-T, with $\ulcorner NA \urcorner$ being understood to be true at a moment M if and only if A is true at the moment M. Prove that, for any wff A of LSQ-TN, A is equivalent to A^*, where A^* is the formula that results when all occurrences of 'N' in A have been deleted. Explain why it would be pointless to add the present-tense operator to LSQ-T.

Appendix I.
LOGISTIC SYSTEM
OF QUANTIFICATION THEORY

In Part Two the valid wffs of LSP were systematized by means of a logistic or formal axiomatic system, system P. In Part Four the valid wffs of LSQ were systematized by means of a natural deduction system, system Q. Natural deduction systems and logistic systems were characterized as different species of formal systems in Section 52.1. Each species has certain advantages over the other. Because it is generally easier in natural deduction systems than in logistic systems to construct proofs of wffs that are theorems, we chose to present a natural deduction system of quantification theory in the body of the text. But it would have been no less inappropriate to present a logistic system of quantification theory, on the grounds that it is generally easier to develop the metatheory of a logistic system than to develop the metatheory of a natural deduction system. But, lest the reader think that quantification theory can be systematized only as a natural deduction system, we now briefly sketch the primitive basis of a logistic system of quantification theory which shall be called "system Q*".

Vocabulary of System Q*

The vocabulary of system Q* is obtained by deleting the three connectives '$\cdot$', '$\vee$', and '$\equiv$', and the quantifier symbol '$\exists$' from the vocabulary of system Q.

Formation Rules of System Q*

We leave it to the reader to state the formation rules of system Q*.

Axioms of System Q*

There are infinitely many axioms in system Q*. They are given by the following six axiom schemata, together with the stipulation

414

that, if A is an axiom of system Q*, then $\ulcorner(a)A\urcorner$ is also an axiom of system Q*.

$A \supset [B \supset A]$

$[A \supset (B \supset C)] \supset [(A \supset B) \supset (A \supset C)]$

$[\sim A \supset \sim B] \supset [B \supset A]$

$(a)A \supset B$, where B is an instance (see Section 52.0) of A

$(a)[A \supset B] \supset [(a)A \supset (a)B]$

$(a)[A \supset B] \supset [A \supset (a)B]$, where a does not occur free in A.

Rules of Inference of System Q*

The sole rule of inference of system Q* is *modus ponens*.

Semantics of System Q*

It is left to the reader to formulate the intended semantics of system Q*.

Exercises

(1) Assuming that system P_2 (see Section 28.1) is complete with respect to validity, prove that every tautologous wff [see Exercise (9) of Section 47] of system Q* is a theorem of system Q*.

(2) Prove that $\ulcorner(a)A\urcorner$ is a theorem of system Q* if A is a theorem of system Q*.

(3) Prove that '$(a)[A \supset B] \supset [(a)A \supset B]$' is a theorem schema of system Q*, that is, prove that every instance of this schema is a theorem of system Q*.

(4) Prove that every theorem of system Q* is valid, that is, that system Q* is consistent with respect to validity.

(5) In the context of system Q* let us understand by a *proof from the hypotheses* $A_1, \ldots, A_n$ any finite sequence of wffs each of which is either an axiom of system Q*, one of the hypotheses $A_1, \ldots, A_n$, or inferable by *modus ponens* from two earlier members of the sequence. Prove that if $A_1, \ldots, A_n \vdash B$, then $A_1, \ldots, A_{n-1} \vdash \ulcorner A_n \supset B\urcorner$. (See Section 30.0 for an explanation of the foregoing notation.)

INDEX

Abbreviative convention, 34–36, 53–54, 60–61, 310
  definition and, 51
  formally acceptable, 35
    See also Ambiguity; Conventions
Absolute completeness, 142 (Ex. 10)
Absolute consistency, 140
Actual truth-value outcome, 163–167, 175–176
AL (alternation left), rule of, 361–362
Algebra, elementary, 41 (Exs. 5–7)
Algorithm, *see* Decision procedure
Alphabetic change of bound variable, 264, 268–269 (Ex. 7), 273 (Ex. 14), 294
Alternation, *see* Disjunction
Alternation left, rule of (AL), 361–362
Alternation right, rule of (AR), 360–361
Alternative semantics ɑ, 385–386
Alternative semantics ß, 385–386
Ambiguity, 5, 104–107, 230, 326
  intolerable, 34
  tolerable, 38–40, 41 (Ex. 6)
Ampersand '&', 11 (Ex. 8), 118
Analytic truth and falsity, *see* Analyticity
Analyticity, 30–32, 163, 180, 260–261
Angle brackets, 356–357, 408
Annotation, 128, 275
Anselmian formula, 204–205 (Ex. 9)
Antecedent, 53
  law of denial of the, 148
AR (alternation right), rule of, 360–361
AR (Aristotelian rule), rule of, 393
Argument (logical), 90–91
  proving correctness of, 89–93
  proving incorrectness of, 93–94
Aristotelian rule (AR), 393
Aristotle, 4

Artificial language, *see* Formalized language
Atom (nominalistic), 308
Atomic analysis, 225, 263
Atomic wff, 13–15, 230–231, 234–235
  semantics of, 234–235
Axiom, 155
Axiom schema, 139–140, 414–415
Axiomatic method, 125
  formal, 127, 155–156
  informal, 127, 156
Axiomatic system, informal, 128
  formal, *see* Logistic system

Barcan formula, 392, 398
  converse, 392, 398
Bernays, Paul, 253
Bestimmheit axiom, 317 (Ex. 1)
Beth, E. W., 358
Biconditional, 54–56, 100
Bilateral reduction sentence, 317 (Ex. 3)
Binary sentence connective, 7
Boolean algebra, 72–73, 76–81
Boolean equations, 76–81
  system of (SBE), 76–81
  translational method, 81
  truth functions of (TFBE), 87–88 (Ex. 5), 196 (Ex. 12)
Bound term (occurrence), 327
Bound variable, 239–240
  occurrence, 239–240
Box '□', 164–169, 389–391, 399
  fundamental set of truth tables for, 167–169
    See also Necessity
Braces, 36, 356
Brackets, 34, 36, 60
  angle, 356–357, 408
  outside pair, 34
    See also Grouping

Calculus, uninterpreted, 207

Calculus of individuals (COI), 307–313

Cantor's antinomy, 261

Cantor's theorem, 253

Carnap, Rudolf, 389

Categorical wff, 344–345

Cd (conditionalization), rule of, 278–279

Cell, 314–315

Characteristic matrix, 142–143 (Ex. 14), 222 (Ex. 12)
 finite, 143 (Ex. 14), 222 (Ex. 12)

Characteristic wff, of a set of truth tables, 199–200
 of a truth table, 45–46, 199

Check mark '√', 360–364, 366–369

Church, Alonzo, 125 n., 337, 385 n.

Church's theorem, 338–341

Church's thesis, 335, 337, 340–342, 369

Church's thesis theorem, 338–339, 341, 343, 369

Circled numeral, 227–230, 237–238, 325–327

Class, 261, 355–357
 empty, 355–356
 ultimate, 261, 316 (Ex. 1)
 unit, 357
 See also Ordered set

Class term, 76–78

Class variable, 73

Closed set of tableaux, 359

Closed tableau, 358

Closed wff, 260–261, 365, 368–369

Closure, universal, 305

Cocchiarella, Nino, 408, 411

COI (calculus of individuals), 307–313

Commutativity of conjunction, 5–6

Compactness theorem, 57, 154, 256 (Ex. 7), 376–378

Compatibility connective '∘', 192–193

Complement (class), 76–79

Completeness, absolute, 142 (Ex. 10)
 ω-completeness, 321–323
 theorem for P, 151–154, 372–375
 theorem for Q, 291, 320, 379–383
 theorem for QI, 306, 313–316
 theorem for QIF, 328

theorem for Q-M, 394–395
theorem for S5, 211–216
theorem for S5', 218
strong theorem for P, 158–159 (Ex. 18)
strong theorem for Q, 292–293
strong theorem for QI, 306
strong theorem for QIF, 328
with respect to a property, 129

Computation problem, 158 (Ex. 13)

Conceivability, 32, 94

Condemned class, 376–377

Conditional, strategy of, 300–301

Conditional wff or sentence, 52–54, 57, 99–100
 antecedent of, 53
 consequent of, 53
 counterfactual, 99–100
 subjunctive, 100
 See also Horseshoe '⊃'

Conditionalization, rule of (Cd), 278–279

Conjunction, 5, 7–8, 96–97
 associated conjunction of a row, 44–45, 198
 commutativity of, 4–6
 continued, 39
 fundamental truth table for, 8
 theorem of infinite, 378 (Ex. 2)
 See also Dot '·'

Conjunction left, rule of (KL), 362

Conjunction right, rule of (KR), 362

Connectives, *see* Sentence connectives

Consequence relation, 57–58, 180, 254

Consequent, 53
 law of affirmation of the, 126

Conservative instance, 284–285, 294, 327

Consistency, absolute, 140
 proof by means of a model, 252–253
 theorem for P, 132
 theorem for Q, 291, 294–296
 theorem for QI, 306
 theorem for QIF, 328
 theorem for Q-M, 394–397
 theorem for S5, 208
 theorem for S5', 218–220
 with respect to a property, 129

Consistent class, 149–154, 211–212, 292, 321–323
Constant, 304
Contingent wff, 20, 179
Continued conjunction, 39
Continued disjunction, 39
Contradictory standard form, 67
Contradictory wff, 28 (Ex. 4)
    truth-functionally, 247–248 (Ex. 10)
Contraposition, converse law of, 126
    law of, 148
Convention 1, 34
Convention 2, 35
Convention 3, 39
Convention 4, 39
Convention 5, 53
Convention 6, 55
Convention 7, 60
Convention 8, 60
Convention 9, 184
Convention 10, 230
Converse Barcan formula, 392, 398
Corners, 16–17
Correct argument, 42, 89–94, 163
Countermodel, 358, 363

Decidability, 336–342
Decision problem, 156, 343
    special cases of, 343–344
Decision procedure, 15, 24, 125, 143 (Ex. 14), 156, 335–337, 343, 369
Dedekind, Richard, 328
Deduction, 275
    finishable, 290–291
    finished, 289–291, 394
    rules of, 275–281, 285–289, 305, 327–328, 392–394
Deduction theorem, for P, 144–147
    for Q*, 415 (Ex. 5)
    for S5, 208–209
Deductive-nomological model, 317 (Ex. 4)
Deductive principle, 110
Deductive strategy, 300–303
Definition, 51, 202
    inductive, 241

See also Abbreviative convention
Deflation theorem, 255 (Ex. 1), 306
Degree (modal), 200–201
Degree (predicate), 226–227
Denumerable set, 251
Designated truth value, 143 (Ex. 14), 222 (Ex. 11)
Determination of interpretation by a tableau, 358–359, 366
Determination of minimal interpretation, 241
Diamond '$\Diamond$', 184–185, 392
    fundamental set of truth tables for, 184
Discreteness, relation of, 307–308
Disjunction, 9–10, 39, 97–98
    continued, 39
    fundamental truth table for, 9
    strong or exclusive, 9–10, 11 (Ex. 1)
    weak or inclusive, 9–10
    See also Wedge '$\vee$'
Dispatching, 360–364, 366–369
Distribution, 345
Domain of discourse, 232–233, 261–262, 264–265
    empty, 259–261
Dot '$\cdot$', 8, 43–46, 48–49, 109, 115–116, 173
    fundamental truth table for, 8
Dual connective, 75 (Ex. 14)
Duality, 72–74
    principle, 72–73
Dummy predicate, *see* Predicate variable
Dummy referring singular term, *see* individual variable
Dummy sentence, *see* Sentential variable

Effective procedure, *see* Decision procedure
EG (existential generalization), rule of, 278
EI (existential instantiation), rule of, 287–288
EL (existential left), rule of, 368
Electrical circuits, 81–86

Elementary logic, 3
  with identity, 3–4
Empty class, 355–356
Empty domain, 259–261
EN, rule of, 299–300 (Ex. 20), 304
Entailment, 3–4, 93, 181, 190
  joint, 57–58
  mutual, 26–27, 42–43, 181, 192
    See also Following from, rela-
      tion of
Enumerating wffs, 157–158 (Ex. 5)
Epimenides, 106
Equality, *see* Identity
Equivalence, 36–38, 42–43, 51, 55–56,
  61–62, 181, 255
Equivalence, strict, 191–193
Equivalence relation, 38
Equivalents, principle of interchange
  of, 113–114, 258 (Ex. 13)
ER (existential right), rule of, 367–
  368
Euclid, 125
Exclusive disjunction, 9–10, 11 (Ex. 1)
Existential generalization, rule of
  (EG), 278
Existential instantiation, rule of (EI),
  287–288
Existential left, rule of (EL), 368
Existential quantifier, 237–238, 263–
  267, 384–386, 405–408, 410
Existential right, rule of (ER), 367–
  368
Explicitation, 95, 101–103
    See also Logistic method
Expressible set, 337–340
Expressive power, 43, 48, 53, 55, 109,
  116, 184, 188, 190, 193–194,
  201
Extension, designator, 325
  of a predicate, 229, 233–234, 325,
    404–406
  of a tensed predicate, 404–406
Extension of an interpretation, 376
Extension to maximal consistent
  class, 150–151

F (future-tense operator), 406–411
Figure (syllogistic), 351–352 (Ex. 11)

First-order logic, *see* Quantification
  theory
Fishhook '⊰', 189–191
  fundamental set of truth tables for,
    189
Flagging, 286, 289–290
Following from, relation of, 42 n., 58
    See also Consequence relation
Formal axiomatic system, *see* Logistic
  system
Formal system, 274
Formalized language, 4–6
Formation rules, 12–13
  elementary algebra, 41 (Ex. 7)
  Polish, 120
  LSM, 165
  LSP, 13–15
  LSQ, 239
  LSQ-M, 389
  LSQ-T, 408
  P, 125–126
  P_1, 139
  P_2, 139
  Q, 275
  Q*, 414
  QI, 304
  QIF, 326
  S4, 222 (Ex. 11)
  S5, 206
  S5', 216
  SBE, 76–77
  TFBE, 87 (Ex. 5)
Formula, 13
  M-formula, 400
  S4-formula, 399
  S5-formula, 399
    See also Well-formed formula
Free term (occurrence), 327
Free variable, 239–240, 307
  occurrence, 239–240, 307
Full and partial truth tables, 165–169
Full disjunctive normal form, 65–71
Fully modalized wff, 216, 218–220,
  393, 401–402 (Ex. 7)
Function, 325
Function variable, 325–327, 332–333
Functional completeness, 43–46, 48–
  51, 116, 198–200

Functional incompleteness, 115–116
Fundamental truth table, *see* Truth tables
Fusion (of individuals), 309
Future-tense operator 'F', 406–411

Gödel, Kurt, 253, 336, 341, 385 n.
Gödel numbers, 336–337
Gödel's incompleteness theorems, 129, 341–342
Goldbach's conjecture, 266, 335–336
Goodman, Nelson, 307
Grammar, 12
    See also Formation rules
Grammatical predicate, 345
Grammatical rule, *see* Formation rules
Grammatical subject, 345
Grouping, 34, 60, 101–102
    See also Brackets

Hempel, Carl G., 317 (Ex. 4)
Hendry, Herbert E., 394 n.
Henkin, Leon, 372
Hilbert, David, 140
Hilbert program, 140
Historical system, 408–411
Horseshoe '⊃', 47, 53, 57
    fundamental truth table for, 47
    self-distributive law of the, 126
Hypothesis, *see* Proof from hypotheses

Identity, 76, 78–81, 259–260, 266–267, 304–308, 313–316
    of indiscernibles, 403 (Ex. 17)
    substitutivity of, rule of (RS), 305, 328
Implication, 56–57, 61–62, 93, 180–181, 254–255, 280
    joint, 57, 254–255
    short-cut test for, 58–59
    truth-functional, 254–255, 276–277
    See also Consequence relation
Implication, material, 191 n.
Implication, strict, 189–191
Impossibility connective '◊', 188
Inclusion (class), 356

Inclusive disjunction, 9–10, 39, 97–98
Inconsequential change of bound variable, 264, 268–269 (Ex. 7), 273 (Ex. 14), 294
Independence, 134–141
Indexical expression, 105–106
    See also Tenses
Indirect proof, 191, 195–196 (Ex. 9)
    strategy of, 303
Individuals, 230, 232
    calculus of (COI), 307–313
    domain of, 232–233, 261–262, 264–265
    product, 313
    sum, 312
Induction by simple enumeration, 110
Induction (mathematical), basis, 110
    hypothesis of, 114
    postulate, 329
    step, 110
    strong, 112–115
    weak, 109–112
Inductive definition, 14, 241
Inference, rule of, 155
    See also *Modus ponens; Modus tollens;* Necessitation; Substitution
Infinity, axiom of, 253
Inflation theorem, 249–251, 306
    generalized, 252–253
Instance, 273–274, 284–285, 327
    conservative, 284–285, 327
Instantiation, variable of, 273, 284–285
Interchange of equivalents, principle of, 113–114, 258 (Ex. 13)
Interpretation, maximal, 250, 314
    minimal, 240–244
    normal (*N*-interpretation), 314–316
    See also Value assignment
Intersection (class), 72, 76–79, 355–356
Invalid wff, 20–21, 179, 248, 259

Joint implication, 57, 254–255
Jointly exhaustive classification, 21

KA, semantics, 397–398

KAB, semantics, 400–401, 408

Kalmár, László, 372

KB, semantics, 398–400

KL (conjunction left), rule of, 362

KR (conjunction right), rule of, 362

Kripke, Saul, 389

Kripke's 1959 semantics, 389–394, 397–398, 401

Language schema M (LSM), 164–205

Language schema P (LSP), 12–75, 89–118

representation in system P, 154–155

Language schema Q (LSQ), 230–273

Language schema Q-M (LSQ-M), 389–403

Language schema Q-T (LSQ-T), 408–415

Language schema Q with identity (LSQ with identity), 259–260

Leibniz, Gottfried Wilhelm von, 32, 403 (Ex. 17)

Lemma, 145

Leonard, Henry S., 307

Lewis, C. I., 205 n.

Lexicographical order, 65 n.

Liar antinomy, 106

Logic, 4, 6, 89–90, 92, 94–95

Logical indeterminateness, 30

Logical truth and falsehood, 29–32, 180, 259–261, 392

Logical word, 3–4, 30–32, 261, 304

Logistic method, 4–6, 127

Logistic system, 127, 155, 274, 414

See also System M; System P; System P₁; System P₂; System Q*; System S4; System S5; System S5′; System S5″

Löwenheim theorem, 251–252, 254, 256 (Ex. 2)

modified, 306, 316

Löwenheim–Skolem theorem, 252–254

Lower predicate logic, *see* Quantification theory

LSM (language schema M), 164–205

LSP (language schema P), 12–75, 89–118

representation in system P, 154–155

LSQ (language schema Q), 230–273

LSQ with identity (language schema Q with identity), 259–260

LSQ-M (language schema Q with modality), 389–403

LSQ-T (language schema Q, tensed), 408–415

Łukasiewicz, Jan, 119, 125 n.

Main connective, 20

Major premiss, 351–352 (Ex. 11)

Material implication, paradoxes of, 191 n.

Mathematical induction, *see* Induction (mathematical)

Mathematical logic, 4, 6, 89–90, 92, 94–95

Matrix, characteristic, 142–143 (Ex. 14), 222 (Ex. 12)

Maximal class, 149–154, 211–212, 321–323

Maximal interpretation, 250, 314

Membership ($\in$), 79, 355

Mendelson, Elliot, 253 n.

Mention and use, 15–17

Metalanguage, 14

Metalinguistic variable, 14, 16–17

Metatheorem, 132

Middle term, 345–346

Minimal interpretation, 240–244

determination of, 241

Minor premiss, 351–352 (Ex. 11)

M-formula, 400

Mirroring of arguments, 91

Modal connective, 187–188, 204

Modal logic, 4, 163–222, 389–403

sentential, 163–222

quantificational, 389–403

Modality, 201–204

Modalization, full, 216, 218–220, 393, 401–402 (Ex. 7)

of variable occurrences, 216, 393

Model, 248, 250–252, 314–316

Model (*Continued*)
  consistency proof by means of, 252–253
  deductive-nomological, 317 (Ex. 4)
  maximal, 250–251, 314
  N-model (normal), 314–316
Model theory, 248–262, 306–307, 314–316, 320–324, 379, 384–388, 390–392, 397–401, 409–411
Modified Löwenheim theorem, 306, 316
Modus ponens, 126, 132–134
Modus tollens, 141 (Ex. 2)
Molecular analysis, 225, 263
Molecular wff, 13
Monadic wff, 344
Mood (syllogistic), 352 (Ex. 11)
Mutually exclusive classification, 21

n-ary connective, 7, 46, 163
n-ary function, 325
Natural deduction system, 128, 239, 274, 414
    See also System Q; System QI; System QIF; System Q-M
Natural language, 4, 89–107, 259–267
NBG, system of (set theory), 253–254
NE, rule of, 298–299 (Ex. 16), 299–300 (Ex. 20), 304
Necessitation, rule of, 220 (Ex. 3)
  rule RN, 393–394
Necessitation of classes, 212–213
Necessity, 163–169, 390, 398–400
Negation, 10, 98–99, 266
  law of double, 148
  converse law of double, 148
    See also Tilde '∼'
Negation left, rule of (NL), 360
Negation right, rule of (NR), 359–360
Nesting, 201, 239, 266
N-interpretation (normal interpretation), 314–316
N-model (normal model), 314–316
NL (negation left), rule of, 360
Nonconjunction sign '|', 49–51, 194
  fundamental truth table for, 49
Nondisjunction sign '↓', 50–51
  fundamental truth table for, 50

Nonnecessity connective '⊡', 188
Nonvalid wff, 20–21
Normal forms, 64–72
  full disjunctive, 65–71; transformational reduction, 67–71; truth-tabular reduction, 68
  prenex, 348–350, 379
  simple disjunctive, 71–72; transformational reduction, 71–72
Normal interpretation (*N*-interpretation), 314–316
Normal model (*N*-model), 314–316
Notation, alternative, 118–122
NR (negation right), rule of, 359–360
NU, rule of, 298–299 (Ex. 16), 299–300 (Ex. 20), 304
N-validity, 314

Object language, 14
ω-complete class, 321–323
Opaque predicate, 228–230, 234
Open set of tableaux, 359
Open tableau, 358
Open wff, 260
Oppenheim, Paul, 317 (Ex. 4)
Opposite truth-value assignments, 73
Opposite truth values, 73
Output, actual, 128–129
Output, intended, 128–129
Ordered *n*-tuple, 357
Ordered pair, 357
Ordered set, 356–357
Ordering of flagged variables, 290
Overlapping, relation of, 308

P (past-tense operator), 405–411
P, system, 125–159, 207, 372–375
PA (Peano arithmetic), system, 328–333, 341–342
Pairing axiom, 316 (Ex. 1)
Paradoxes of material implication, 191 n.
Paradoxes of strict implication, 191
Paraphrase, 6
Parentheses, 36, 239
Parenthesis-free notation, 119–122
Partial and full truth tables, 165–169
Partition, 315

Part-whole relation, 307–308

Past-tense operator 'P', 405–411

Peano, Giuseppe, 328

Peano arithmetic (PA), 328–333, 341–342

Peano's postulates, 328–329, 341

P-language, 27, 43, 48, 55, 57, 89–107, 109

Plenary set of truth tables, 177–178

Polish notation, 119–122, 182 (Ex. 12)

Possibility, 163, 183–185

Possible truth-value outcome, 164–167, 175–176

Postulate set, 307

Postulate system, 307

Power set, 253–254

Predicate, 226–231

  n-ary, 226–227

  opaque, 228–230, 234

  tensed, 404–406

  transparent, 228, 233–234

Predicate variable, 230–231, 233–234, 237–238, 313, 332–333, 408

Premiss, major, 351–352 (Ex. 11)

  minor, 351–352 (Ex. 11)

  of a line, 275–276

  of arguments, 91

  rule of (RP), 275–276

Premisses, proof from, 292, 306

Prenex normal form, 348–350, 379

Prenex quantifier, 301, 343–344

Present-tense operator 'N', 413

Primitive basis, 126–127

  of system M, 400

  of system P, 125–126

  of system P_1, 139

  of system P_2, 139–140

  of system Q*, 414–415

  of system S4, 222 (Ex. 11)

  of system S5, 206

  of system S5', 216

Primitive symbol, 12

Principal interpretation, 132, 135

Projective geometry, 72

Proof (formal), 127–128, 207, 274–275, 286, 291, 394

Proof from hypotheses, 144, 155–156, 208, 283 (Ex. 7), 415 (Ex. 5)

  notation '⊢', 145, 208, 306

Proof from premisses, 292, 306

Proper subset, 356

Pure validity, 261

Q, system, 275–304, 320–324, 336–342, 414

Q*, system, 414–415

QI, system, 304–319, 336–342

QIF, system, 326–342

Q-language, 235, 259, 261–267

Q-M, system, 392–397

Quadruple bar '≡', 191–192

Quantification theory, 225–303, 320–324

  tensed, 404–415

  with identity, 304–319

  with identity and function variables, 325–343

  with modality, 389–403

Quantifier strategy, 301

Quantifiers, elimination of (finite domains), 246–247 (Exs. 6–7)

  existential, 237–238, 263–267, 405–408, 410

  temporal, 407–408, 410

  universal, 238, 263–267, 407–408, 410

Quine, W. V. O., 17, 227, 275, 376, 378 (Exs. 2, 5)

Quotation marks, use of, 15–17

RA (Robinson arithmetic), system of, 337–338

Rank order of connectives, 35, 60, 190 n.

Reduction of decision problem, 348–350

Reduction of modal wffs, 201

Reduction to disjunctive normal form, 67–72

Reduction to prenex normal form, 348–350, 379

Reference, 25–26, 232–234

Referring singular term, 226

  See also individual variable

Reflexive relation, 38

Relevance relation (possible worlds), 398–400
RI (self-identity), rule of, 305
RN (necessitation), rule of, 393–394
Robinson arithmetic (RA), 337–338
RP (rule of premiss), rule of, 275–276
RS (substitutivity of identity), rule of, 305, 328

S4, system, 205 n., 222 (Ex. 11), 400
S4 system of worlds, 399
S4-formula, 399
S5, system, 205–217
S5 system of worlds, 399
S5-formula, 399
S5′, system, 216–220
St. Anselm, 204
Satisfaction (Tarski), 386
Satisfiable class, 151–154, 252–253
Satisfiable wff, 248, 391
Satisfiability, in a domain, 248–249, 253, 391
    of classes, 151–154, 252–253
    of wffs, 248, 391
    simultaneous, 252
        See also Löwenheim–Skolem theorem; Löwenheim theorem; Skolem–Gödel theorem
SBE (system of Boolean equations), 76–81
Schema, axiom, 140
Schema, theorem, 147
Scope, 200–201, 239–240, 266
Secondary interpretation, 135–139
Selective quotation, 16–17
Self-identity, rule of (RI), 305
Semantic tableaux, 358–371, 380
    closed, 358
    closed set of, 359
    interpretation determined by, 358–359, 366
    open, 358
    open set of, 359
    splitting, 361–362
    terminal set of, 363, 367–369
Semantics, 12, 18
    KA, 397–398

KAB, 400–401, 408
KB, 398–400
Sense, sameness of, 25–27, 232–234, 262
Sentence, 259
Sentence connective, binary, 7
    main, 20
    modal, 187–188, 204
    n-ary, 7, 46, 163
    rank order, 35, 60, 190 n.
    singulary, 10, 46 n.
    truth-functional, 7–11, 46–58, 163–165, 187, 195 (Ex. 7)
    truth-tabular, 185–205
Sentential variable, 12, 18 (Ex. 8), 27, 237–238
Sentential wff, 247 (Ex. 8)
Serial order, 408, 412 (Ex. 5)
Set, *see* Class
Sheffer's stroke '|', 49–51, 194
    fundamental truth table for, 49
Short-cut test for validity and implication, 58–60, 358
Simple disjunctive normal form, 71–72
Simplification (electrical circuits), 85–86, 89 (Ex. 14)
Simultaneous satisfiability, 252
Simultaneous substitution, 131 (Ex. 11)
Singular terms, 225–226, 325
Singulary connective, 10, 46 n.
Skolem–Gödel theorem, 292, 320–321, 328
Skolem paradox, 254
Sound argument, 42, 91
Soundness (deductions), 280–281
    in a deduction, 277, 280, 394
Spectrum problem, 251–252, 306–307
Splitting (semantic tableaux), 361–362
Stage (tableau construction), 362
Standard form, 64–72
    contradictory, 67
        See also Normal forms
Star connective '✡', 193–194
Starred line (deduction), 277
Stars (premiss), 275–276

Strategy, deductive, 300–303
  of indirect proof, 303
  of the conditional, 300–301
  of truth functions, 302–303
  quantifier, 301
Strict equivalence, 191–193
Strict implication, 189–191
  paradoxes of, 191
Strong completeness theorem, *see*
  Completeness
Strong disjunction, 9–10, 11 (Ex. 1)
Strong mathematical induction, 112–115
Subset, 356
  proper, 356
Substitution, rule of, 126, 133–134
  simultaneous, 131 (Ex. 11)
Substitutivity of identity, rule of
  (RS), 305, 328
Subsystem, 179–180, 207, 217
Successful design, 129
Switching circuits, 81–86
Syllogism, 344–348 ·
  rules of, 346
Syllogistic term, 345–346
Symbolic language, 4–6
Symbolic logic, 4, 6, 89–90, 92, 94–95
Symmetrical relation, 37
synonymy, 25–27, 232–234, 262
Syntax, 12
  See also Formation rules
Synthetic truth and falsehood, 31–32
System M (of Feys-von Wright), 400
System NBG of set theory, 253–254
System of Boolean equations (SBE),
  76–81
System of worlds, 390, 397, 399–400
System P, 125–159, 207, 217
System P₁, 139
System P₂, 139–140
System Q, 275–304, 320–324, 336–342, 414
System Q*, 414–415
System QI, 304–319, 336–342
System QIF, 326–342
System Q-M, 392–397
System S4, 205 n., 222 (Ex. 11), 400
System S5, 205–216, 217

System S5′, 216–220
System S5″, 220–221 (Ex. 3)
System SBE (system of Boolean equations), 76–81
System TFBE (truth functions of
  Boolean equations), 87–88 (Ex.
  5), 196 (Ex. 12)

Tableau-construction rules, 359–369
Tableau method, *see* Semantic
  tableaux
Tarski, Alfred, 385–388
Tarski's semantics for quantifiers,
  385–386
Tautologous wff, 182 (Ex. 11), 242
  (Ex. 9), 255, 343–344
Tautology, 28 (Ex. 4)
Telescopic set of truth tables, 195
  (Ex. 7)
Temporal quantifiers, 407–408, 410
Tense logic, 404–413
Tense operator, 405–411
Tensed predicate, 404–406
Tenses, 264–266, 404–413
Terminal set of tableaux, 363, 367–369
Term, 326–327
  bound occurrence of a, 327
  class, 76–78
  free occurrence of a, 327
  major, 345
  middle, 345
  minor, 345
  of QIF, 326–327
  referring singular, 226
  singular, 225–226, 325
  syllogistic, 345
TF (truth functions), rule of, 276–277
TFBE (truth functions of Boolean
  equations), system of, 87–88
  (Ex. 5), 196 (Ex. 12)
Theorem (of a system), 128, 132, 274,
  283 (Exs. 8–9), 291, 293, 394
  Δ-, 307
  notation '⊢', 148, 209, 217
Theorem schema, 147
Three-step evaluational procedure,
  19–25

Three-valued interpretation, 135–139

Tilde '∼', 10, 43–46, 48–49, 109, 118
    (Ex. 7), 170–171
    fundamental set of truth tables for,
        170–171
    fundamental truth table for, 10

Token-reflexive expression, 105–106
    See also Tenses

Traditional logic, 268 (Exs. 3–6), 345–
    348, 351–352 (Exs. 9–11)

Transformational method, reduction
    to normal form, 67–72

Transitive relation, 37

Translation (logical), 94–103, 262–
    267

Transliteration, 121

Transparent predicate, 228, 233–234

Triple bar '≡', 54–56
    fundamental truth table for, 54, 118
        (Ex. 7)

True of, notion of, 228–229

Truth conditions, 65–66, 71

Truth-functional connective, 7–11,
    46–58, 163–165, 187, 195 (Ex. 7)

Truth-functional implication, 254–
    255, 276–277

Truth functions, rule of (TF), 276–
    277

Truth functions of Boolean equations,
    system of (TFBE), 87–88 (Ex. 5),
    196 (Ex. 12)

Truth tables, 21–25, 46–48, 135–139
    Boolean, 78–81
    full and partial, 165–169
    in modal logic, 165–205
    plenary sets of, 177–179
    sets of, 169–173
    telescopic sets of, 195 (Ex. 7)

Truth-tabular connective, 185–205

Truth-tabular method, reduction to
    normal form, 68

Truth values, 4, 25–26, 135–139, 142–
    143 (Ex. 14)
    designated, 143 (Ex. 14), 222 (Ex.
        11)

Truth-value assumption, 104–107

Truth-value outcome, 163–167, 175–
    176

Turnstile '⊢', 145, 208, 306

UD, see Universe of discourse

UG (universal generalization), rule of,
    285–286, 288–289

UI (universal instantiation), rule of,
    277–278

Union (class), 72, 76–79, 355

Universal class, 76–77

Universal closure, 305

Universal generalization, rule of
    (UG), 285–286, 288–289

Universal instantiation, rule of (UI),
    277–278

Universal left, rule of (UL), 365–366

Universal quantifier, 238, 263–267,
    384–386, 407–408, 410

Universal right, rule of (UR), 366–367

Universe, 313

Universe of discourse (UD), 232–233,
    261–262, 264–265

UN, rule of, 299–300 (Ex. 20), 304

Use and mention, 15–17

Vacuous quantification, 245–246 (Ex.
    3), 260, 285–286, 288
    and the empty domain, 260

Vagueness, 104–105

Valid argument, see Correct argument

Valid wff, 20, 78, 135, 143 (Ex. 14),
    179, 248, 259–261, 280, 335, 392,
    411

Validity, in an historical system, 411
    in a domain, 249, 391
    in a system of worlds, 391
    N-validity, 314
    pure, 261

Value assignment, 18–27, 77–78, 104–
    106, 175–177, 232–235, 240–244,
    252, 376, 384–388, 390, 397, 399,
    409
        See also Model; Secondary in-
            terpretation

Value of a wff under a value assign-
    ment, 19, 77–78, 234–235, 241–
    244, 326–327, 384–388, 390–391,
    397–400, 409–410

Variable, 27, 237–238
  bound, 239–240
  class, 73
  flagged, 286, 289–290
  free, 239–240, 307
  function, 325–327, 332–333
  individual, 230–233, 237–238
  metalinguistic, 14, 16–17
  of instantiation, 273, 284–285
  predicate, 230–231, 233–234, 237–
    238, 313, 332–333
  propositional, *see* Sentential varia-
    ble
  sentential, 12, 18 (Ex. 8), 27, 237–
    238
  truth-value, *see* Sentential variable
Variant interpretation, 384–385, 391

Variant wff, 144
Venn diagram, 344–347
Vocabulary, 12
von Neumann, J., 253
Voting circuits, 84

Weak disjunction, 9–10, 39, 97–98
Weak mathematical induction, 109–
  112
Wedge 'V', 9, 43–46, 48–49, 109, 115–
  116, 118 (Ex. 7), 171–173
  fundamental set of truth tables for,
    171–173
  fundamental truth table for, 9
Well-formed formula (wff), 13–15
  atomic, 13–15, 230, 234–235